COMPLETE GUIDE TO
SERVICE
HANDGUNS

*Other Stoeger books
by Gene Gangarosa Jr.:*

MODERN BERETTA FIREARMS

P.38 AUTOMATIC PISTOL — THE FIRST 50 YEARS

COMPLETE GUIDE TO COMPACT HANDGUNS

COMPLETE GUIDE TO
SERVICE
HANDGUNS

BY
GENE GANGAROSA JR.

STOEGER PUBLISHING COMPANY

I dedicate this book to my family

COVER DESIGN and PHOTOGRAPH:
Matt C. Wells and O. Ray Wells
BOOK DESIGN and DIGITAL PRODUCTION:
Loretta Luongo Associates

FRONT COVER:
The service handguns pictured on the front cover are (left to right):
the Colt Model 1911, the Smith & Wesson Model 66 Revolver
and Beretta's 9mm Model 92F.

Published by Stoeger Publishing Company
5 Mansard Court
Wayne, New Jersey 07470

International Standard Book Number: 0-88317-204-6
Library of Congress Catalog Card No.: 96-071004

Manufactured in the United States of America

In the United States, distributed to the book trade and to the sporting goods
trade by:
Stoeger Industries
5 Mansard Court
Wayne, New Jersey 07470
Tel.: 973-872-9500 Fax: 973-872-2230

In Canada, distributed to the book trade and to the sporting goods trade by:
Stoeger Canada Ltd.
1801 Wentworth Street, Unit 16
Whitby, Ontario, L1N 8R6, Canada

PREFACE

Service handguns—those pistols and revolvers whose primary use is to arm military personnel and police officers—represent the earliest handguns ever made, and they are still being produced and sold in great quantities today. While handguns receive less attention from military planners than do rifles and larger weapons, a pistol or revolver has saved many a soldier's life when a larger weapon was either unavailable or too slow into action. For this reason handguns remain highly desirable in military circles.

While most on-duty police officers are authorized to carry handguns (except in some countries, notably Great Britain, where only certain police officers may carry a handgun), military forces tend to be far more stringent in such authorizations. Despite this official reluctance to grant handgun carry and use to any but a select few, in a shooting war military personnel invariably go to great lengths to acquire handguns any way they can. To the police officer, a service handgun (if authorized) is both a symbol of authority and a potentially lifesaving tool. In addition to arming the military and police, service handguns sell widely to collectors, sport shooters and people who desire solid, sturdy handguns for self-defense.

THE COMPLETE GUIDE TO SERVICE HANDGUNS covers revolvers and pistols that have gained official acceptance by military and/or police forces at some time in their history. It also details guns which, due to their larger size and configuration compared to compact guns, offer the potential for official acceptance and service. For the reader's convenience, the book has been divided into five sections. The first is historical in nature, covering the evolution of the handgun as a weapon and a tool of self-defense. It's followed by a section on the classic service revolvers, which in some cases date back a century or more. The third section covers current service revolvers, while parts four and five concentrate on classic and contemporary automatic pistols.

The purpose of this book is to enable prospective buyers of service pistols or revolvers—whether handgun enthusiasts or historians—to review the characteristics of a large number of handguns all at once. By following the development of each gun and its production history, the reader will have a better idea of how widespread the issue on guns has become, and where one might expect to encounter a given model. The dimensions of each gun are given, too, including width and height, probably the two most important dimensions for those who carry a handgun, but which are unaccountably omitted in other books on the subject. Another positive aspect of this book—and its companion volume, THE COMPLETE GUIDE TO COMPACT HANDGUNS—is its detailed coverage of more models than virtually any other handgun book now available.

It seems advisable at this point to forewarn all readers of this book how important it is to exercise utmost care and caution in handling a gun. Because handguns are short, their muzzles can swing widely with even a relatively small movement. Never point a gun at something you do not intend to shoot. Never take someone's word for it that a gun is "unloaded" without verifying that condition for yourself. Remember, you can remove the magazine from an automatic pistol and still have a round lurking in the chamber, ready to punish an act of carelessness with one fatal stroke. Finally, never rely on any mechanical safety device as an excuse for sloppy, inconsiderate gun handling.

ACKNOWLEDGMENTS

No book of this magnitude can be completed by one person, and I am greatly indebted to many people for making it possible. First and foremost, my deepest thanks and gratitude extend to my family: my lovely wife Lynn and our children, Megan and Tyler, without whom nothing I do would be worthwhile. Next, my thanks go to the terrific people of Stoeger Publishing Company, especially Robert Weise, former executive vice-president, and David C. Perkins, his successor, and Bill Jarrett and Charlene Cruson Step, the wonderfully talented and cooperative editorial team whose efforts I deeply appreciate. The many businesses and individuals who gave generously of their time and resources to help make this book possible also have my deepest thanks and gratitude. There are too many to list, but they know who they are and I appreciate all of them. When all is said and done, however, I accept sole responsibility for any errors that may have found their way into the text.

BY AND ABOUT
THE AUTHOR

I have enjoyed shooting since I was a little boy, and all my early exposures were to long arms. The first handgun I ever fired was the Colt M1911A1 during my service with the U.S. Navy, in which I served from 1977 to 1981 as a helicopter air crewman. Although my squadron's primary mission was antisubmarine warfare, I also did a considerable amount of rescue and intelligence-gathering work, which I personally found most gratifying. Naturally, I had occasion to work with my standard Navy firearms and for a time carried a Walther P.38 as my personal sidearm. Since my collateral duty was intelligence, I had considerable exposure to firearms used in various countries.

As a rescue swimmer, I flew in several rescue sorties for which I received letters of commendation. We were not technically at war during my enlistment, but the cold war was raging and I was involved in a supporting role during the Iranian hostage rescue attempt in May 1980. Afterward I attended college and commenced a teaching career. I began writing firearms articles a number of years ago and have since written well over 100 of them, along with several books (this is my third book).

Because of the circumstances under which I first began using handguns in the Navy, I've leaned mostly toward the service-type automatic pistols and revolvers; I think, therefore, primarily in terms of each gun's usefulness in self-defense situations. I believe that we live in a world in which it is often easier and more natural for evil to triumph — at least temporarily — over good. In such a world, it is prudent to take all appropriate safety precautions, and in some professions and circumstances it may be appropriate for law-abiding citizens to arm themselves. I oppose gun control, basing my position on the belief that human beings should be treated as responsible moral agents and should be made to face the consequences of their actions. Thus I consider the punishment of criminals a much more effective crime-fighting tactic than outlawing guns or their law-abiding owners who pose no threat to society. In my opinion, when society learns to punish malefactors swiftly and effectively, things will improve.

Regarding handgun selection, I've gravitated mostly toward the major gun types over the years and feel that almost all of them will do the job as long as the owners are well practiced and pay close attention to what they are doing. When testing a gun, I always assume it has something to offer. I work hard to discover its good points and try to be as open-minded as possible. I also believe that subjectivity and ego have no place in gunwriting; I have no personal axes to grind and am always willing to listen to other points of view. So be it.

CONTENTS

1. EVOLUTION OF THE HANDGUN.............................. 11
2. CLASSIC SERVICE REVOLVERS 23
3. SERVICE REVOLVERS.................................... 49
4. CLASSIC SERVICE PISTOLS 97
5. SERVICE PISTOLS — 9MM, .40 AND .45 CALIBER......... 157
6. EMERGING TECHNOLOGIES AND FUTURE TRENDS......... 291
7. DISASSEMBLING WALTHER PP-TYPE PISTOLS............. 295
8. HANDGUN SAFETY.................................... 298
    INDEX.. 301

1. EVOLUTION OF THE HANDGUN

Handguns have evolved greatly over the centuries. Compare the Turkish flintlock single-shot pistol made in the 18th century (top) with the 9mm Canadian-made Inglis High Power pistol (below) made in 1944.

The history of firearms stretches back more than 600 years. From its origins in China during the 10th century or perhaps earlier, blackpowder made its way to Europe during the Crusades. The earliest known European "recipe" for gunpowder appeared in the writings of Roger Bacon around 1280. After that, it took little time for clever inventors to develop workable rockets and firearms. By 1346, at the Battle of Crecy during the Hundred Years' War, the English army had already organized field artillery units. And while archers won that battle for England and remained in service until almost 1600, the future of weaponry was clearly founded in the "gonnes" used by a few of the English troops at Crecy.

Despite the primitive, unstable nature of the earliest firearms, their influence was far-reaching. Cannons especially proved effective in assaulting strong castles and quickly became the decisive weapons of their day. The early cannons were cast mostly from bronze—an alloy of tin and copper—but soon iron took over, forming a marriage with gunpowder that has lasted for centuries. Although iron was, and remains, one of the most abundant materials in the earth's crust, it took decades for people to learn by trial and error which manufacturing methods and materials worked best in making firearms. After a German blacksmith invented the first blast furnace in 1311, cast iron quickly became the favored gun material.

Later, when the primacy of gunpowder had been established, clever inventors began seeking ways to miniaturize firearms so that every soldier could carry one. By 1350, firearms that could be carried and fired by individual soldiers had come into use; and by the 1500s a major part of the armed forces of the more technologically advanced nations were carrying these weapons. It took a long time, howev-

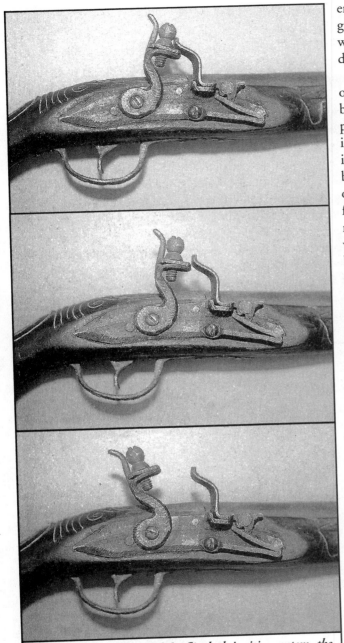

Despite the limitations of the flintlock ignition system, the flintlock pistol saw wide military and personal use for nearly two centuries. The hammer had three positions: firing position (top); half-cock position (center); and full-cock position. Pressure on the trigger tripped the sear, releasing the hammer. The hammer struck the flint against the frizzen, creating a shower of sparks that ignited the powder charge and fired the pistol.

er, for inventors to devise portable handguns that were reliable enough to compete with edged weapons, such as swords and daggers.

First, problems of metallurgy had to be overcome. Early guns had a nasty habit of blowing up in their owners' faces. This problem was eventually alleviated through increased knowledge of heat treatments and improved manufacturing methods. Early blast furnaces used charcoal, but as supplies of wood became scarce, another source of fuel had to be found. Finally, in 1709, a new method for creating coke from coal was perfected by the English. In addition to being a more abundant raw material than charcoal, coke burned hotter, thus making possible a higher quality of cast iron. Lighter, stronger and more reliable firearms were the result.

Another innovation occurred in the 1730s, when an Englishman named Benjamin Huntsman undertook the large-scale manufacture of steel. Stronger, lighter and much more consistent than cast iron, steel quickly became the chief component of better guns, a position it maintains to this day.

Eventually, governments instituted standard proof-firing procedures, requiring gunsmiths and manufacturers to fire double charges of powder and shot, which became known as a proof load. The reasoning behind this regulation was that the manufacturer would, out of enlightened self-interest, make guns that were far stronger than necessary. Guns that survived this process received a stamp of approval called a proofmark.

While advances in metallurgy improved quality control, the search continued for a reliable source of ignition. The hot coals used to ignite the powder charges in early field artillery, and the glowing fuses used to fire shoulder firearms, proved impractical for weapons designed for operation with one hand. Not until the early 16th century was this problem solved with the introduction of the wheellock mechanism. With this a coiled spring produced enough energy to turn an iron wheel against a flint. The sparks that were created from this simple procedure proved sufficient to fire a powder charge. Thus did the wheellock make a practical, albeit expensive pistol possible, enough to equip elite cavalry units and high-ranking officers from the 1500s to the early 1600s.

Later in the 17th century, the flintlock came into use. Simpler and cheaper to make than the wheellock, the flintlock ignition system resulted in rifles, smoothbore muskets and pistols that were more rugged and practical than the wheellocks. Despite its obvious limitation—a single shot followed by a slow reload—the flintlock pistol saw wide use as an offensive cavalry and personal-defense weapon for nearly two centuries. Not only was it the first practical handgun suitable for mass production, the flintlock system was a huge advance over anything that had preceded it. The flintlock pistol was used even at sea, where it became a favored weapon of boarding parties.

Despite the flintlock's unquestioned superiority over its predecessors, there was still plenty of room for improvement, especially regarding its reliability. For this reason, experiments in finding alternate types of ignition continued until the early 1800s, when the percussion cap was invented. This system involved the crushing of a small metal cap containing an unstable compound—originally fulminate of mercury—by a falling hammer. The result was a new source of ignition for the main powder charge, a concept that has carried over in modified forms to modern cartridge firearms.

THE FIRST REVOLVERS

During this same era, the first truly practical repeating handguns were developed, the most famous and significant of which was the revolver. Developed by Samuel Colt beginning in 1836, various revolver designs, notably the Paterson revolver and the improved .36- and .44-caliber Navy and Army models, saw extensive use in the U.S. Civil War (1861–1865) and in Europe. Colt also mechanized manufacture of his firearms, still another innovation that eventually led to the mass production of large quantities of nearly identical weapons with interchangeable parts. Colt was also a great salesman whose success at convincing governments of their need for his weapons has been envied by gunmakers ever since.

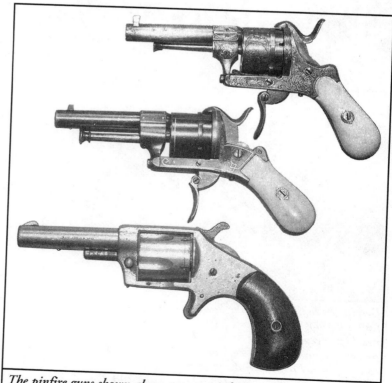

The pinfire guns shown above were carried in gentlemen's coat pockets from the 1850s onward. The folding triggers aided concealment as well as safety.

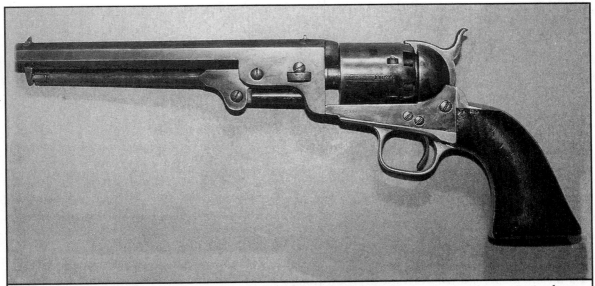

The early revolvers created by Colt, such as the 36-caliber Model 1851 Navy, saw extensive service in the Civil War (1861–1865).

Even though other firms produced excellent arms—notably Smith & Wesson in the U.S. and Adams in England (creator of the first practical double-action revolver)—the name Colt was for decades dominant in revolver manufacture.

The importance of Colt's early revolvers cannot be overestimated. Not only were they the most advanced firearms of their day, produced using the latest manufacturing techniques, they were widely

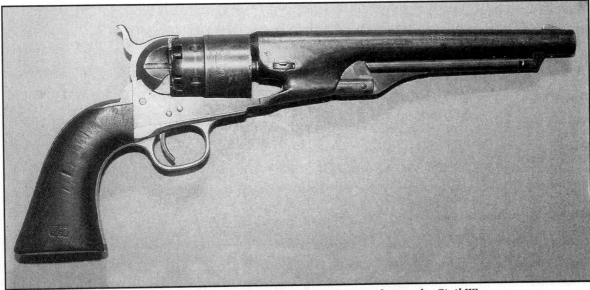

Colt's Model 1860 Army in .44 caliber was another sidearm favorite during the Civil War.

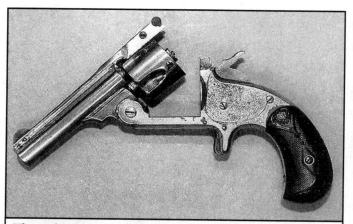

The multi-shot capabilities of the revolver created a booming market for civilian defensive firearms in the post-Civil War era. From the 1870s onward, this top-break revolver type was popular because it permitted rapid loading and unloading. The divided frame, however, weakened this critical component, limiting such guns to low-powered cartridges.

available and practical arms capable of firing a serious combat cartridge. They made their mark on infantry and cavalry tactics in the Civil War and did much to change the way military engagements were fought.

Rifling, primitive though it was, came into use as early as 1490, when an Austrian named Gaspard Kollner cut straight grooves down the bore of a gun barrel. The exact purpose of this first attempt at rifling remains unclear. Perhaps it was to collect powder fouling, enabling soldiers to fire more times before having to clean their weapons. August Kotter, a German, refined this early rifling about 1520 by cutting spiral grooves, rather than straight ones, into gun barrels. This spiraling stabilized the bullet by spin-

ning it, a concept that has led directly to the production of today's modern firearms that exhibit extreme accuracy.

It took literally centuries before rifling became universally popular, however. At first, only a tiny fraction of firearms—and almost none of the military types—used rifled barrels. Their rate of fire was far too slow for most military purposes; moreover, guns so equipped required meticulous maintenance. By the time of the U.S Civil War, virtually all firearms (including pistols but not shotguns) then in use by front-line military units bore rifled barrels.

The next major advance in firearms design was the creation of revolvers with cylinders bored all the way through. This invention was attributed to Rollin White, an employee of Colt's, in April 1855. The innovation allowed the use of centerfire cartridges, which combined the bullet, percussion cap and powder charge all in

Smith & Wesson's Safety Hammerless (top) and Colt's Lightning (bottom) were two early double-action handguns dating from the late 1870s (Lightning) and late 1880s (Safety Hammerless).

In its time, Colt's Single Action Army revolver (made from 1873 on) was considered by many to be the ultimate centerfire cavalry revolver. Rugged, reliable, powerful and accurate, it has been widely copied over the years and remains in production even today.

This early Smith & Wesson Hand Ejector revolver produced in the 1890s later evolved into the extremely popular Military & Police (Model 10), which many believe to be the best-selling handgun of all time.

one metal-cased projectile called a cartridge or round. The creation of centerfire cartridges allowed a degree of uniformity and standardization of ammunition previously unattainable. Numerous practical centerfire revolver designs followed—first single-action, then double-action. Notable among these rugged revolvers were the British Webley introduced in 1867; Smith & Wesson's Russian Model of

1871; the Colt Single Action Army of 1873; the French Model of 1892; and the Belgian/Russian Nagant of 1895.

The pinnacle of revolver development, though, was undoubtedly the introduction in 1899 of Smith & Wesson's Military & Police Revolver. This outstanding weapon (still sold by Smith & Wesson as the Model 10) has remained in continuous production for almost a century, during which time over four million units have been manufactured. The distri-

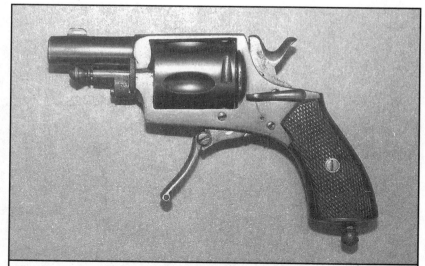

Another popular handgun type was the tiny "Velo Dog" revolver, intended for personal protection in a compact, portable package. Note the folding trigger on this example imported from Belgium.

bution and use of Smith & Wesson's Military & Police revolvers have literally spanned the globe, arming untold numbers of police, military and civilians. Adapted to a variety of calibers, it has also served as the basis for most modern revolver designs.

In 1856 — the year after Rollin White's cylinder patent — Sir Henry Bessemer of England invented a method of mass-producing steel by blowing air through a large pot full of molten cast iron. The air removed excess carbon, thus strengthening the metal; and while the iron was still hot, other desirable materials could be added to the mixture, further strengthening the steel. A modification of Bessemer's basic converter, called the Basic Oxygen Process, is still in use. These devices continue to make possible the manufacture of steel in enormous quantities and at high speed. Thus have these and other metallurgical developments greatly aided the firearms industries of the world.

In the late 19th century, blackpowder began to give way to a smokeless powder mixture that offered cleaner burning with a smaller charge. Major firearms advances have, almost without exception, been based upon advances in ammunition; and in this case, smokeless powder made possible a new generation of repeating firearms, called automatic or self-loading weapons.

AUTOMATIC PISTOLS

The first practical automatic pistols did not lag long behind the refinement of smokeless powder; indeed, by the 1890s a growing number of workable automatic pistol designs were already in production. Several of these, notably the Mauser C.96 — known affectionately as the "Broomhandle" because of the odd shape of its grip — and Fabrique Nationale's (FN) Model 1900, were tremendous commercial successes, with production and sales in the hundreds of thousands all over the world. With growing experience and confidence, designers quickly refined the techniques of making automatic pistols, which were soon offered in a variety of sizes and calibers.

By 1914, when World War I began in Europe, automatic pistols had made tremendous inroads into the revolver business in the three major markets: military, police and civilian. The two most important classic designs of this period—the Colt M1911 and Luger Parabellum P08—are still in production. During the war, automatic pistols largely replaced revolvers among most of the world's major armies. Between World Wars I and II, the refinement of automatic pistols continued, many of which have proved remarkably successful. Some authorities argue that, with the perfection of the Colt M1911 design in 1926 (Model M1911A1) and the introduction of other models—such as Walther's Model PP (*Polizei Pistole*) in 1929, Beretta's Model 1934, the FN High Power of 1935, and the Walther P.38—automatic pis-

By the 1890s, early automatic pistols were making their first tentative forays into a handgun market that had been dominated for six decades by revolvers. Shown at top is a Mauser C.96 "Broomhandle" with the Luger Parabellum P08 below.

Colt's Model 1911 pistol is considered by many to be the greatest automatic military handgun ever made. This Remington-Rand M1911A1 was made for the U.S. Armed Forces during World War II.

The German-made Walther Models P.38 (top) and PP (below) introduced the double-action trigger to the world of automatics.

tols have reached a state of development unlikely to be exceeded until the next breakthrough in ammunition is achieved. Indeed, all of the guns mentioned above remain in production and widespread use despite the appearance of more modern designs.

Until the development of the two landmark Walther pistols—the P.38 and PP—most automatics were of single-action design; i.e., the shooter had to cock the hammer by hand before the trigger could be released to fire the pistol. Walther's P.38 and PP introduced the double-action trigger to the world of automatics, and since then both single-action and double-action designs have fought for supremacy. They were joined later by double-action-only pistols, which use a revolver-like double-action pull for each shot. Arguments over the relative merits and demerits of these three systems continue to this day.

An increasing emphasis on human engineering, or ergonomics, has produced handguns that are subtly but significantly improved over the guns of a generation ago. Even those who argue that the classic Colt M1911 or FN High Power are the ultimate handgun designs are impressed by the improved sights and safety catches found on the latest versions of these classic models. Such innovations as the Novak sights, found on many custom pistols and on most production Smith & Wesson pistols, greatly improve a gun's handling. But while such innovations occur each year, most of what is happening appears to be little more than refinements of existing ideas. New materials—most recently the lightweight but rugged polymer plastics, stainless steel and investment-cast parts—are coming into use all the time.

THE HANDGUNS OF TOMORROW

The next major leap in handgun development and design, however, will almost certainly occur in the area of ammunition. Several companies, one of which is Heckler & Koch, are now working on caseless cartridges, thereby eliminating the metal casing that has made its mark on centerfire ammunition for more than a century. The entire case of this new cartridge, consisting of the powder charge and primer shaped into a hard block, is consumed upon firing; this eliminates the extraction and ejection cycle known to cause problems in many handguns. The status of caseless ammunition for handguns remains uncertain, and undoubtedly conventional cartridge handguns will continue in use for some time even after a caseless-ammunition handgun has been perfected and marketed. But one thing is

Modern handguns, like this Glock Model 17 pistol, often combine the best of the old and new. Glock uses an early-1900s' adaptation of John Browning's successful short recoil system along with a new polymer frame that is strong but much lighter than steel.

certain: more has happened in the area of ammunition development for handguns in the past ten years than has occurred since the beginning of the 20th century.

Numerous studies done around 1990 have attempted to define effective handgun ammunition performance, including the interesting and controversial publication in 1992 of Marshall and Sanow's book, *Handgun Stopping Power*. In it, the authors tried to determine precisely which factors influence handgun ammunition performance and how it could be improved. Although its conclusions have not met with universal agreement, this book's contribution to the continuing debate on handgun ammunition is unquestioned.

A selection of common handgun ammunition includes (left to right): .22 Long Rifle, .25 ACP, .380 ACP, 7.62x25mm (also called 7.63 Mauser or 7.62 Tokarev), 9mm Parabellum, .38 Special, .40 S&W and .45 ACP. The two rounds on the far right (for comparison purposes) are modern military rifle rounds: the .223 and .308. The next major leap in handgun development and design will undoubtedly occur in the area of ammunition.

Within the U.S. Armed Forces, the role played by the handgun has been—and remains—strictly that of emergency defense. The days when a handgun formed the primary armament of a cavalryman ended around the turn of the century. Today, the only personnel in military uniform who carry a handgun as a primary weapon are mostly high-ranking officers who are not expected to do any actual fighting themselves, or personnel whose duties involve working in confined spaces where the more effective long gun might get in the way. In general, the military establishment holds handguns in low esteem. On the other hand, most combat troops greatly prize handguns and will go to great lengths to acquire them.

Among state and local police units, a handgun is seldom the first choice of armament when shooting is anticipated, in which case a shotgun, rifle or submachine gun gets the nod. But when a shooting situation is encountered unexpectedly and is forced upon an officer, the handgun can be invaluable and even life-saving. Much the same applies to civilians who are legally armed and responsibly trained in handgun use.

In the sections that follow, classic service revolvers and pistols are described in detail. The "classics" are those that have stood the test of time—in terms of design, reliability and practicality. Contemporary service handguns are also discussed at length. These are the revolvers and automatics that are in common use around the world by military and law-enforcement personnel, sporting shooters and civilians who are concerned about self-defense.

2. CLASSIC SERVICE REVOLVERS

CONTENTS

British Service Revolvers
  Enfield No.2 / Webley Mark IV 24
Colt
  New Service 27
  Police Positive/Police Positive Special 29
  Python 30
  Single Action Army (SAA) 32

Nagant Model 1895 35
Ruger Security Six 37
Smith & Wesson
  Model 10 Military and Police 39
  Model 19 Combat Magnum 42
  Model 27 44
  Model 29 48

After single-shot pistols, the next class of handguns to see widespread military and police use was the revolver. Beginning in the early to mid-1800s, the revolver quickly supplanted single-shot pistols in most military and police organizations. It reigned supreme until automatic pistols began to appear half a century later. In many of the world's armies and navies, and in most police forces, revol-vers have continued in service to the present day, despite the growing popularity of automatic pistols. For those individuals who wish to add a used but still serviceable revolver to their collection, the rising tide of acceptance for automatic pistols among official bodies bodes well. Indeed, a well-made revolver is still a good choice for many handgun users.

This section covers revolvers made by such giants of industry as Colt, Ruger, Smith & Wesson and Webley. These guns have established worldwide reputations for ruggedness and reliability under adverse conditions, but remember that some of these revolvers are now very old. A gun that has been around for a century or more may have had at least several owners. One can't know for certain how those owners handled their guns, so the wise buyer should have his new purchase thoroughly checked out by a competent gunsmith before attempting to fire it.

BRITISH SERVICE REVOLVERS
ENFIELD NO. 2/WEBLEY MARK IV

During World War I, the .455 Webley Mark VI revolver served the British forces admirably, with more than 300,000 units produced by Webley & Scott between 1914 and 1918. After the war, though, the Royal Army questioned the revolver's considerable weight and recoil. These were excellent characteristics for an army consisting of seasoned professional soldiers; but a smaller, lighter revolver that fired a reduced-caliber bullet was considered a more reliable weapon for use by the less experienced soldiers who were likely to man the ranks in future conflicts. Therefore, in 1922 the British government asked Webley & Scott to look into the possibility of building a smaller revolver in 9mm (.38 caliber).

Unfortunately, the British gunmaking firm worked at such a slow pace to fulfill this mandate that the military was forced to take over the whole project in 1926. Thus did the Royal Small Arms Factory at Enfield Lock in England assume development of the revolver begun by Webley & Scott. Nevertheless, it wasn't until 1931 that series production began. Finally, on June 2, 1932—a full ten years after the project was initiated—the British armed forces accepted the revolver, which was dubbed "Pistol, Revolver, No. 2, Mark 1." While this improved revolver still resembled a Webley & Scott product (notably its distinctive flat-sided barrel), its hammer and cylinder lockwork were quite different in design. Unfortunately, it still broke open from the top and simultaneously extracted all cartridges—up to six of them in the cylinder—as the Webleys and some early Smith & Wesson revolvers had done.

Eventually the Enfield revolver went through three major evolutions, with the first version—Pistol, Revolver, No. 2, Mark 1—being accepted in 1931. It featured a hammer spur that offered the option of cocking the hammer for more precise single-action shooting or firing double action simply by pulling through on the trigger. Its large hammer spur had an annoying and potentially fatal habit, however, of getting caught inside the armored tanks of the Royal Tank Corps. The resulting modification to the Enfield pattern was approved on June 22, 1938 and became known as the Pistol, Revolver, No. 2, Mark 1*.

In this Mark 1* version, the hammer spur and the hammer's single-action notch were removed, rendering the gun capable of firing only in the double-action mode. To improve the revolver's accuracy, its mainspring was lightened slightly to allow an easier trigger pull. Most early No. 2, Mark 1 revolvers were converted to this 1* pattern during the British Army's maintenance system, making the original No. 2, Mark 1 quite rare today.

Prior to 1938, a 200-grain soft lead bullet was the standard loading for the Enfield revolver, producing a rather slow muzzle velocity of only 650 feet per second. In 1938, concern over the inhumane wounding qualities of the soft lead bullet led to the adoption of a new jacketed bullet weighing 185 grains. The wounding power of this cartridge was even less, but for a pistol meant to be used at short range it was sufficient. In addition to the British ammunition, standard .38 S&W caliber cartridges—NOT .38 Special—also chamber and fire in these revolvers (the .38 S&W round made in the U.S. uses a 146-grain roundnosed lead bullet).

Still an accurate handgun, the Webley Mark IV revolver produced this five-shot 1.6-inch group from a distance of 25 feet.

The third and final version of the No. 2 revolver was the Pistol, Revolver, No. 2, Mark 1**. Introduced on July 29, 1942, this wartime variant was simplified in order to accelerate production. Changes in the lockwork— particularly the omission of the revolver's hammer stop—allowed the manufacturer to produce a gun in considerably less time than with earlier versions. A serious problem arose with the No. 2, Mark 1**, however, with the discovery that the weapon could fire accidentally when dropped. This proved so unsatisfactory that after the war virtually all Mark 1** revolvers were rebuilt according to the earlier Mark 1* pattern.

During World War II, Albion Motors, Ltd. of Glasgow, Scotland built approximately 24,000 Enfield No. 2 revolvers. The Singer Sewing Machine Company in the nearby town of Clydesbank also made parts for No. 2 revolvers, with final assembly taking place at RSAF Enfield.

Under the mounting pressure of war, the Webley & Scott company returned to the military revolver business with what amounted to a reincarnation of the revolver as it had evolved between

1922 and 1926. Called the Webley Mark IV or No. 4 revolver, it closely resembled the Enfield No. 2 except for the original lockwork, including a spur hammer. It also had plastic stocks with a prominent "W&S" logo. With orders to proceed in the dark days of World War II when Britain stood alone against Nazi Germany, Mark IV production began in early 1942 and continued in large numbers until 1944; the gun remained in general issue until June 1963.

During the war years, the British also purchased more than a million Smith & Wesson M&P model revolvers from the U.S. Most of these Smith & Wesson revolvers chambered the .38/200 British service cartridge, not the .38 Special favored by Americans who owned the Smith & Wesson revolver. Both the No. 2 and Mark IV revolvers served the British armed forces reasonably well, becoming standard equipment for artillerymen and armored vehicle crew members. Interestingly, elite units with a heavy emphasis on pistol training did not favor the double-action-only trigger found on the No. 2, Mark 1* and Mark 1** revolvers. In addition, the ever-increasing popularity of the 9mm Parabellum caliber Sten submachine gun reduced the demand for handguns in the British army; moreover, the No. 2 revolver looked downright archaic compared to more modern automatic pistols like the Walther P.38. Despite all the factors conspiring against its widespread use, the No. 2 revolver served well and was not formally retired from military service until it was replaced by the FN High Power automatic pistol in 1957.

Many British wartime .38 revolvers still remain in use throughout former British colonies and the Commonwealth countries, and as our testing demonstrates, the gun is quite accurate. One five-shot offhand group measured 1.6 inches wide when fired from 25 feet, all in double-action mode. These guns have mild recoil, a smooth trigger pull, and the popular feature of simultaneous extraction and ejection of all cartridges.

BRITISH SERVICE REVOLVERS (ENFIELD NO. 2/WEBLEY MARK IV)

Manufacturer	Years Produced	Caliber/Capacity	Dimensions
Enfield No. 2: RSAF Enfield/Albion Motor Co./ Singer Sewing Machine Co., Clydesbank Webley No. IV: Webley & Scott Ltd., Birmingham	Enfield No. 2: 1931–1945 Webley Mark IV: 1940–1944	.38/200 (.38 S&W)/ up to 6 rounds	(Enfield No. 2) Barrel Length: 5.0" O.A. Length: 10.25" Height: 5.7" Width: 1.4" Weight: 27 oz. (unloaded); 31 oz. (loaded)

COLT NEW SERVICE

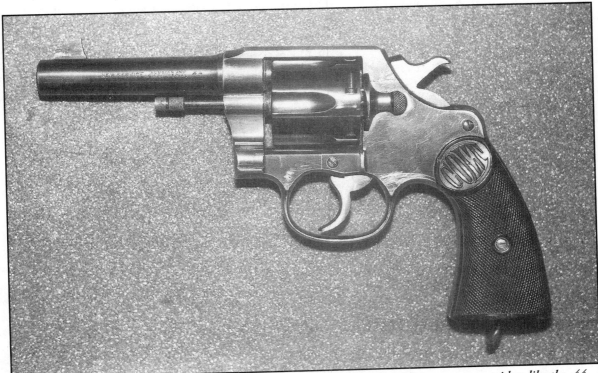

Although double-action prototypes of Colt's revolvers were developed for experimental use as early as the 1850s, the company was slow to adopt double-action revolvers for series production. Once it did, however, several good ones, including the New Service, emerged. Introduced in 1898, it proved to be one of the best and remains a viable service handgun to this day. A large, powerful revolver, the New Service was intended from the beginning to compete for the many military and police contracts that opened up in the 1890s and the early part of the 20th century.

By 1894, Colt had perfected its double-action service revolver design with the New Army & Navy Model. The New Service was essentially an enlarged version of this gun, made stronger to handle more powerful cartridges. The initial chambering was for .45 Colt, the same as Colt's famous Single Action Army model (*see* page 32), which introduced this popular caliber. In time, Colt offered the New Service in 17 other calibers, notably .44 Special and .45 ACP.

One mark of an outstanding handgun is an ability to retain its popularity relatively unchanged over a long period of time, as opposed to being constantly upgraded and modified. Aside from a special competition version called the Master Shooter, with its high-polish finish and adjustable target

Colt's New Service revolver proved a solid and reliable handgun capable of firing strong cartridges like the .44 Special.

sights, the New Service has remained essentially the same throughout its production run.

Among the most famous users of this world-famous revolver have been Canada's Royal Mounted Police and the U.S. Armed Forces. The Mounties used the New Service in both .455 and .45 Colt calibers from 1903 until 1954. Although total procurement was relatively small (about 3,195 units) this was considered a "prestige order" that any gun manufacturer would be happy to fill. As for the U.S. Armed Forces, more than 21,000 New Service revolvers (in .45 Colt caliber) were bought between February 1909 and April 1911, making this the last revolver to serve as a primary service standard handgun for the U.S. military. During World War I, the U.S. ordered New Service revolvers to augment its M1911 automatic pistol, which could not be produced fast enough to satisfy the needs of America's rapidly expanding armed forces. In 1917 the War Department ordered 150,000 New Service revolvers (chambered for the same .45 ACP cartridge used in the M1911 automatic pistol), along with an equal number of Smith & Wesson revolvers of similar configuration.

The War Department's decision to augment automatic pistol issues with these revolvers made sense. The guns had already seen considerable military service and the manufacturing capacity to mass-produce them already existed. The decision to chamber the revolvers for the .45 ACP round, however, created a slight mechanical problem. Most revolver cartridges have a pronounced rim, or flange, located at the rear of the casing. Its purpose is to keep the loaded rounds from moving too far forward into the cylinders, thereby preventing their rotation and jamming the weapon. This rim or flange also gives the extractor star (at the rear of the cylinder) something to push against as it lifts the spent cartridges clear of the cylinder after firing and prior to reloading with fresh ammunition.

A solution to this problem was quickly found. To accommodate the rimless .45 Auto round to their Model 1917 .45 ACP revolvers, Colt and Smith & Wesson both installed small "half-moon clips" each holding three rounds. Later on, Colt added a small step to the forward portion of each firing chamber in the six-round cylinder. Adding this stepped portion not only made certain the firing pin would hit the primer, it also did away with the clips (although this meant the spent cartridges had to be forcibly removed from the cylinder). Eventually, the need for separate metal clips on the .45 Auto Rim cartridge was eliminated altogether.

Once these problems of chambering and extraction were solved, the New Service revolver proved a great success in U.S. military service despite stiff competition from other large double-action military revolvers, such as Smith & Wesson's Model 1917 and the new automatic pistols. By the time New Service production was halted in 1944, total production exceeded 356,000.

Today, the New Service remains a viable combat handgun. Its size and weight provide a relatively soft recoil despite the power of the cartridges it uses. The gun's smooth trigger pull is highly conducive to good accuracy despite its undersized sights. Among the New Service's weak points are its size and weight, plus a trigger reach in the double-action mode that is a real stretch for most shooters. Finally, with the New Service becoming a collector's item, prices have approached the point where their owners hesitate to carry or fire them lest their value suffer adversely.

COLT NEW SERVICE

Manufacturer	Years Produced	Caliber/Capacity	Dimensions
Colt Industries Firearms Division Hartford, CT	1898–1944	.45 ACP & others/ 6 rounds	Barrel Length: 5.5" O.A. Length: 10.8" Height: 6.0" Width: 1.4" Weight: 41 oz. (unloaded); 46 oz. (loaded)

COLT POLICE POSITIVE/ POLICE POSITIVE SPECIAL

When Colt realized how much success Smith & Wesson was enjoying with its Military & Police revolver, Colt decided to make a firearm that would compete with it. The result was the Police Positive revolver, which made its first appearance in 1905 and was kept in production until 1943. Chambered in .38 S&W, this model saw wide use among military and police forces the world over, with total production exceeding 200,000. A slightly smaller .32 Colt caliber Police Positive variant appeared in 1907 and, despite the low-powered cartridge, it also became immensely popular with police forces in the U.S. and Canada.

Another larger, more powerful version—the so-called Police Special—also appeared in 1907. This one, in .38 Special, featured a cylinder that was 1/4-inch longer than the earlier Police Positive revolvers and could be chambered in a variety of calibers, including .38 S&W, .32 Colt and .32-40 Winchester. A variety of barrel lengths up to 6 inches was also available. And although it weighed about 5 ounces more than the earlier Police Positive model, the "Special" was still noticeably lighter and slimmer than Smith & Wesson's competing Military & Police Model. In time, the Police Positive Special became one of Colt's more successful revolver designs. It remained in production until 1973, by which time more than 750,000 were built.

Although Police Positive and Police Positive

Slightly smaller than its rival, the Smith & Wesson Model Military & Police, Colt's Police Positive Special proved accurate and reliable. This version sported a nickel-plated finish for superior corrosion resistance.

Special revolvers are still in service among police forces worldwide, many one-time buyers are switching to more modern handguns, mostly automatic pistols, leaving large numbers of Police Positive and Specials on the used firearms market. Of these guns, only the .38 Special caliber Police Positive Special has the requisite stopping power to make it a truly viable self-defense gun—but only on an emergency basis when nothing better is available.

COLT POLICE POSITIVE / POLICE POSITIVE SPECIAL

Manufacturer	Years Produced	Caliber/Capacity	Dimensions
Colt Industries Firearms Division Hartford, CT	1905–1973	.32 Colt, .38 S&W (PP), .38 Special (PPS)/ 6 rounds	(Police Positive) Barrel Length: 4.0" O.A. Length: 8.5" Height: 5.1" Width: 1.3" Weight: 20 oz. (unloaded); 25 oz. (loaded)

COLT PYTHON

Like the snake that shares its name, the Colt Python is huge, powerful, efficient and deadly. Introduced in 1955, this deluxe shooting machine has always boasted meticulous hand-fitting and polishing of parts, features that are reflected in the gun's significantly higher price. Its most distinctive external feature is a massive barrel,

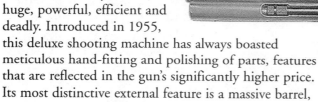

Colt's Python ranks among the most impressive handgun designs of all time, attracting a strong following. This snubnosed model, with blued finish and 2 1/2-inch barrel, is now out of production.

with a ventilated rib on top and a full-length shroud for the ejector rod underneath.

Internally, the Python's most outstanding feature is its trigger pull, which is extraordinarily smooth. That and its well-designed target sights contribute to the gun's accuracy. The Python does not conceal easily, however; even the

This five-shot offhand group made by a Colt Python at a distance of 25 feet measures a remarkable 1¼ inches, attesting to its accuracy.

smallest 2½-inch barreled variant (now out of production) is more than 8 inches long and weighs nearly 38 ounces loaded. The Python's one real failing, though, is its high price. The 1996 retail figure was close to $900 for the least expensive model, while the most costly variant with high-polish stainless finish cost nearly $1,000. But discriminating shooters, including many policemen, are willing to pay top dollar for a gun on which they can literally stake their lives. Consider, too, the Python's excellent resale and collector's value; even if a shooter were to buy one and later switch to another gun, selling the Python will present little problem. It's an excellent gun and a true classic.

COLT PYTHON

Manufacturer	Years Produced	Caliber/Capacity	Dimensions
Colt Industries Firearms Division Hartford, CT	1955–Present	.357 Magnum/6 rounds	Barrel Lengths: 2.5", 4", 6" or 8" O.A. Length: 9.25" (w/4" barrel) Height: 5.7" Width: 1.55" Weight: 38 oz. (unloaded); 44 oz. (loaded)

COLT SINGLE ACTION ARMY (SAA)

The appearance in 1873 of the immortal Single Action Army (SAA) revolver rescued Colt's Patent Fire-Arms Manufacturing Company from a period of weakness and stagnation. Between 1873 and 1941, the Colt firm produced over 350,000 of these revolvers, with the U.S. Army taking 37,075 and the balance going to militia units, police forces and private citizens in the U.S. and all over the world. Manufacture of the Single Action Army stopped in 1941 to make room for wartime production; but after World War II ended, a resurgence of interest in "six-shooters" related to the Old West generated a tremendous demand for the gun's revival. Colt thereupon resumed production in 1956 and has been making the SAA ever since. However, the need to concentrate on more modern firearms eventually predominated, forcing Colt to quit cataloguing the Single Action Army (although it continued to offer the gun through its Custom Shop). But, in 1992, the company reintroduced the SAA again into full production, with a wide choice of barrel lengths, calibers and finishes, including polished nickel and royal blue with color casehardened frame.

Ranked among the most famous handguns in the world, the Single Action Army has gone through countless variations and has been offered in at least 30 different calibers (.45 Colt has always

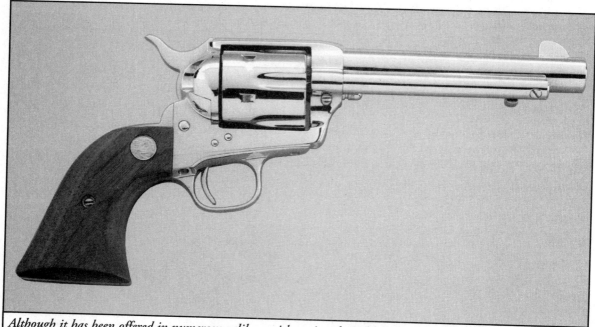

Although it has been offered in numerous calibers with various barrel lengths, the classic lines of Colt's famous Single Action Army (SAA) revolver are unmistakable and are recognized worldwide. This contemporary version with full nickel finish bears the traditional walnut grips and Colt medallion.

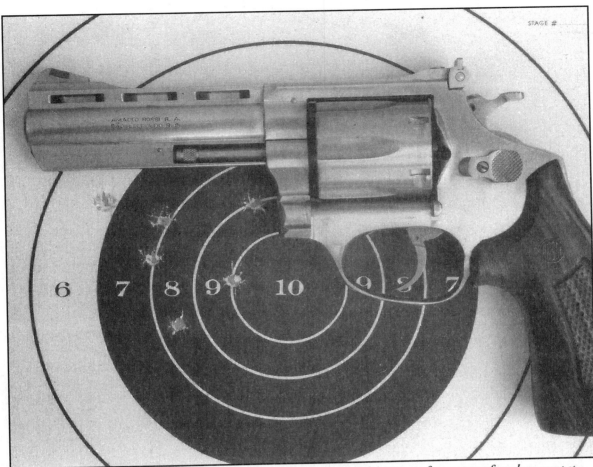

The fully underlugged barrel and ventilated sighting rib on the Model 851 are features not found on competing revolvers in the same price range. In terms of accuracy, our test firing from 25 feet with a six-shot offhand group measured 2.9 inches.

revolvers—and at a considerably lower price. For those who need a well-made, full-sized combat revolver backed by a top-flight manufacturer and importer, the Model 851 deserves a close look, particularly for those whose budgets don't allow an extra $100 or so for a Smith & Wesson of comparable size and features.

ROSSI MODEL 851

Manufacturer	Years Produced	Caliber/Capacity	Dimensions
Amadeo Rossi S.A. Sao Leopoldo, Brazil Imported by: Interarms Alexandria, VA	1991–Present	.38 Special/up to 6 rounds	Barrel Length: 3" or 4" O.A. Length: 8" or 9" Height: 5.1" Width: 1.4" Weight: 27.5 or 30 oz. (unloaded) 30.5 or 33 oz. (loaded)

ROSSI MODEL 971

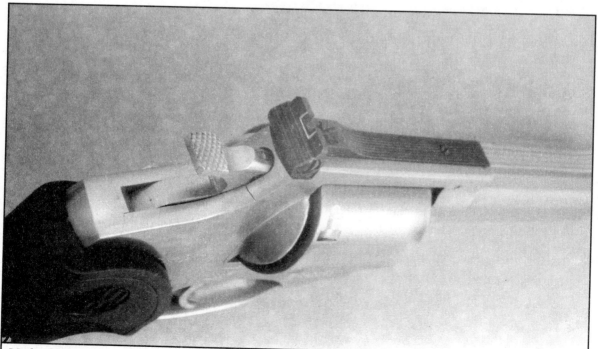

The Model 971 is one of the most popular guns in the Rossi line. Consequently, it offers several variations, including a blued model with fluted cylinder and 4-inch barrel, and stainless-steel versions with 4- or 6-inch barrels and unfluted, smooth-surfaced cylinders. The stainless 971 VRC with vented rib is shown at right.

Rossi began making its stainless Model 971 with built-in recoil compensator in 1993. Whatever barrel length or finish they have, all Model 971s are equipped with six-shot cylinders made for the powerful .357 Magnum cartridge (or the slightly shorter .38 Special round). The rear sight, which is outlined with a thin white line, is adjustable and, unlike the Model 851, is made of blued steel rather than stainless. The front sight features a non-snag ramp design that's pinned in place on the heavy rib above the barrel. It also has a red insert on the rear surface to help catch the shooter's eye. Grips are usually made from checkered rubber with finger rests, although wooden grips are also available.

Handling is not as good as that found on most competing revolvers in this caliber. The trigger pull is rough, and the cylinder latch and ejector rod are not particularly good. Despite these shortcomings, the Model 971 we tested demonstrated surprisingly good accuracy out to 25 feet. The best six-shot, rapid-fire offhand group fired from 25 feet, using Winchester 110-grain jacketed hollowpoint rounds,

Made of blued steel rather than stainless, the excellent rear sight on Rossi's popular .357 Magnum Model 971 contributes greatly to the gun's fine accuracy.

The Model 971 is available in a number of configurations, including this compensated version with unfluted cylinder and neoprene stocks. The six-shot offhand group shown above measures 1.6 inches. From a distance of 25 feet, all shots were fired in the heavier double-action trigger mode. Single-action shots with their lighter trigger pull tend to provide better accuracy.

spanned just 1.6 inches; at 50 feet, our best group (fired in double-action mode) went into 4.9 inches.

In sum, numerous manufacturers—including Colt, Ruger, Smith & Wesson and Taurus—all have truly excellent revolvers in .357 Magnum caliber. The chief advantages of Rossi's Model 971, shared by most other Rossi revolvers, are its adequate performance and low price.

ROSSI MODEL 971

Manufacturer	Years Produced	Caliber/Capacity	Dimensions
Amadeo Rossi S.A. Sao Leopoldo, Brazil Imported by: Interarms Alexandria, VA	1990–Present	.357 Magnum/up to 6 rounds	Barrel Length: 4" or 6" O.A. Length: 9.2" or 11.2" Height: 5.3" Width: 1.5" Weight: 35 or 41 oz. (unloaded) 37.5 or 43.5 oz. (loaded)

RUGER GP100

When Sturm, Ruger and Company began making firearms in 1949, its first product— the Standard Automatic pistol in .22 Long Rifle—was an immediate and enduring success. Ruger soon followed with its single-action revolvers after Smith & Wesson successfully debuted theirs. Since then, Ruger has introduced a large number of high-quality guns for civilian, military and police use. Its police revolvers—including the Speed Six, Service-Six and Security-Six—have since 1969 made significant inroads into the U.S. police market, traditionally dominated by Colt and Smith & Wesson. The Ruger revolvers all proved extremely useful and successful, gaining a reputation for durability, reliability and accuracy.

As good as these revolvers have been, though, Ruger wanted to make something better. Accordingly, the company decided in 1988 to update its police revolver line by introducing the powerful, medium-frame GP100 and the small-frame SP101 (*see* separate listing). The GP100's rugged, modularized frame is easily disassembled. An exposed hammer, typical of most double-action revolvers, can either be thumb-cocked for single-action firing with a short, light trigger stroke or pulled all the way through a much longer, heavier travel for double-action shooting.

The all-steel construction of the GP100 helps make it strong and tames recoil. Workmanship is up to Ruger's typically excellent standard. Both blued and stainless steel versions are available, as are numerous variations in barrel length, making the GP100 useful for every shooting purpose from concealed-carry to hunting. A coil mainspring is standard. The grips are mostly rubber with wood inserts and are exceptionally comfortable. The cylinder, which holds up to six rounds, features a release that pushes in, much like the magazine release on an automatic pistol. As with all .357 Magnum handguns, .38 Special ammunition can also be fired. The ejector rod is not especially smooth in operation, but considering the GP100's 4-inch barrel, it's long enough to extract the empty cartridges after firing.

The sight's excellent fixed pattern provides a large, easy-to-use picture. In common with virtually all service revolvers manufactured since

The GP100 (top) is shown in standard service configuration with fixed sights and 4-inch barrel. It's roughly the same size as the Israeli-made Baby Eagle, a CZ-75 9mm clone (bottom).

1968 for sale in the U.S., the GP100 features a transfer-bar safety mechanism that prevents the hammer from reaching the firing pin until the trigger has been pulled all the way to the rear at the moment of firing.

The GP100 fits comfortably in the hand and balances well. Recoil is calmed by the weight of the gun and its excellent grip design. The trigger pull, while long and gritty, is not excessively heavy. As for the GP100's accuracy, our best five-shot offhand efforts measured 1.7 inches at 25 feet using Winchester 110-grain JHP. At 25 feet, using Cor-Bon +p+ .38

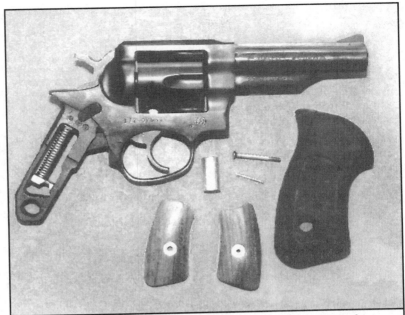

The GP100 is easily disassembled without tools, as shown. Note the wooden inserts in the live-rubber stocks.

The GP100's accuracy is evident in this five-shot, 25-foot offhand group measuring 1.7 inches.

Special JHP ammunition, a five-shot group spanned 1.9 inches; and with .357 JHP at 50 feet the group measured 5.2 inches. All test-firing was done in double-action mode.

In a world where the high-capacity automatic pistol is considered state of the art, a traditional "sixgun" like the GP100 may be regarded by some as a dinosaur, but be assured that this excellent revolver is far from outdated. Loaded with suitable ammunition (the .357 Magnum is recommended), this weapon can be formidable.

RUGER GP100

Manufacturer	Years Produced	Caliber/Capacity	Dimensions
Sturm, Ruger & Co., Inc. Southport, CT	1988–Present	.357 Magnum/ 6 rounds	Barrel Length: 3", 4" or 6" O.A. Length: 9.4" w/4" bbl. Height: 4.75" Width: 1.5" Weight: 35-46 oz. (unloaded); add about 2.5 oz. (loaded)

RUGER REDHAWK

Ruger introduced the Redhawk in 1979, followed by the even larger Super Redhawk in 1987. although these massive weapons are best suited for hunting and handgun shooting competition, either gun — especially the Redhawk with its shorter (5½ inches) barrel — is accurate and powerful enough to serve as a defensive firearm.

For Ruger, the Redhawk represented an important transition from the company's Security-Six (1969) and GP100/SP101 series revolvers, introduced from 1988 on. Like other Ruger revolvers, the Redhawk features a coil mainspring, a transfer-bar safety mechanism, easy

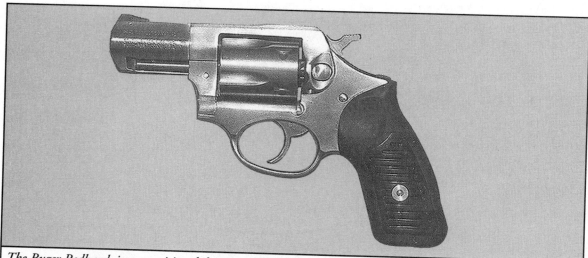

The Ruger Redhawk is a transitional design connecting the original Ruger double-action revolvers, such as the Security Six, with modern revolvers like the SP101 shown above.

The Redhawk's cylinder release latch consists of a button lying almost flush with the frame, which the user pushes in to open the crane.

disassembly (without a side-plate) and a cylinder latch. Like most .44 magnum revolvers, recoil is impressive with full-power loads; yet it's easy to keep on target and shoots with authority and accuracy.

Ruger makes the Redhawk in both blued and stainless steel finishes. Its front sight is a wide ram with an orange insert, while the rear sight is adjustable. The stocks are huge wooden types that flare out toward the bot-

The Redhawk is both accurate and powerful. This six-shot offhand group, fired from a distance of 25 feet, measures 1.9 inches.

tom of the frame and are well-shaped for all but the smallest hand.

Considering how difficult it is to find a Ruger revolver that doesn't offer excellent performance at a reasonable price, the Redhawk is a superior large-caliber revolver and a fine representative of the Ruger line of handguns.

RUGER REDHAWK

Manufacturer	Years Produced	Caliber/Capacity	Dimensions
Sturm, Ruger & Co., Inc. Southport, CT	1979–Present	.44 Magnum/.44 Special up to 6 rounds	Barrel Length: 5.5" or 7.5" O.A. Length: 11" (w/5.5" bbl.) Height: 6.0" Width: 1.6" Weight: 50 oz. (unloaded); 56 oz. (loaded)

RUGER SINGLE-ACTION REVOLVERS

In the 1950s when Colt temporarily discontinued production of its Single Action Army (SAA) Revolver, Ruger took up some of the slack by building several of its own single-actions. Beginning with smaller rimfire models (the Single-Six in 1953 and the Bearcat in 1958), Ruger competed more directly with Colt by introducing the Blackhawk in 1955. While its version looked much like the SAA (but with improved adjustable sights), Ruger showed some originality by replacing the SAA's leaf springs with coil springs and instituting an improved firing-pin design.

Ruger's great success at selling SAA clones was, in fact, a major factor in Colt's decision to resume SAA production in 1955. The only fly in the ointment for Ruger was the gun's safety. Early Ruger knockoffs were too much like the SAA in that they too were unsafe to carry with a round in the chamber beneath the hammer. When several accidental shootings occurred, some of them fatal, Ruger offered a free retrofit program for its early Blackhawk, Super Blackhawk, Single-Six and Bearcat models. Since 1973, these guns all have been equipped with a transfer-bar safety mechanism that reduces accidental discharges to a minimum. Note that if any of these four guns is marked "New Model" on the frame, then it has already been fitted with the modern safety devices. If one of these models is not so marked, owners who desire the modifications may contact the manufacturer at the following address:

Sturm, Ruger and Company, Inc., Lacey Place, Southport, CT 06490

Ruger will send instructions on how to return the gun to the factory for the safety retrofit.

Ruger still makes a number of SAA-type guns. The Bearcat is now called the New Bearcat and comes with two cylinders, enabling shooters to change from .22 Long Rifle to .22 Magnum at will. The Single-Six is available in two variations: the New Model Single-Six, chambered for the .22 LR and .22 Magnum cartridges, and the New Model Super Single-Six, which is available in .32 H&R Magnum caliber and a .22LR/.22WMR combination package.

Ruger's Bisley closely resembles the revolver of the same name that was made by Colt from 1894 to 1915. Primarily a target-shooting variant of the accurate SAA, the Bisley made by Ruger comes in

Ruger's New Model Single-Six is a re-issue of the original Single-Six introduced in 1953. The "New Model" designation indicates improved lockwork, which reduces the danger of accidental discharge should a loaded gun be dropped. Also available in a stainless steel finish, this gun fires two calibers—either .22 Long Rifle or .22 Magnum—simply by changing cylinders.

.22 LR, .32 H&R Magnum, .357 Magnum, .41 Magnum and .45 Long Colt calibers, with barrel lengths of 6.5 or 7.5 inches.

The New Model Blackhawk remains an SAA-type gun with adjustable sights, available in .30 carbine, .357 Magnum, .41 Magnum, and .45 Colt calibers. The New Model Super Blackhawk is available in .44 Magnum caliber only. The New Model Super Blackhawk Hunter, with its integral scope rings on a heavy, ribbed barrel (making it especially suited for hunting), sports a 7.5-inch barrel, stain-

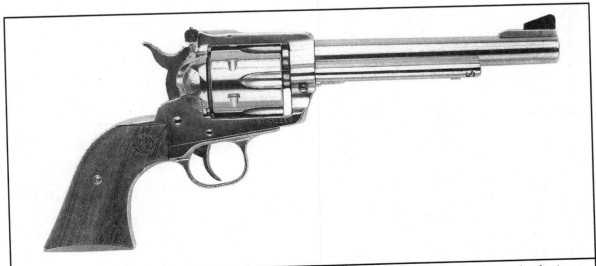

The Ruger New Model Blackhawk features adjustable sights but is otherwise almost identical to the classic Single Action Army design.

The Ruger Bisley is a copy of Colt's most famous variation of the Single Action Army Revolver. Complete with fluted, roll-engraved cylinder, the beauty is reminiscent of turn-of-the-century Bisleys.

less finish, and laminated wood grips. These features help make this model especially well suited for rugged service in the field.

The latest Ruger single-action, introduced in 1994, is the Vaquero (Spanish for "cowboy"), a fixed-sight version of the Ruger Blackhawk. Ruger makes the Vaquero in three calibers—.44-40, .44 Magnum and .45 Long Colt—and three barrel lengths: 4 5/8, 5 1/2 and 7 1/2 inches. Two finishes are available—one with a blued barrel and cylinder with color casehardened frame, and the other a high-gloss bright stainless steel (shown on page 72).

Despite the many excellent Single Action Army copies being produced in Germany, Italy and elsewhere, U.S. gunmakers still dominate the manufacture of this all-American gun. The SAAs made by Colt and the Ruger variations continue to rank among the finest handguns available for their beauty and rugged performance.

RUGER SINGLE-ACTION REVOLVERS

(Made by Sturm, Ruger & Co., Inc., Southport, CT)

Dimensions for selected Ruger Single-Action Revolvers

Model	Barrel Length*	Overall Length**	Weight (unloaded)	Caliber/Capacity
BISLEY	7.5"	13.0"	48 oz.	.45 LC, .357 Mag. .44 Mag.+/6 rounds
NEW MODEL BLACKHAWK	4.6"	10.25"	39 oz.	.357 Mag., .45 LC/ 6 rounds
SINGLE-SIX	4.6"	9.9"	32 oz.	.22 LR or Mag./6 rounds
VAQUERO	4.6"	10.25"	39 oz.	.44-40, .45 LC .44 Mag.+/6 rounds

*other barrel lengths available   **varies with barrel length   +other calibers available

SMITH & WESSON MODEL 15

Smith & Wesson's Model 15 made its debut in 1950 as the "Combat Masterpiece," a K-frame revolver similar to the classic Military & Police Model (Model 10) but equipped with adjustable sights and an improved trigger. In 1957, when Smith & Wesson supplemented its model names with numbers, the Combat Masterpiece became the Model 15. In 1962, the U.S. Air Force—never happy with its M1911A1 automatic pistols—made the decision to change over to revolvers and, beginning in 1963, ordered from Smith & Wesson 15,205 modified Model 15 revolvers with 2-inch barrels. This began a series of large-scale revolver purchases by the U.S. armed forces that contin-

Smith & Wesson's Model 15 (top) is, like the FN High Power shown below, a solid and reliable handgun. This Model 15 has a 4-inch barrel, while the U.S. Air Force has for decades opted for the 2 1/2-inch barrel version.

The Model 15 proves its accuracy with this five-shot offhand group measuring 1.1 inches from 25 feet.

ued until the early 1980s, by which time testing for a new 9mm service pistol was well underway.

Easy to shoot and extremely accurate, the Model 15 is a sensational revolver, built to a flawless standard of fit, finish and workmanship. The adjustable sights offer a good sight picture without being so large as to hinder concealment. With its standard 4-inch barrel, the Model 15 is about the same size as a CZ 75 or an FN Browning High Power pistol. It is indeed an excellent gun capable of rugged and reliable service.

SMITH & WESSON MODEL 15

Manufacturer	Years Produced	Caliber/Capacity	Dimensions
Smith & Wesson Springfield, MA	1950–Present	.38 Special/up to 6 rounds	Barrel Length: 4" O.A. Length: 9.3" Height: 5.3" Width: 1.4" Weight: 32 oz. (unloaded); 35 oz. (loaded)

SMITH & WESSON MODELS 57, 58 AND 657

In an attempt to make a truly powerful handgun, one that would be easier than the massive .44 Magnum for hunters and police to control, Smith & Wesson introduced the .41 Magnum Model 57 in 1963. Conceived primarily as a hunting and target model, it sported an adjustable rear sight. The Model 58, which appeared the following year, came with a fixed rear sight and 4-inch barrel only. The stainless steel Model 657 (shown above), which is identical to the Model 57 except for its metallurgy, appeared in 1986.

Smith & Wesson's goal in developing the .41 Magnum was to split the difference between the .357 Magnum on the low end and the .44 Magnum on the high end. The company sought a gun/cartridge combination that would be at once easier to shoot and more powerful than the .357 and still approach the power level of the .44 Magnum. Consider these numbers:

- With a 170-grain bullet, a standard Remington-made .41 Magnum cartridge develops a muzzle velocity of 1420 fps, while another Remington load, using a 175-grain cartridge, travels at 1250 fps. To reduce recoil, Remington also makes a "medium velocity" magnum loading, firing a 210-grainbullet at a muzzle velocity of 965 feet per second. The maximum energy of the .41 Magnum in a factory loading is 760 foot-pounds.
- For factory-loaded versions of the .44 Magnum, the top figures equal a 180-grain bullet traveling at 1610 fps and producing 1035 foot-pounds of energy.
- For the .357 Magnum, the figures for factory-loaded ammo come out to a 125-grain bullet at 1450 fps producing 585 foot-pounds of energy.

From these ballistics figures, it appears that Smith & Wesson and the ammo makers succeeded, at least from a technical standpoint, in creating an intermediate magnum cartridge between the .357 and .44 Magnums.

Despite this achievement, the .41 Magnum apparently never caught on in popularity, dealing a particularly hard blow to the Model 58. A large police department in California, for example, discovered that its officers were having difficulty shooting the .41 Magnum with enough accuracy to pass the qualification tests. In addition to control problems among users who were trained to handle the milder .38 Special and .357 revolvers, the .41 Magnum name itself proved a poor choice for police departments ever alert to possible litigation. Several commentators who like the cartridge suggested that the .41 Magnum would have been easier to sell to police administrators with a name like ".41 Police" or ".41 Special." At any rate, the Model 58, which was available in standard blue or special-order nickel finishes, went out of production in 1991. The Models 57 and 657 are still listed in Smith & Wesson's catalogs, but they are certainly not among the top sellers.

Meanwhile, relatively little business exists for the .41 Magnum cartridge, which proved at once promising ballistically and disappointing financially. The Model 57/58/657 series is no larger in size than the more popular Model 625 in .45 ACP, and they fire a far more effective cartridge for hunting purposes. Why these .41 Magnum guns have not enjoyed greater success remains a mystery. Still, the promise of an effective intermediate cartridge crops up from time to time. The .41 Action Express, the 10mm Auto and the .40 S&W have all been more or less successful attempts to produce an intermediate-level cartridge in the wake for the ill-fated .41 Magnum.

SMITH & WESSON MODELS 57, 58 AND 657

Manufacturer	Years Produced	Caliber/Capacity	Dimensions
Smith & Wesson Springfield, MA	1963–Present (57) 1964–1991 (58) 1986–Present (657)	.41 Magnum/up to 6 rounds	Barrel Length: 6" or 8.4" O.A. Length: 11.4" (w/6" barrel) Height: 5.8" Width: 1.6" Weight: 48 oz. (unloaded); 54 oz. (loaded)

SMITH & WESSON MODEL 625

Although the .45 ACP cartridge is best known for its use in automatic pistols, mainly the Colt Model M1911 introduced in the early 1900s, its history with revolvers stretches back nearly as far. During America's involvement in World War I, both Colt and Smith & Wesson produced large quantities of revolvers chambered for the .45 ACP round to supplement M1911 issues. The Smith & Wesson M1917 version of the .45-caliber revolver became quite popular and continued to be produced after the war. In 1955, Smith & Wesson introduced an improved version of this revolver, known as the Model 25 (now out of production). A stainless steel variant of this revolver—the Model 625, with additional refinements to the stocks and sights—joined the Smith & Wesson line in 1989.

Because it is made on S&W's N frame, the Model 625 is a hefty gun. Available with a 5-inch barrel only, it does not have a transfer-bar

Smith & Wesson's Model 625 (top) is a massive N-frame revolver whose large size is readily apparent when compared to S&W's Model 4516 automatic pistol (below) in the same caliber. Because of the tremendous variety of .45 ACP ammo available, Smith & Wesson wisely included an adjustable sight on its Model 625.

This five-shot offhand group measuring 1.8 inches was fired from a Model 625 at a distance of 25 feet. Unlike many .45-caliber automatic pistols, this revolver can feed and fire all types of .45 ACP ammunition with reliability.

mechanism to reduce the chances of unintentional discharge; instead, it uses a hammer-mounted firing pin and rebound slide. This keeps the firing pin away from the cartridge primer until the trigger is pulled. The effect is the same as with a transfer bar and makes the gun much safer to carry with a loaded chamber directly under the hammer than was the case with older revolvers.

The front sight on the Model 625 is a prominent Patridge type, with the rear sight featuring S&W's famous micrometer adjustable unit. These target-type adjustable sights are all black, with no dots, lines or other markings to complicate the sight picture. The semi-target type hammer is .4 inch wide, and the trigger is an efficient, smooth-faced combat type. Like Colt's King Cobra, the Model 625 has a fully underlugged barrel; but in all other respects the Model 625 closely follows Smith & Wesson's N frame in form and practice.

As all .45-ACP revolvers, the Model 625 is best reloaded from clips, either the "full-moon" type holding six rounds (enough to recharge the entire cylinder) or "half-moon" clips that hold only three rounds. While full-moon clips offer the advantage of rapid reloading, they are quite bulky, measuring 1.5 inches across and weighing about 5 ounces. The half-moon clips are much easier to conceal, although two are needed for a complete reload. The .45 Auto Rim round, now out of production, also works in this revolver since the cartridge itself supplies its own rim against which the extractor works. The standard .45-ACP round can also be loaded without a clip, but a pencil or similar implement will be needed to extract the empty cartridge casings after firing.

The Model 625-4 tested for this book was quite accurate. It's a comfortable gun to shoot, and its recoil levels are not excessive. The standard Smith & Wesson revolver trigger is smooth, slick and well suited to rapid double-action shooting. The 625's sole weakness is its size. The Smith & Wesson Model 4516 automatic pistol in the same caliber holds one more round and is over three inches shorter. A competent gunsmith, however, can easily shorten the barrel on a Model 625 to as short as 2.5 inches in overall length. With a shortened barrel, rounded lower grip (butt) and concealment-type stocks fitted, this model can be a fine, concealable piece with a lot of power. Otherwise, for those who want to carry a gun this size, the other Smith & Wesson N-frame revolvers are chambered in more potent magnum cartridges.

SMITH & WESSON MODELS 625

Manufacturer	Years Produced	Caliber/Capacity	Dimensions
Smith & Wesson Springfield, MA	1989–Present	.45 ACP/up to 6 rounds	Barrel Length: 5" O.A. Length: 10.5" Height: 5.8" Width: 1.5" Weight: 45 oz. (unloaded); 50 oz. (loaded)

SMITH & WESSON MODEL 629

Although Smith & Wesson's Model 29 revolver in .44 Magnum remained extremely popular with collectors and shooters, experienced handgunners familiar with full-power cartridges reported problems with the durability of this model. At the same time, Ruger's introduction of the Redhawk (*see* page 70) caused Smith & Wesson to consider ways of creating a stronger version of its Model 29. The result—the Model 629 series—began production in 1990. These improved Model 29s, featuring stainless steel

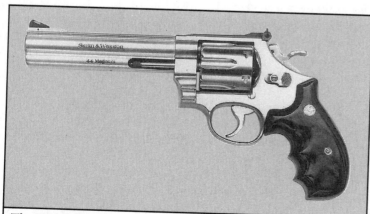

The Model 629 Classic DX, with interchangeable front sights, represents one of Smith & Wesson's latest efforts to compete in the .44 Magnum revolver market.

construction, include a number of major variations:

• Model 629—standard version, which is simply a Model 29 in stainless steel with 4-, 6- or 8 3/8-inch barrel;

• Model 629 Classic—this has a strengthened frame and cylinder and is available in barrel lengths of 5, 6 1/2 or 8 3/8 inches;

• Model 629 Classic DX—identical to the Model 629 Classic, but with interchangeable sight assemblies and in barrel lengths of only 6 1/2 or 8 3/8 inches; and

• Model 629 Powerport—

with Patridge front sight, adjustable black blade rear sight and 6¹/₂-inch barrel;
  • Mountain Revolver—equipped with 4-inch barrel only.

Introduction of the Model 629 series has given the entire Model 29 line new popularity. Because of their large size and heavy recoil, though, these handguns are not for everyone. Still, the .44 Magnum revolvers in general, and the Model 29 line in particular, remain great favorites with many shooters, particularly those in the U.S.

SMITH & WESSON MODELS 629 (CLASSIC WITH 5" BARREL)

Manufacturer	Years Produced	Caliber/Capacity	Dimensions
Smith & Wesson Springfield, MA	1990–Present	.44 Magnum/up to 6 rounds	Barrel Length: 5" O.A. Length: 10.5" Height: 5.7" Width: 1.6" Weight: 51 oz. (unloaded); 59 oz. (loaded)

SMITH & WESSON MODEL 686

When it became apparent that Smith & Wesson's Models 19/66 "Combat Magnums" were not holding up under the constant pounding of hot .357 ammunition, the company saw the need to introduce a heavier revolver. The first of the new "L frames," which fell in size between the handy K frame (as used in the Models 10, 19, 66, among other highly successful revolvers) and the massive N frame (as used in the Model 27), appeared in 1981. Since then the L-framed Model 686 has become a successful police and civilian gun, competing on essentially equal terms with Ruger's GP100 and Colt's King Cobra (*see* separate listings).

In addition to being much larger in the cylinder and upper frame (all stainless) than the Model 19, the Model 686 also has larger stocks and grips. As a result, its chief advantage lies in its considerable increase in strength, albeit at the expense of more size and weight. Still, the Model 686, while nearly as strong, remains much smaller

Unlike some older Smith & Wesson revolvers, the Model 686 does not use counterbored cylinders to enclose the cartridge rims.

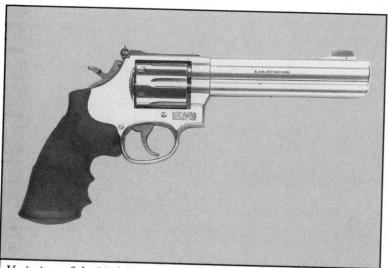

Variations of the Model 686 include the 686 Powerport, which features a 6-inch full lug barrel with integral compensator, Hogue square-butt rubber grips and black-pinned Patridge front sight.

than the brawny N-framed Model 27. Typical of Smith & Wesson products, fit and finish are outstanding, with all controls operating smoothly. One cost-cutting measure that is readily apparent, however, involves the cylinders, which are no longer counterbored to enclose the cartridge rims as in older S&W revolvers.

Variations of the Model 686 include the 686 Powerport, featuring a 6-inch full lug barrel with integral compensator, Hogue square-butt rubber grips and black-pinned Patridge front sight; and the 686 Plus Distinguished

In size the Model 686 falls between the massive N-framed Model 27 and the K-framed Model 19. Using a Model 686, this five-shot offhand group fired from 25 feet measured 2.2 inches.

Combat Magnum, with 2¹/₂-, 4- or 6 -inch full lug barrel.

Despite its size, the Model 686 is well suited for combat purposes and is comfortable to shoot as well. Its smooth-faced trigger is a real plus in rapid, double-action shooting, and the trigger pull is smooth and easy. Despite the power of the .357 Magnum round, recoil is not a problem; and the stocks, while bulky, are easy to hold.

Accuracy results with the Model 686 during rapid double-action shooting were good. Our best five-shot, 25-foot group measured 2.2 inches across; and at 50 feet the group measured 4.1 inches across. In general, the Model 686 handled well using both 110-grain jacketed hollowpoints and the heavier 158-grain bullets. So if you can conceal the bulk of this gun, especially when compared to the Model 19, this fine Smith & Wesson revolver is an excellent choice.

SMITH & WESSON MODELS 686

Manufacturer	Years Produced	Caliber/Capacity	Dimensions
Smith & Wesson Springfield, MA	1981–Present	.357 Magnum/up to 6 rounds	Barrel Lengths: 2¹/₂", 4", 6", 8³/₈" O.A. Length: 7.5" Height: 5.9" Width: 1.5" Weight: 36–53 oz. (unloaded) 39.5–56.5 oz. (loaded)

TAURUS MODEL 44

To compete with its long-established rivals—Smith & Wesson, Colt and Ruger—Taurus introduced its .44 Magnum Model 44 in 1995. Whether this bold move will succeed for Taurus remains to be seen, but the Brazilian designers certainly crafted an interesting .44 Magnum handgun. Features include the same grip size as that of other Taurus .357-caliber models, with the forward portion of the frame and barrel enlarged. Hand-filling santoprene stocks—sorely needed in a hefty .44 Magnum revolver—add to shooting comfort and recoil control. Both blued and stainless steel models are available.

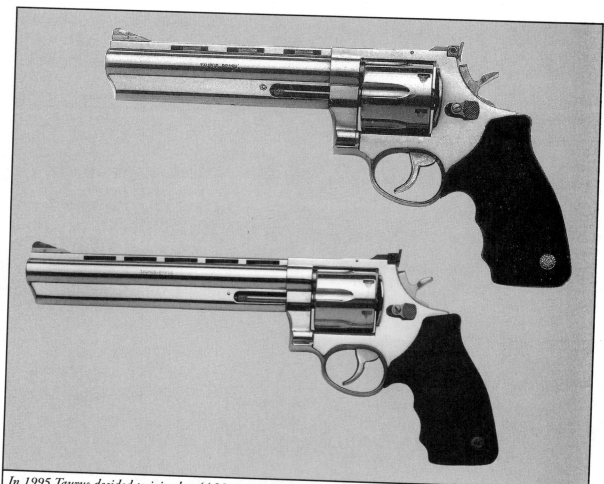

In 1995 Taurus decided to join the .44 Magnum competition with its Model 44. Available in several versions, the six-inch vent-barrel model comes with a blued finish (top), while the longest version in stainless sports an eight-inch barrel similar to the largest versions of Smith & Wesson's Model 29.

All the Model 44 variations—even the short four-inch barrel version shown on the previous page—have an integral compensator system consisting of four holes drilled on each side of the front sight to vent powder gases straight up. The longer barrel versions work better, of course, because their greater length increases the downward force, thus adding enough leverage to counteract muzzle rise. The four-inch barrel variation has a heavy solid rib atop the barrel, while the other two versions feature ventilated ribs that allow for scope mounting. On all variations, the rear sight is adjustable, enabling shooters to zero in with a particular brand or bullet weight of ammunition.

TAURUS MODEL 44

Manufacturer	Years Produced	Caliber/Capacity	Dimensions
Forjas Taurus S.A. Porto Alegre, Brazil Imported by: Taurus Int'l Miami, FL	1995–Present	.44 Magnum/6 rounds	Barrel Length: 4", 6.5" or 8.4" O.A. Length: 9.5", 12.0" or 13.9" Height: 7.9" Width: 1.45" Weight: (w/4" bbl.) 44 oz. (unloaded) 49 oz. (loaded)

TAURUS MODEL 65

When Taurus introduced its Model 65 and 66 in 1978, its intent was to compete with Smith & Wesson's Model 19/66 as low-cost, high-quality service revolvers using the powerful .357 Magnum round. The Model 65 became the company's economy model featuring 2 1/2-, 3- and 4-inch barrels and a fixed sight system. The Model 65 also offers grips made from attractive and durable checkered Brazilian hardwood. The Model 66 with its adjustable sights, offered more options.

Although it's not quite as good as a Smith & Wesson Model 19, the Model 65 shoots well. Recoil is manageable, but recoil-sensitive shooters may prefer using .38 Special +P rounds rather than full-power .357 Magnum loads. We chose to test this revolver with the .357 Magnum, and our best five-shot rapid-fire offhand group fired at 25 feet measured 3.0 inches using Winchester 125-grain jacketed hollowpoint rounds.

Overall, the Model 65 is an excellent revolver, made all the more attractive with a cost that's considerably lower than its equivalent at Smith & Wesson.

TAURUS MODEL 65

Manufacturer	Years Produced	Caliber/Capacity	Dimensions
Forjas Taurus S.A. Porto Alegre, Brazil Imported by: Taurus Int'l Miami, FL	1978–1996	.357 Magnum/6 rounds	Barrel Length: 3" or 4" O.A. Length: 8.5" Height: 5.3" Width: 1.45" Weight: 34 oz. (unloaded) 37.5 oz. (loaded)

TAURUS MODEL 66

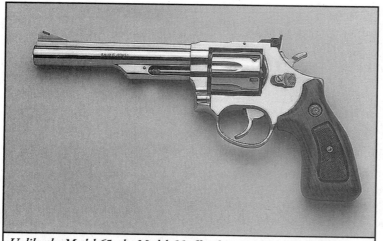

The Model 66 made by Taurus has become one of the most popular revolvers in the company's line. Initially conceived as an improvement over its rather pedestrian Model 80 (*see* next listing), Taurus has created an extremely versatile revolver, one that's been offered in three barrel lengths and three finishes. It also served as the inspiration for the company's more advanced Model 669 (*see* page 91).

In addition to being extraordinarily well built, the Model 66 is easy to shoot. Its wide target-type hammer, grooved trigger and adjustable sights may not be every shooter's favorite features on a service-type or defensive revolver, but most of us can learn to live with them. As for accuracy, results during rapid, double-action test firing were good. Our best six-shot, 10-foot group measured 1.6 inches across, and at 25 feet the next group measured 3.0 inches across (at 50 feet, the result was 4.6 inches). Interestingly, the Model 66 worked well with both .38 Special and .357 Magnum rounds. Most .357 Magnum revolvers don't shoot as accurately with the shorter .38 Specials compared with the .357 Magnum rounds for which they were designed.

Unlike the Model 65, the Model 66 offered more options, including an adjustable rear sight and six-inch barrel version.

As with the slightly less expensive Model 65, the Taurus Model 66 is a good choice as a defensive handgun for those who prefer the handling and features of Smith & Wesson's Combat Magnum series of revolvers but can't afford them. With a properly tuned trigger and other refinements, the Taurus holds promise as a target revolver, too, particularly since it does so well with both .38 and .357 ammunition.

TAURUS MODEL 66

Manufacturer	Years Produced	Caliber/Capacity	Dimensions
Forjas Taurus S.A. Porto Alegre, Brazil Imported by: Taurus Int'l Miami, FL	1978–1996	.357 Magnum/6 rounds	Barrel length: 3", 4" or 6" O.A. Length: 8.5" Height: 5.3" Width: 1.45" Weight: 35 oz. (unloaded); 38.5 oz. (loaded)

TAURUS MODELS 80, 82 AND 83

Taurus's Model 80, which dates from 1971, is essentially a clone of Smith & Wesson's Model 10. It enjoyed wide use in South America and the Middle East as a police and military handgun and was the backbone of the Taurus handgun line until it was discontinued in 1997.

Available in blued or satin nickel finishes, the Model 80 used the same narrow barrel common to the original Smith & Wesson Model 10, rather than the heavy barrel found on many Taurus revolvers. Everything on the Model 80 is simple, reliable and quite accurate. Our best six-shot group fired from 10 feet measured only 1.1 inches across—about the distance one would have to fire at close range in self-defense. Our best six-shot, 25-foot group measured 3.3 inches across, and at 50 feet the group measured 6.6 inches across.

The Model 82 (shown above) is quite similar to the Model 80, and was introduced shortly after it. The Model 82 has also been compared to the Smith & Wesson Model 15. A specialized version—the Model 83—appeared in 1977, featuring a four-inch heavy barrel, enlarged target-type stocks and adjustable sights. Its accuracy is quite good, with one six-shot rapid-fire offhand group fired from 10

The close-range accuracy of the Model 82 is impressive, as shown by this six-shot 1.25-inch group fired from 10 feet (four of those shots landed in a 1/2-inch pattern in the bull's-eye).

feet measuring 1.25 inches (four of those shots landed in a 1/2-inch pattern in the bull's-eye). At 25 feet, a full cylinder of six shots produced a 2.6-inch pattern. Two different six-shot offhand groups fired from 50 feet went into four inches, which is good performance for most shooters in double-action revolver shooting.

Overall, the Model 83 displays great solidity and consistency, earning its recognition as Taurus's best-shooting .38 Special revolver. Despite its large grips and thick barrel, which complicate concealment, the Model 83 remains a useful gun for most purposes.

TAURUS MODELS 82 AND 83

Manufacturer	Years Produced	Caliber/Capacity	Dimensions

Forjas Taurus S.A.
Porto Alegre, Brazil
Imported by:
  Taurus Int'l
  Miami, FL
	1970s–Present	.38 Special/6 rounds	Barrel Length: 3" or 4"
			O. A. Length: 9.25" w/4" bbl.
			Height: 5.6" Width: 1.4"
			Weight (w/4" bbl.): 34 oz. (unloaded)
			  37 oz. (loaded)

TAURUS MODEL 431

The Taurus Model 431 appeared about the same time as Rossi's Model 720 in early 1993. It filled the void left by the demise of Charter Arms's popular Bulldog (ironically, production of the Bulldog resumed within a year, thanks to a reconstituted Charco, Inc.). Still, the Taurus and Rossi .44 Special offerings remain excellent guns and warrant a close look by those who appreciate guns in this famous, well-regarded caliber.

Taurus revolvers are basically built along Smith & Wesson lines, but with certain modifications. One of these is the floating firing pin, that is located in the frame, not the hammer. Linked to the hammer by a transfer bar, the pin can be raised only by pulling the trigger, thus representing an improvement over Smith & Wesson's design. The fixed rear sight on the Model 431 is a square notch cut into the top strap of the frame; the front sight is a serrated ramp, integral with the barrel. The finish on the Taurus Model 431 is

The Model 431 (top) was Taurus's answer to demand for a small .44 Special defensive revolver. Rossi's Model 720 pictured below it was its chief competitor.

The Model 431 fired from a distance of 25 feet with Winchester 200-grain Silvertip ammunition produced this five-shot offhand group, measuring 3.6 inches (disregard the last shot because the shooter failed to follow through on the final shot).

blue, stainless steel or the attractive satin nickel. Thick, checkered Brazilian hardwood is used for the grips, which are comfortable to hold but quite large for concealment purposes.

The Model 431 is not as smooth in operation as the Rossi Model 720 or a comparable Smith & Wesson revolver. Recoil is not objectionable, which is one of the attractions of the .44 Special caliber. It gets its stopping power from a large bullet rather than from elevated pressures and high velocity. The trigger is a grooved target type—not a popular choice for a double-action revolver intended mainly for defensive shooting (as this gun definitely is). Our best five-shot rapid-fire offhand group from 25 feet measured 3.6 inches. This .44 Special revolver performed best with the Winchester Silvertip 200-grain hollowpoint round, probably the best factory-made defensive load made in this caliber.

Overall, the Model 431 is a good choice for a defensive weapon in this caliber. Because of its added weight and size it will likely prove more durable than its chief competitors. Although its larger size may be a hindrance to effective concealment, it does add to one's shooting comfort and should not be a problem when carried in a quality holster.

TAURUS MODEL 431

Manufacturer	Years Produced	Caliber/Capacity	Dimensions
Forjas Taurus S.A. Porto Alegre, Brazil Imported by: Taurus Int'l Miami, FL	1992–1996	.44 Special/5 rounds	Barrel Length: 3" O.A. Length: 8.5" Height: 5.5" Width: 1.45" Weight: 37 oz. (unloaded); 40 oz. (loaded)

TAURUS MODEL 607

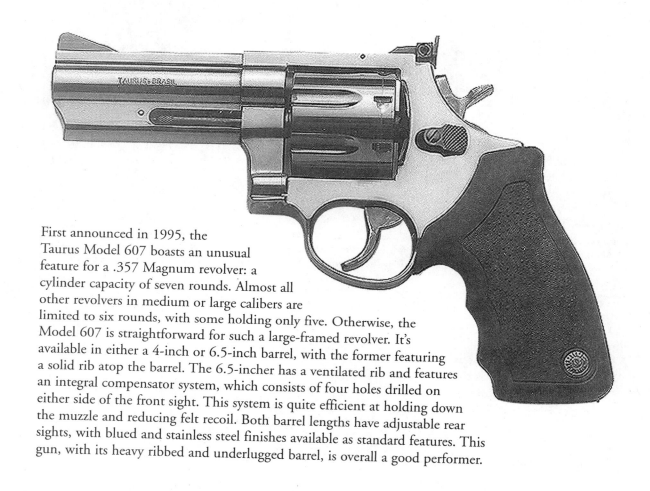

First announced in 1995, the
Taurus Model 607 boasts an unusual
feature for a .357 Magnum revolver: a
cylinder capacity of seven rounds. Almost all
other revolvers in medium or large calibers are
limited to six rounds, with some holding only five. Otherwise, the
Model 607 is straightforward for such a large-framed revolver. It's
available in either a 4-inch or 6.5-inch barrel, with the former featuring
a solid rib atop the barrel. The 6.5-incher has a ventilated rib and features
an integral compensator system, which consists of four holes drilled on
either side of the front sight. This system is quite efficient at holding down
the muzzle and reducing felt recoil. Both barrel lengths have adjustable rear
sights, with blued and stainless steel finishes available as standard features. This
gun, with its heavy ribbed and underlugged barrel, is overall a good performer.

TAURUS MODEL 607

Manufacturer	Years Produced	Caliber/Capacity	Dimensions
Forjas Taurus S.A. Porto Alegre, Brazil Imported by: Taurus Int'l Miami, FL	1995–1996	.357 Magnum/7 rounds	Barrel Length: 4" or 6.5" O.A. Length: 11" Height: 7.9" Width: 1.45" Weight (w/4" bbl.): 44 oz. (unloaded) 48.5 oz. (loaded)

TAURUS MODEL 669

The Model 669, first announced in 1988, is Taurus's answer to the .357 Magnum revolvers made by Colt, Rossi, Ruger and Smith & Wesson. Like all other modern Taurus revolver, it resembles a Smith & Wesson equivalent, with its cylinder lockup and controls. In particular, it's modeled after S&W's K-framed Model 19, not the larger L-framed Model 686. It also features the frame-mounted firing pin and transfer-bar safety of other Taurus revolvers, with considerable similarity to the company's earlier Model 66.

The Model 669 tested for this book was blued, but Taurus also offers it in stainless steel. The gun we tested had a 4-inch barrel, but a 6-inch barrel option is available that's better suited for target shooting or hunting. The stocks, made from checkered hardwood, are narrow at the top and swell out slightly at the bottom, making them comfortable to hold.

The Model 669 has adjustable sights similar in appearance to those found on Smith & Wesson revolvers (but without S&W's colored insert on the front sight). For those who desire more advanced target-acquisition arrangements, the Model 669 is available with an optional laser sighting package that fits under the barrel. This high-tech feature is also an option for the PT-92/99 series of automatic pistols.

The most interesting feature available on the Model 669, aside from the optional laser sight, is its ported barrel. This variation—sold as the Model 669CP—has four holes drilled through the top of the barrel on either side of the front sight. Upon firing, some of the gases escape through these eight ports, thereby reducing muzzle climb. This porting system, however, has no effect on the shooter's sight picture at the moment of firing.

The Model 669 shoots well, with recoil and performance about on a par with Smith &

The Model 669 (top) like other Taurus revolvers, is based on Smith & Wesson revolvers, but with slight modifications and improvements. Shown below is Smith & Wesson's Model 19, the original Combat Magnum.

Some shooters prefer a high-capacity 9mm automatic pistol like the 15-shot CZ 75 (bottom), while others want a six-shot .357 Magnum revolver like the Taurus Model 669 (top).

Wesson's Models 19 and 686. Our best five-shot offhand group fired from 25 feet measured 2.5 inches; at 50 feet, a five-shot group measured 4.1 inches across using .357 magnum ammunition (.38 Special rounds will also work).

The Model 669 remains one of the top revolvers in the Taurus line. Well-made and sturdy, it's worth serious consideration as a defensive handgun.

TAURUS MODEL 669

Manufacturer	Years Produced	Caliber/Capacity	Dimensions

Forjas Taurus S.A.
Porto Alegre, Brazil
Imported by:
  Taurus Int'l
  Miami, FL
	1988–Present	.357 Magnum/7 rounds	Barrel Length: 4" or 6" O.A. Length: 9.2"
			Height: 5.9" Width: 1.4"
			Weight: 37 oz. (unloaded); 41 oz. (loaded)

TEXAS LONGHORN ARMS

TEXAS LONGHORN ARMS
GROVER'S IMPROVED NO. 5

One of the projects undertaken by Elmer Keith, the legendary expert among "six-gun" shooters, was to improve one of his favorite revolvers: the Colt Single Action Army. Keith was also active in ammunition research and a proponent of the .44 Magnum cartridge, which led to its introduction in 1955. Grover's Improved No. 5 revolver, made by Texas Longhorn Arms, perpetuates both of these Elmer Keith endeavors.

Originally developed in 1926–27 with the cooperation of a Philadelphia gunsmith named Harold Croft, the No. 5 was a masterpiece of engineering. Firing the .44 Special cartridge, it was a combination of Colt Single Action Army and Bisley parts intermingled to produce a reliable, accurate single-action revolver. Although Colt declined to produce Keith's revolver, his No. 5 became a legend in the handgun industry, loved by anyone who fired it or even held it.

It all came together in 1986 when Bill Grover of Texas Longhorn Arms set out to reproduce and improve Keith's famous redesign. The result was "Grover's Improved No. 5," which debuted in 1988. The influence of Keith's No. 5 on Grover's new revolver was most evident in the lockwork and grip contour. Another useful feature was a strengthened base pin that was easy to remove, yet controlled unwanted movement under recoil. Grover's Improved No. 5, like the Keith arm that inspired it, is in

Grover's Improved No. 5 revolver (top), made by Texas Longhorn Arms, is loosely based on the design of Colt's Single Action Army (bottom), but with numerous modifications.

This five-shot offhand group fired with Grover's Improved No. 5 from 25 feet measured a remarkable .6 inch. At 50 feet, another five-shot offhand group measured 1.8 inches.

every respect a dramatic update of Colt's SAA concept, taking the classic single-action design about as far as it could go. Major improvements include adjustable sights, a modern trigger linkage and a reshaped grip. The firing pin, located within the frame, is a rebounding type.

Despite its considerable size, the Improved No. 5 is comfortable to hold and shoot. Incredibly smooth in operation, its hammer effortlessly cycles through four distinct clicks, similar to the best Colt SAAs. The trigger, descibed as a "shotgun-type," sits far back in the trigger guard, moving forward only slightly as the low Bisley-type hammer is cocked. Only when it is pulled all the way back does the trigger release the hammer to fire. Trigger pull is light and crisp, allowing precise firing movements that hardly disturb sight alignment, creating extraordinary accuracy. Interestingly, the Improved No. 5 is a "right-handed" reloader, with its loading gate on the left side of the cylinder opening to the left.

Our best five-shot offhand group fired from a distance of 25 feet measured an incredible .6 inch, and at 50 feet the results were equally impressive. Reloading is slow, of course, because of the ejector rod-gate system; but with this kind of accuracy and power numerous follow-up shots probably become unnecessary. Overall, the Improved No. 5 is a beautiful and highly functional revolver, capable of protecting its owner and bringing in game animals as well.

TEXAS LONGHORN ARMS GROVER'S IMPROVED NO. 5

Manufacturer	Years Produced	Caliber/Capacity	Dimensions
Texas Longhorn Arms Richmond, TX	1988–Present	.44 Magnum/6 rounds	Barrel Length: 5.5" O.A. Length: 11.6" Height: 5.3" Width: 1.6" Weight: 44 oz. (unloaded); 49 oz. (loaded)

DAN WESSON MODEL 14-2/714-2

If the name "Wesson" brings to mind "Smith & Wesson," it's not by accident. Dan Wesson, founder of Wesson Firearms, was, in fact, a descendant of Daniel Baird Wesson, who co-founded Smith & Wesson in 1852, then left the company in 1869 to build his own version of the ideal revolver. Since then, the Dan Wesson company has had its share of difficulties (it even went bankrupt at one point), but has managed to become an important force on the American revolver scene.

Among the numerous unique touches found on Dan Wesson revolvers is a transfer bar that prevents the hammer from reaching the firing pin until the shooter pulls the trigger all the way to the rear. This causes the transfer bar to rise and allows the hammer and firing pin, which is mounted in the frame, to meet. Unlike most revolvers, its cylinder release latch is located at the front of the cylinder crane, not the rear. This placement gives the Dan Wesson system exceptional rigidity and contributes to the accuracy of the company's line of revolvers. Many shooters—especially those who've become accustomed to firing revolvers made by Smith & Wesson, Colt and Ruger—find this latch placement and the downward motion required to open it an awkward arrangement.

Many innovative and useful features are offered on Dan Wesson's Model 714-2 that help make it an outstanding choice. The latch, for example, is located ahead of the cylinder, rather than behind it as in most competing models. This feature provides a smooth contour not likely to injure the shooter's thumb upon recoil, a common complaint with other revolvers.

Another quality feature on Dan Wesson revolvers is a screw placed inside the rear of the trigger guard to prevent trigger backlash and ensure accuracy. Most Dan Wesson revolvers also feature a system of interchangeable barrels, which enable the shooter to swap barrels of varying lengths from 2 to 8 inches, depending upon need. The barrel retaining-nut system adds rigidity to the whole system and improves accuracy still further. Some of the newer Dan Wesson revolvers, however, including the smaller "Li'l Dan," lack this interchangeable barrel feature.

In addition, all Dan Wesson revolvers have a one-piece stock held in place by a single screw found in the bottom of the butt. Once this screw is loosened, several different stocks of various sizes and shapes can be fitted to suit one's preference (Ruger used this same feature as an inspiration for its

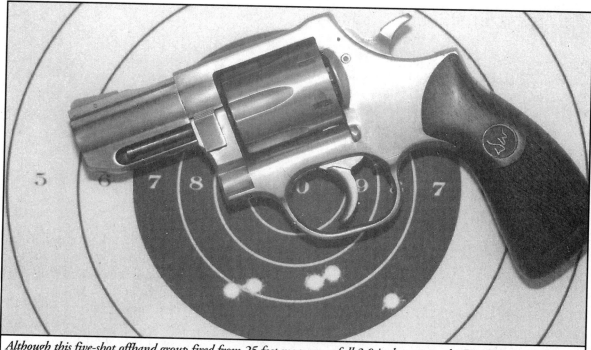

Although this five-shot offhand group fired from 25 feet measures a full 3.0 inches across, the Dan Wesson trigger design is so smooth that this group required only two seconds to fire!

GP-100 series). Dan Wesson revolvers come in brushed stainless steel or high-gloss blued finishes; and both fixed and adjustable sights are available. With all of these advanced features, many of the Dan Wesson revolvers fall in the same price range as comparable Colt and Smith & Wesson revolvers, making them excellent values.

One model in particular—the stainless steel .357 Magnum Model 714-2 with 2.5-inch barrel—contains one of the best fixed-sight systems found anywhere, featuring a wide serrated ramp in front and large, square-cut notch in the rear. This same model boasts excellent handling qualities and accuracy. The short barrel offers comfortable balance, and the grips are quite comfortable and controllable. The trigger is smooth and light, better even than a competing Smith & Wesson revolver. Almost the same size as S&W's classic Model 19 Combat Magnum, the Dan Wesson Model 714-2 offers a number of new features. It, along with the other Dan Wesson revolvers, is well worth a close look by those who seek a versatile revolver of modern design. The system of interchangeable barrels makes these Dan Wesson guns outstanding target and hunting revolvers as well as self-protection arms.

DAN WESSON MODEL 14-2/714-2

Manufacturer	Years Produced	Caliber/Capacity	Dimensions
Wesson Firearms Company Palmer, MA	1993–1995 1997–Present	.357 Magnum/ up to 6 rounds	Barrel Lengths: 2.5", 4", 6" or 8" O.A. Length: 9.25" (w/2.5" barrel) Height: 5.4" Width: 1.4" Weight: 30 oz. (unloaded); 33 oz. (loaded)

4. CLASSIC SERVICE PISTOLS

CONTENTS

Astra
    Model 400 99
    Model 600. 100
Beretta
    Model 92 106
    Model 950. 102
    Model 951 104
Colt Model 1911/1911A1. 109
CZ Model 52. 115
    Model 75 117
FN Browning High Power 120
French Model 1935A 123
Llama Model XI "Especial" 127

Luger Parabellum 129
Mauser C.96 "Broomhandle" 134
Radom VIS-35 138
SIG Model P210 140
Smith & Wesson
    Model 39 141
    Model 59 142
Star Model A 145
    Model B Series 147
Tokarev Model TT-30/33 148
Walther
    Model P.38 150
    Model PP 154

Around the turn of the century, automatic pistols began a long, steady process of supplanting the revolver in military service. Most armies preferred the automatic pistols' improved ruggedness and higher rate of fire compared to revolvers; so when finances permitted, they traded revolvers for automatic pistols. As early as World War I several of the warring countries were already fielding automatic pistols in the millions. Between World Wars, particularly from the mid-1930s on, more countries joined the race and switched to automatics. As a result, many more automatic pistols saw military service during World War II than revolvers. By mid-century, even such holdouts as Great Britain and Russia had retired most of their military revolvers. More recently, automatic pistols have made serious inroads into the market for police handguns, too. The revolver is by no means

extinct in military service—it remains in use by police forces in even greater numbers—but far more service pistols are now in circulation, and in a wider variety of brand names and calibers, than are revolvers.

This section covers the classic service automatic pistols that have made their mark in history through the bloody wars of this century. Many of their names—Astra, Browning, Colt, Mauser, Walther, Radom and Tokarev, for example—conjure up images of desperate fighting around the world. Aside from their great historical importance, these arms represent solid, workable examples of useful handguns. As each pistol went into service, it represented a state-of-the art handgun design, painstakingly developed at great cost by a national arms factory or large private concern. Before being accepted for service, each pistol had to pass rigorous tests devised to uncover design flaws or other shortcomings. The official acceptance that resulted carried with it a seal of approval and a powerful endorsement of the pistol's shooting and handling qualities, as well as the materials and workmanship that went into it.

Because most models have remained in production for many years and were produced in large quantities, spare parts—including the all-important magazines—generally remain in abundant supply. Still, many of these guns have seen rough service and hard use; even a seemingly well-preserved example may conceal serious damage that could compromise its function or even the shooter's safety. Therefore, as with any old, well-used firearm, the usual cautions prevail. Be sure to have each one tested and checked by a competent, experienced gunsmith.

ASTRA MODEL 400

Astra introduced its Model 400 pistol in 1921. Based on Spain's earlier Campo-Giro service pistol, the Model 400 shows significant influence from Fabrique Nationale's (FN) Model 1910 (*see* COMPLETE GUIDE TO COMPACT HANDGUNS), particularly in the construction of its barrel bushing and barrel-retaining system. Other distinctive features of the Model 400, aside from its overall quality construction, include the extended bottom magazine release and grip safety (a magazine safety was added later). Spain's military-issue Model 1921 pistols have wooden grips, while commercial Model 400s have checkered hard rubber grips. Unlike virtually all other large-caliber handguns, the Astra Model 400 does not have a breech-locking mechanism; instead, it is a pure blowback pistol like most small automatic pistols.

The Model 400 was a great success for Astra. In addition to the Spanish armed forces (which referred to the gun as the Model 1921), the armed forces of Chile, France and Nazi Germany all took quantities of the pistol. The German order—over 6,000 pistols—was especially large. By the time its production ended just after World War II, Astra had made 106,175 Model 400s. The pistol remained in service with the Spanish armed forces until the competing Star Model B Super made its debut in 1946. The Chilean navy also kept the Model 400 in service until the 1980s.

Among the Model 400's many strong points are its quality construction and sturdiness. It is capable of excellent accuracy by pistol standards; in fact, a Model 400 in good condition and with proper ammunition will shoot competitively with almost any modern service pistol. Its weak points include a high price, stiff trigger, tiny sights and a poor grip angle. The slide is quite stiff, too,

The Astra Model 400 is extremely accurate, despite its small sights and rough trigger. This 5-shot offhand group fired from a distance of 25 feet measures 2.2 inches across.

The Astra Model 400 disassembles into the following components (top to bottom): slide, a strong recoil spring, barrel and muzzle bushing, grips and frame.

because of a strong recoil spring, making it difficult for someone with weak hands to operate.

Although the Model 400 can reputedly handle a variety of pistol cartridges other than the 9mm Largo for which it was designed, such accounts should be looked upon with great skepticism. As a general rule, it is extremely unwise to fire a gun with ammunition other than that for which it was designed.

Because of the recent importation of large quantities of military-surplus pistols from Spain, Chile and elsewhere, the Model 400 is currently enjoying a resurgence of popularity in the U.S. More importantly, importers are also bringing in the ammunition for which the gun was designed.

ASTRA MODEL 400

Manufacturer	Years Produced	Caliber/Capacity	Dimensions
Astra Unceta y Cia, Guernica, Spain	1921–1946	9mm Largo/8 rounds (Bergman-Bayard)	Barrel Length: 5.9" O.A. Length: 9.25" Height: 5.5" Width: 1.1" Weight: 31 oz. (unloaded); 37 oz. (loaded)

ASTRA MODEL 600

During World War II, Germany approached Unceta y Cia (Astra) requesting a slightly modified Astra Model 400 pistol (*see above*), one that was more reliable with 9mm Parabellum ammunition. Subsequently, Unceta y Cia created a smaller version of the Model 400 rechambered from the 9mm Largo ammunition to the slightly shorter (19mm) round in 9mm Parabellum. After 50 test samples were received by the Germans in 1943, an order for 50,000 Model 600 pistols (known as the *Pistole Astra 600/43*) was received. Deliveries began in May 1944, when 10,450 guns were delivered to the German forces occupying France. When the Allied armies invaded France a few weeks later, further deliveries were cut off. The remaining pistols—32,750 in number—were later sold (from 1951 on) to West

This five-shot offhand group fired from a distance of 50 feet away with an Astra Model 600 measures only 1.4 inches across. It was a popular service gun during World War II.

Germany. Another 3,550 were exported to various countries, including Chile, Costa Rica, Egypt, Jordan, the Philippines, Portugal and Turkey.

The Model 600 shares all the features—both good and bad—of the earlier Model 400. On the plus side were its sensational accuracy and stellar reliability, even when used with modern hollowpoint ammunition. On the bad side were its undersized sights and stiff trigger pull. The gun's "hammerless" design (actually, there is a hammer concealed within the frame that's not visible when the pistol is assembled) bothers those who desire a visible hammer. Because of its unlocked breech (blowback) construction, the Astra Model 600 calls for a strong recoil spring to contain the chamber pressures. The result is a stiff slide that is difficult for some to retract. And, since the hammer is contained within the slide, there's no exposed hammer to cock, thereby lessening pressure on the slide and making it easier to pull back. Because of that stiff recoil spring, disassembly is difficult—and reassembly is harder still. Despite these shortcomings, the Model 600 is an excellent service pistol, one that combines great accuracy, ruggedness and reliability.

ASTRA MODEL 600

Manufacturer	Years Produced	Caliber/Capacity	Dimensions
Astra Unceta y Cia Guernica, Spain	1943–1945	9mm/8 rounds	Barrel Length: 5.2" O.A. Length: 7.9" Height: 5.1" Width: 1.3" Weight: 35 oz. (unloaded); 41 oz. (loaded)

BERETTA MODEL 950

Soon after World War II ended, the Beretta company began long-range planning to develop new pistols to supplement and eventually replace its old wartime guns. One of the first and most successful of the company's brilliant postwar designs was the Model 950. Introduced in 1950, this pistol has since been made in Italy, Brazil and the United States and remains in full production more than 40 years after its appearance.

The chief attractions of the Model 950 are its extremely small size and light weight; and yet it is superbly reliable. Many small automatic pistols, being so tightly fitted and with little margin for error, have a tendency toward fussiness and unreliability, but this has never been a problem for even the smallest Beretta pistols.

Mechanically, the Model 950 runs well off the beaten path. Its barrel is hinged near the muzzle, which, when released, springs straight up to allow easy reloading or cleaning. Typical of almost all Beretta pistol designs, the Model 950 features an open slide, with the magazine release located near the bottom of the left grip. Oddly, the Model 950 has no extractor; spent cartridge casings are simply blown clear of the firing chamber once fired. Naturally, elimination of the extractor mechanism greatly simplifies manufacture, making the Model 950 extremely competitive in price with other small pistols made by top-flight firearms companies. On the debit side, this feature can theoretically lead to malfunctions related to poor extraction, although in actual practice this is rarely the case.

Among the numerous variations of the Model 950 are the 950B, which uses a double recoil-spring arrangement, and the Model 950BS, which added a manual safety. In the U.S., Beretta's .22-caliber version of the Model 950 went by the trade name "Minx" (the .25 version was called "Jetfire"). The Minx offered a stan-

Despite its diminutive size, the Beretta Model 950 is capable of impressive accuracy, as this rapid-fire eight-shot burst at 10 feet indicates.

Full field-stripping of the Model 950 reveals the slide (top), frame with tipping barrel—one of its more interesting features—still attached (middle), and magazine (bottom). The tipping barrel is used in the disassembling process as well as for loading and unloading the gun.

When loading the Model 950, the barrel latch must be released and the first round inserted into the firing chamber.

dard-length (2.4") or long (3.7") barrel.

Because of their small size, the guns in the Model 950 series fell under the restrictions of the Gun Control Act of 1968, effectively halting their importation. But in 1978 Model 950BS manufacture began in the U.S. at the Firearms International factory in Accokeek, MD, which later became the nucleus of the Beretta U.S.A. operation.

The Model 950 is extraordinarily reliable and surprisingly accurate, despite its miniscule sights. Although not strictly a service pistol because of its size, it has been widely used for clandestine purposes and is a popular backup choice for police and as a concealed-carry piece for civilians. Its workmanship, fit and finish are excellent, which is to be expected in a Beretta-made firearm. About its only shortcomings are the weak cartridges it uses and the possibility that, because it locks an extractor, a misfired cartridge could tie up the gun for precious seconds in a close-quarters battle. Shooters must remember to activate the barrel latch to throw the dud round clear. Working the slide, as in most other automatic pistols, will do no good under thesecircumstances.

BERETTA MODEL 950

Manufacturer	Years Produced	Caliber/Capacity	Dimensions
Pietro Beretta S.p.A., Gardone, V.T., Italy	1950–Present	.22 Short/6 rounds .25 ACP/8 rounds	Barrel Length: 2.4" O.A Length: 4.5" Height: 3.4" Width: 1.0" Weight: 10 oz. (unloaded); 11 oz. (loaded)

BERETTA MODEL 951

Just before World War II began, the Beretta company, while still selling its small .380-caliber Model 1934 pistol as fast as it could make them, realized that the future of military handguns lay with a larger, more capable weapon that fired a more powerful cartridge. Beretta sensed accurately that the military pistol cartridge of the future was the 9mm Parabellum. Consequently, the company began to develop a Model 1938, which was basically a Model 1934 enlarged to accommodate the 9mm Parabellum cartridge.

Although the blowback mechanism of the Model 1938 proved inadequate to handle the recoil forces and stresses of the 9mm round, Beretta had made a huge step forward into a lucrative postwar market that was to culminate, many years later, in the fabulously successful Model 92 pistol series. Before Beretta could proceed any further with its 9mm pistol designs, however, World War II intervened.

Following the war, the Italian armed forces, impressed with the German P.38, asked Beretta to develop a similar weapon. Beretta's development work began around 1949, and by 1950 several prototypes were available to test the merits of various systems of operation. First, a blowback model was rejected quickly as unsatisfactory; then a new version featuring a Browning-type locked breech controlled by a tipping barrel was found lacking. Finally, a pistol with a modification of the P.38's locking system proved superior and was tentatively adopted in 1951.

This new Model 951 soon developed problems of its own. In an effort to hold down its weight, Beretta had made the frame of this pistol from an aluminum alloy called "Ergal," which it had used earlier in the smaller Model 1948 pistol. While the Model 951 with aluminum-alloy frame weighed only 25 ounces, making it easy to carry, it also had excessive recoil and lacked the durability necessary for a military pistol. As a result, the alloy-framed Model 951 was dropped almost immediately.

Beretta set out at once to redesign the frame in steel, and by

The Model 951, in its Egyptian-made Helwan version, shows off its accuracy with this five-shot, 25-foot offhand group measuring 2.9 inches.

1955 the improved Model 951 was at last ready for series production. The new pistol attracted the attention of the Egyptian government, which ordered a large quantity for its armed forces. So successful was the Model 951 in Egyptian service that in the 1960s the Maadi Company of Cairo negotiated a licensing arrangement with Beretta to build the Model 951. Known locally as the "Helwan" pistol, it remains in production and was, until 1995, imported into the U.S. by Interarms.

The lower grip area of Beretta's Model 951 includes a long finger-rest extension on the magazine bottom, a lanyard loop at the bottom rear, and a push-buttom magazine release.

In 1957, after finishing the initial Egyptian contract, Beretta went into full-scale commercial production of the Model 951. Large arms shipments were made to military and police forces in Israel, Italy, Sudan, Haiti, Nigeria, Iraq, and a number of other countries. The Israelis still use the Model 951 extensively, although in recent years the Browning High Power has usurped its popularity. Nigeria negotiated a production license from Beretta, and around 1976 so did Iraq (examples of the Iraqi-built Model 951, called the Tariq, were captured during the 1991 Gulf War). Beretta halted its own Model 951 production in May 1983, but the Helwan, which is identical except for its markings and poorer finish, remains in production in Egypt.

The only real problems with the Model 951 concern its awkward operating controls. The manual safety is a cross-bolt push button located on the upper portion of the grip, making it difficult to reach with the thumb of the shooting hand. In most Model 951s, the magazine release is also a push button, located near the bottom rear of the grip; but those early versions made under the Egyptian contract featured a P.38-style, heel-mounted magazine release. Interesting to note, in producing its early Model 92 pistols Beretta discarded the 951's awkward safety, but kept the low-mounted magazine release button. The prominent hooked finger rest on the Model 951's magazine bottom—a carryover from the Model 1934 series—may irritate some shooters and could compromise a rapid draw from under clothing. Despite these idiosyncratic handling characteristics, the Model 951 has proven an excellent pistol—at once accurate, reliable and powerful.

BERETTA MODEL 951

Manufacturer	Years Produced	Caliber/Capacity	Dimensions
Pietro Beretta S.p.A., Gardone, V.T., Italy	1951; 1955–Present	9mm/8 rounds	Barrel Length: 4.5" O.A. Length: 8" Height: 5.6" Width: 1.1" Weight: 31.4 oz. (unloaded); 36 oz. (full)

BERETTA MODEL 92

In 1976, Beretta launched its third "Wondernine" (i.e., 9mm) pistol: the Model 92. This new model became a legend when the U.S. military selected it in 1985 to replace the Colt M1911A1(*see* separate listing) as the armed forces' M9 service pistol.

Mechanically, the Model 92, with its open slide, owes a great deal to previous Beretta handguns and to the Walther P.38 as well. Essentially a Model 951 (*see* previous listing), its double-action trigger system was adapted from the P.38, while its 15-shot magazine was similar to that found on the FN High Power. In its earliest versions, the Model 92's magazine release was placed on the lower left portion of the grip, the same position as the magazine release on the Model 951.

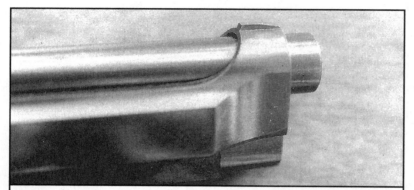
Among the improvements Beretta has made in the Model 92 line are the enlarged, improved sights compared to the tiny front sight on the original Model 92 shown here.

Although Beretta had never before made a double-action 9mm pistol prior to the Model 92, the company already had a wealth of experience in building high-quality firearms, including excellent military pistols like the Model 1934 (*see* COMPLETE GUIDE TO COMPACT HANDGUNS) and Model 951. Beretta had also made excellent sporting weapons and military rifles, submachine guns and machine guns, earning the company an outstanding reputation and great respect. As a result, Beretta had no trouble establishing the Model 92 in what had become an increasingly crowded handgun category.

The first major success for the Model 92 actually occurred in 1977, only a year after full-scale production had begun, when Beretta won a military order from Brazil for 40,000 guns. The contract called for domestic production of the pistols, which Beretta arranged through its subsidiary in Sao Paulo. Once the order had been complet-

In 1981, Beretta introduced a firing-pin lock and ambidextrous safety lever with its Model 92SB.

Beretta has expanded its Model 92 line to include compact as well as full-sized versions. Beretta 9mm pistols have come a long way since the Model 92 of 1976 (top) and the Model 951 of 1957 (bottom).

ed, Beretta sold the factory in 1990 — complete with machinery, tools and drawings — to the Forjas Taurus company, which now produces a Model 92 clone called the Taurus PT-92.

The original Model 92, which was kept in production until February 1983, had a safety system similar to that of the M1911A1, the Browning High Power, and the CZ 75 (*see* separate listing). When the manual safety was pushed all the way up, the slide, hammer and sear were locked, preventing the pistol from firing. In 1976, Beretta introduced a slight variation, called the Model 92S, whose manual safety was applied by pushing it down, thereby decocking the hammer. Beretta calculated correctly that this feature would appeal to military and police buyers who were leery of the Model 92's earlier cocked-and-locked capabilities. Between May 1976 and February 1983, total production of the original Model 92 numbered only 52,000 pistols, while production of the Model 92S lasted from 1976 to 1981 and totaled 140,000 guns.

In 1981, Beretta introduced the improved Model 92SB, based on the Model 92S but outfitted with ambidextrous controls, better sights, a magazine release (repositioned to the rear of the trigger guard), a firing-pin lock (deactivated only when the trigger was all the way back), grooving on the front and rear gripstraps (to improve the shooter's hold) and an overtravel shelf on the rear face of the trigger. This beautifully made gun re-equipped the Italian armed forces and remained in production

10 years until 1991.

U.S. military "XM9" testing of Beretta pistols began as early as 1979, with Model 92Ss modified to 92SB standards. For a second round of testing in 1981, Beretta submitted its Model 92SB, and for the third—and, as it turned out, decisive—round of XM9 testing in 1984, the company submitted its Model 92SB-F. A much-modified 92SB, this new model featured a squared trigger guard, matte black finish, reshaped grip, extended magazine baseplate, repositioned lanyard loop, and chrome-lined barrel. Known as the Model 92F, this pistol was produced for police and civilian use as well as military use.

U.S. military acceptance of the Model 92F created a storm of controversy, with several competing companies, notably Smith & Wesson and SIG, protesting the outcome and demanding a rematch. This uproar ironically made Beretta's new star an "overnight" success nine years after its introduction, and opened up the U.S. market to 9mm and double-action pistols more than all the Walthers, Brownings or Smith & Wessons had been able to do thus far. Within a few years, the Beretta Model 92—usually in its -SB or -F form—went on to arm more than a thousand police forces in the U.S. alone. These pistols became exceedingly popular overseas as well, re-equipping the French armed forces and police in another major commercial coup that took place in 1991.

Opposition to adopting the Model 92 continued to mount in the U.S. A series of slide failures, wherein the lightweight, open-topped slides broke at the rear and struck the shooter, forced Beretta to modify the pistol to accept a "slide retention device." It also tarnished the image of the U.S. military's newest pistol. But when the Model 92F went on to win still another round of testing in 1988–89, the Army reaffirmed it as the military's top choice; subsequently, M9s served capably in military operations in Panama, Kuwait and Somalia. Despite a desire on the part of U.S. elite forces to purchase a new .45-caliber "Offensive Handgun System," and despite continued use of the M1911A1 by individual soldiers and even whole units, the Model 92FS/M9 continues to serve the U.S. and other armed forces.

Beretta has also made a number of other successful offshoots of the basic Model 92 pistol, including 13-shot and 8-shot compact models, the Model 93R machine pistol, and various engraved presentation models. Several competition versions are under development, and Beretta has offered the pistol in 7.65mm (.30 Luger) caliber as well.

Despite the controversy surrounding it, the Model 92 offers many positive qualities, including surprising accuracy and extraordinary reliability. Considering its size, the pistol handles well, particularly in the later versions, and is well suited for use by left-handed shooters. Negative factors include complaints about its size, a heavy trigger pull, and a feeling that it is not sturdy enough for arduous service. For all this, the Model 92 has served with distinction for nearly two decades and will likely continue to do so for many more years.

BERETTA MODEL 92

Manufacturer	Years Produced	Caliber/Capacity	Dimensions
Pietro Beretta S.p.A., Gardone, V.T., Italy	1976–Present	9mm/15 rounds	Barrel Length: 4.9" O.A. Length: 8.5" Height: 5.3" Width: 1.45" Weight: 34 oz. (unloaded); 41 oz. (loaded)

COLT MODEL 1911/1911A1

In 1900, the U.S. Army tested its first Browning-designed pistol manufactured by Colt: the Model 1900. It was a .38-caliber weapon firing a semi-rimmed cartridge 23mm long and was loaded with smokeless powder. Having been more impressed with this Colt pistol than the Mauser C.96 (*see* separate listing) it had tested at the same time, the Army decided to test the Model 1900 further. Beginning in February 1900, a board of Army officers test-fired one Colt Model 1900 pistol a total of 5,800 times, suspending the tests only because they had no more funds with which to purchase ammunition. The pistol had a few mechanical failures, but these were easily fixed. On the whole, the Board was extremely impressed with the Colt-Browning pistol and recommended a limited purchase for troop trials and the adoption of a larger caliber. Both suggestions were acted upon, with 100 Model 1900 pistols in .38 caliber going to troops in the Philippines, Cuba and Puerto Rico, with mostly positive results. The Navy also bought 100 Model 1900 pistols for testing, and another 3,300 or so were sold commercially.

While U.S. Army testing of the Model 1900 continued, Colt introduced several variations to the commercial market that proved moderately successful. All of these pistols— the Model 1900, the Sporting Model of 1902, the Military Model

This Argentine Model 1927, a licensed copy of the Colt M1911, was introduced shortly after the U.S. Army standardized the M1911A1 pattern in 1926. All parts interchange with pre-Series '80 Colt pistols.

of 1902 (200 of which the Army bought, with another 16,000 or so selling to civilians), and the .38 Pocket Model of 1903 (not to be confused with the considerably smaller Pocket Model in .32 and .380 caliber described earlier)— are eagerly sought by collectors. *Caution:* They are not safe to shoot with modern .38 Super ammunition and are in any case so rare and valuable that they should be left in their original condition and not fired at all.

In 1905, Colt introduced a slightly larger and sturdier gun modified by John Browning to accept a more powerful .45-caliber cartridge. This followed a series of tests made famous in 1904 by Colonels John Thompson and Louis LaGarde, which indicated that a .45-caliber bullet would work best in any new automatic pistol. Colt was anxious to get a large-caliber handgun into production as quickly as possible, but the Model 1905 proved to be a disappointment. The British tested one in late

1905 for possible service use and the U.S. Army bought 201 Model 1905 pistols in 1907 for tests. When Colt finally ended Model 1905 production in 1911, however, fewer than 6300 had been made. The Army turned it down chiefly because it had no manual safety device and lacked durability. The locking system used two links, one at the front (which was especially prone to breakage) and one at the rear of the barrel.

Despite its lack of success, the Model 1905 established Colt as a serious maker of .45-caliber auto-

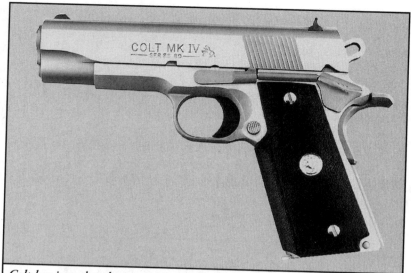

Colt has introduced numerous variations to the basic M1911A1 design. This Combat Commander has a shorter barrel but a full-size steel frame. A similar gun, the Commander — with its aluminum-alloy frame — is much lighter but recoils harder.

matic pistols. In 1906–1907 the company built a slightly improved design with a grip safety; this answered a major Army objection to earlier pistols and introduced a feature carried over later by Colt into the Model 1911. Army testing in 1907 narrowed the choices down to two: the Colt model and a new pistol made by Savage. In a further round of testing in 1909, a redesigned Colt pistol very similar in form to the later Model 1911 attracted favorable comment. This pistol used the same magazine release, grip safety, and single-link locking system as the M1911. A 1910 version came even closer in form; and in a 1911 test, during which the Savage pistol foundered in a 6,000-shot endurance test, the improved Colt pistol functioned almost perfectly. The Army board of officers then recommended adoption of the Colt pistol designed by John Browning, and on March 29, 1911, the Secretary of War approved its purchase as the U.S. Model 1911. This excellent gun is still serving American and numerous other armed forces more than 85 years later.

Experience in World War I demonstrated the M1911's capabilities in close-quarters combat. Colt, along with the government's Springfield Armory and Remington, all produced M1911 pistols during the war, and over 700,000 were produced by 1919. It would have been output in far larger numbers had the war gone on; indeed, North American Arms Company (Montreal, Canada) made 100 pistols before the Armistice halted production, and plans were in the works to open up additional production lines in the U.S.

Post-World War I Adaptations. Despite its outstanding wartime performance, a few changes were called for in the Model M1911, beginning in 1923 as a result of combat experience. The trigger was shortened, the frame around the trigger was relieved, the grip safety tang was lengthened, and the mainspring housing was arched to change the angle of the backstrap. All changes were intended to benefit small-handed shooters — and most of the modifications actually did help— although many shooters still prefer the original straight mainspring housing. The resulting pistol, renamed the

M1911A1, came on line officially in May 1926; but with the lean budgets of that period, upgrading old pistols and buying new ones had become low priorities. Over several decades, the Army gradually phased out the old-style M1911 by changing the pistols to M1911A1 standards after they had come into the depots for repair.

Commercial Variations. Between World Wars I and II, Colt also introduced several commercial variations of the M1911 design, including in 1929 an M1911A1 chambered in a new .38 Super caliber. This version held nine .38 rounds instead of seven .45 rounds. Another change of caliber occurred in 1931 with the emergence of the Ace, which was chambered for .22 LR rimfire rounds (to allow low-cost practice shooting). This model was supplemented in 1937 by the Service Ace, whose floating chamber allowed the recoil from the small .22 cartridge to mimic that of the full-sized .45 ACP round. Colt also sold conversion kits, which enabled owners of .45-caliber M1911 pistols to convert to .22 caliber, and for owners of .22 Ace pistols to convert to .45 ACP.

Both the Ace and Service Ace were moderately successful. Ace production lasted until the U.S. entered World War II in late 1941 and resumed after the war's end in 1945; Colt produced the Service Ace throughout the war, stopping its manufacture in 1945. These guns served as training pistols in small numbers with the U.S. armed forces and were popular with civilian shooters too. Still another M1911 variant used between wars was the super-accurate National Match Model. Introduced in 1933, this gun used specially selected, hand-fitted parts and improved sights. Both pistols — the Ace and the National Match — proved that the basic M1911 design was capable of great accuracy.

During World War II, when manufacture of the M1911A1 was given a fairly high priority, several companies were directed to aid Colt in its manufacture. The Singer Company built 500 M1911A1 pistols before transferring its pistol manufacturing equipment to the Ithaca Gun Company, which built 369,000 more. Remington-Rand produced slightly over one million M1911A1 pistols during the war, while Union Switch and Signal made 55,000. And during the war years,

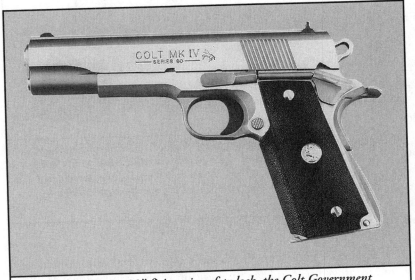

Except for its "Series 80" firing-pin safety lock, the Colt Government Model made in the late 1980s is almost identical to wartime M1911A1 pistols.

Colt turned out some 500,000. Total production of M1911A1 pistols during WW II for the U.S. armed forces exceeded 1.8 million pistols, while total U.S. government purchases of M1911-type pistols between 1912 and 1945 exceeded 2.4 million.

Immediately after the war, the U.S. Army, impressed by the German P.38, briefly flirted with the idea of replacing the trusty M1911A1 with a new pistol. Among the characteristics it desired were lighter weight and possibly a double-action mechanism. Like the German Luger, the P.38 and the Belgian-made FN High Power (*see* separate listings), the specified caliber was 9mm Parabellum. The Army took this opportunity to test several guns, one of which later evolved into Smith & Wesson's Model 39, while another became the Colt Commander. Although the Army took no definite action at this time mostly because of its huge inventory of M1911A1 pistols, the need for a change found its fruition several decades later when, in 1985, it adopted Beretta's Model 92SB-F as the now famous M9 service pistol.

When it was introduced commercially in 1950, the Colt Commander, with its new aluminum-alloy frame, was significantly lighter than the M1911A1. In addition, the Commander's barrel and slide were shorter than those of the M1911A1; otherwise, the two guns' performance and handling characteristics were identical. The chief disadvantage of the Commander was increased recoil caused by its lighter overall weight (26 oz. unloaded), which was 13 oz. less than the M1911A1. Later, in 1971, Colt's new steel-framed Combat Commander reduced recoil to a lower, more tolerable level.

In 1957, Colt also added a target-shooting version of the M1911A1. Called the Gold Cup, this pistol further improved the

One of the few weak points of the M1911A1/Government Model is its relatively complicated disassembly procedure, due mostly to its detachable muzzle bushing (shown just ahead of the barrel) and recoil spring plug. Later pistols have improved on this design by eliminating some parts.

pre-World War II National Match by adding a lightweight trigger with an overtravel stop, adjustable sights, a tightened barrel bushing, and improved sear linkage. In addition to the standard .45 ACP chambering, Colt made a .38 Super version of the Gold Cup. Many features of this excellent and accurate pistol, which remains in production, are found in the latest enhanced version of the Government Model (the commercial name for the M1911A1).

Colt's excellent Officer's Model, which made its debut in 1983, was smaller and lighter than the Combat Commander. It offered big-bore firepower in a compact package (7 1/4 inches long) and a lightweight alloy frame (24 oz. unloaded as opposed to 34 oz. for the all-steel version). About the same time, Colt introduced "Series 80" improvements to its entire Government Model line. The barrel bushing was strengthened and a passive firing-pin lock added, positively blocking the firing pin's path to a chambered cartridge. All earlier M1911-type pistols relied on an inertia firing pin, which assumed (falsely) that the firing-pin spring's resistance to compression would, in the event of a sharp blow, prevent the firing pin from moving forward and igniting a cartridge in the firing chamber.

Opinions vary on the desirability of these Series 80 changes. By introducing several small additional parts that might break after extensive firing, they undoubtedly added complexity to the mechanism. On the other hand, with the firing pin positively locked until the trigger was pulled all the way through its travel, the gun was now much safer to carry loaded.

Colt addded still another caliber choice to the Government Model line when, in 1987, it introduced the Delta

The Officer's ACP, which debuted in 1983, was a smaller, lighter variation of the 1911A1 than the Combat Commander. It offered big-bore power in a compact package, a lightweight alloy frame and the then-new "pebbled" neoprene wraparound, combat-style grips.

Elite in 10mm. At the time, the 10mm concept — an attempt to combine the best features of the .45 ACP and the 9mm Parabellum — lay moribund. Colt's decision to chamber the 10mm in the Delta Elite gave the cartridge a major boost and doubtless contributed indirectly to the development of the .40 S&W cartridge several years later (Colt began making a .40 S&W version of the Government Model in 1992).

Other variations of the M1911A1 were the Delta Elite, introduced in 1987, and the Delta Gold Cup (shown above), which followed it. Chamberd in the powerful 10mm cartridge, both guns are now out of production.

Dozens of countries have either bought or been given M1911s for their armed forces. In addition, foreign production of M1911-type pistols has been extensive. Argentina and Norway, for example, have been licensed by Colt to make M1911-type pistols. Spain and China are among other countries that have made copies, or near-copies, of the M1911A1. In the U.S., several companies now produce M1911A1 clones.

The worldwide success of the M1911/M1911A1/Colt Government Model series during the past 80 years or more is no accident. It is a powerful and accurate gun whose long years of service have guaranteed the availability of numerous spare parts, including those necessary to customize the basic pistol.

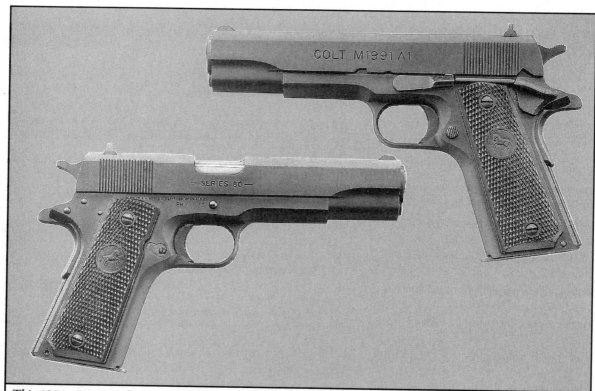

This 1991-vintage Colt Government Model (classic GI service .45 ACP) features composite grips, Parkerized finish, fixed sights, and the Series 80 firing-pin lock.

These include extended and/or ambidextrous safety levers, exotic materials for the grips, improved sights, and so on.

Disadvantages. As for the disadvantages of the M1911 series, most are easily corrected with proper training or sensible gunsmithing. For example, the single-action mode of operation requires a high level of training and confidence on the part of the shooter to ensure safe and effective handling. The standard sights on most older M1911/GM pistols are too small; the pistol is poorly suited for left-handed operation; and the recoil is more pronounced than that encountered on most 9mm pistols. Finally, the feeding reliability of the standard pistol with hollowpoint ammo was, until recently, only fair.

The M1911-series pistol remains a true classic, however, the kind one is likely to encounter virtually anywhere. With proper training on the shooter's part, this pistol will serve its owner quite well.

COLT MODEL 1911/1911A1

Manufacturer	Years Produced	Caliber/Capacity	Dimensions
Colt Industries, Firearms Division Hartford, CT	1911–Present	.45 ACP/7 rounds	Barrel Length: 5.0" O.A. Length: 8.5" Height: 5.2" Width: 1.3" Weight: 39 oz. (unloaded); 46 oz. (loaded)

CZ MODEL 52

Following World War II, Czechoslovakia, which had been an independent armsmaker of high repute, fell under Soviet domination. During the first few years of the Cold War, the Czechs used mainly Russian-designed weapons, including the TT-33 Tokarev pistol (*see* separate listing) and its 7.62x25mm cartridge. But with the passage of time, the Czechs resumed a course independent of the Soviets in the design and manufacture of firearms. As a result, the Czech armed forces let it be known in the early 1950s that a new pistol of domestic design and manufacture was needed to replace the Tokarev. This new pistol was to be an eight-shot type made to fire a variant of the 7.62x25mm handgun and submachine-gun cartridge loaded to more powerful levels than the service round made by the USSR.

At least three pistols were considered: 1) a locked-breech adaptation of the prewar Model 38, which was rejected almost immediately; 2) the ZKP 524, which closely resembled Browning's locked-breech pistols, particularly the M1911; and 3) the CZ Model 52, which was officially accepted as the service standard in Czechoslovakia on May 17, 1952.

The Model 52 had much in common with Germany's MG42 machine gun of World War II fame, including a roller-locking mechanism that held the breech shut at the moment of firing. When not in use, the rollers sit in recesses machined into the inside of the slide; but upon firing, the recoil impulse forces the rollers out of engagement with the slide. While unnecessarily complicated and quite expensive to manufacture, this system proved both strong and reliable.

The Model 52 is unusual in other ways. For example, the manual safety lever decocks the hammer, a function rarely found in a single-action pistol of this vintage (except the earlier Radom pistol made in Poland). Another

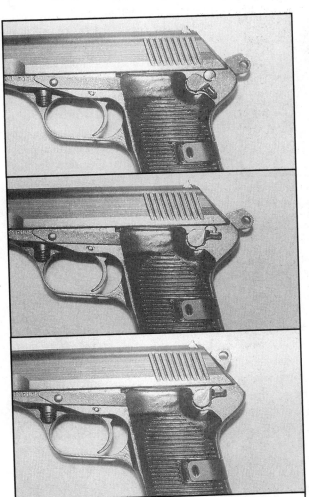

The Czech Model 52 boasts an interesting three-position manual safety lever. In its full down position (top), the pistol can be fired when the hammer is cocked; the normal on-safe position (center) prevents the pistol from firing, while at the same time pushing the safety lever to its uppermost position (bottom), safely decocking the hammer without firing the gun.

The Czech Model 52, with its roller-locking mechanism and straight-recoiling barrel, can produce excellent accuracy, as this five-shot, 50-foot offhand group measuring 2.4 inches indicates.

singular feature of the 52 is its ribbed plastic grip panel, reminiscent of those used on wartime-era P.38s.

The CZ 52 saw considerable use in Czechoslovakia and was for many years the standard military handgun of the Czech armed forces. Then beginning in 1982, it was replaced gradually in front-line service by the Model 83 pistol in 9mm Makarov caliber, but continued to be held in reserve for several more years. Model 52s also served in several Third World armies, and were unfortunately supplied to terrorist units as well. Still, despite its undeniable efficiency, the CZ 52 lacked the appeal of such competitive Western designs as the FN High Power and Colt M1911A1.

For many years the Model 52 remained exceedingly rare in the U.S, forcing collectors to pay premium prices approaching $1000 for one in excellent condition. Finally, in the early 1990s, the Czechs released large numbers of stored 52s for sale to international arms dealers. The pistol is now available in the U.S. from Century International Arms, which offers the CZ 52 in both the standard 7.62mm chambering and, since 1993, the more popular 9mm Parabellum round. Prices are now quite reasonable, leaving those who paid four figures for these same guns in the early 1980s not a little regretful.

Disadvantages. Although the Model 52 remains a reliable and reasonably accurate pistol, it's not especially noteworthy or impressive. Moreover, it's more complicated than it needs to be, particularly its roller-actuated breech mechanism. Also, because its recoil spring is so strong, disassembly is much more difficult than what one might encounter with, say, the more traditional designs produced by Colt and Browning. The sights on the CZ 52 are small by modern standards, a fault shared with most military pistols until the late 1970s or early 1980s. Also, its magazine release is located at the base or heel of the grip, a location that bothers many American shooters especially.

The new version recently converted to 9mm Parabellum caliber is a promising step in the right direction — particularly in the U.S., because of the easy availability of high-quality hollowpoint ammunition.

CZ MODEL 52

Manufacturer	Years Produced	Caliber/Capacity	Dimensions
Ceska Zbrojovka Strakonice, Czechoslovakia	1952 – c. 1956	7.62mm/8 rounds	Barrel Length: 4.7" O.A. Length: 8.25" Height: 5.4" Width: 1.3" Weight: 34 oz. (unloaded); 40 oz. (loaded)

CZ MODEL 75

The introduction by Smith & Wesson of the first high-capacity double-action 9mm automatic pistol, the Model 59, soon attracted attention overseas. While Steyr of Austria was still struggling in 1975 to get its 18-shot "Wondernine" pistol into production, Ceska Zbrojovka of Czechoslovakia introduced its Model 75. The CZ 75 has become a legendary pistol and remains very much in full production, having been adopted by numerous armies and police forces the world over. It has also been bought by untold thousands of civilians, who've willingly paid premium prices of $1500 or more for a single pistol.

The CZ 75 is the most copied modern handgun design, with exact (or nearly exact) clones produced in such diverse places as England, Italy, Switzerland, and China. Many people rate the CZ 75 as perhaps the best handgun of its type ever made, a reputation it did not achieve overnight. In fact, numerous factors militated against it, so that its survival, much less its considerable success, remains a tribute to its superb design.

Advantages. Some of the CZ 75's features include a slide that sits inside the frame (as in the SIG P210), and an especially innovative double-action trigger mechanism that provides a remarkably smooth trigger pull. Considering how crucial a quick double-action first shot must be, the CZ 75's trigger pull is far superior to that of any Walther, Beretta or Smith & Wesson pistol. Like many Ruger firearms, the CZ 75 makes considerable use in its construction of strong but inexpensive investment castings. It also has fewer separate components than competing designs from, say, Beretta or Smith & Wesson, leaving little that can go wrong. The CZ 75's design is also extremely well-sealed against the ingress of dirt, sand or other foreign material into the mechanism, making it less likely to jam under even the most arduous service conditions.

Because of the way its safety is arranged, the CZ 75 offers the shooter a choice of a double- or single-action first shot— a characteristic that appeals to a large num-

The large but graceful CZ 75 handles well and is capable of exceptional accuracy, as this five-shot, 50-foot offhand group measuring 2.5 inches across demonstrates. Note how the double-action first shot is pulled away from the single-action four-shot group that followed. This shift in point of impact is common to all double-action pistols, but is far less pronounced in the CZ compared to other guns of inferior design.

The excellent design of the CZ 75 has inspired these copies and clones (clockwise, from top left): the Italian-made EAA Witness Compact, the Czech CZ 75 Compact, Spain's Star Firestar, and the Spanish Star Model 31.

ber of shooters, many of whom regard a double-action trigger as an annoyance at best and a potential danger at worst. They prefer to load the CZ 75 and then apply the safety, blocking the cocked hammer and sear in what is popularly called the "cocked-and-locked" carry. A simple downward movement of the right thumb as the shooter assumes the firing position is all that is needed to get off a first shot with a light single-action trigger pull; or, the shooter can elect to lower the hammer, controlling it with his thumb as he pulls the trigger, thereby gently easing the hammer to its down position without firing a shot. The pistol is then ready for a double-action first shot.

The lack of a mechanical decocking/safety lever, such as one finds on the Walther and Smith & Wesson double-action pistols, limits the CZ 75's appeal in some quarters; but it is not inherently unsafe to handle as long as extreme care is taken in lowering the hammer, with the barrel pointed in a safe direction. Then, even in the event of an accidental discharge, the bullet will travel in a direction not likely to endanger lives or property.

Considering its size and high magazine capacity, the CZ 75 has, like the FN High Power, one of the most comfortable and forgiving grips of all high-capacity 9mm pistols, particularly among shooters with smaller hands. Still another desirable characteristic of the CZ 75 is that all its controls function in much the same manner as those on the immortal M1911A1, ensuring its continued popularity.

The earliest version of the CZ 75 had a rounded hammer, wooden grips and no half-cock notch on the hammer. It also had a short bearing surface between the slide rails and the frame, giving the front area of this pistol a distinctly slab-sided appearance. It also had a lanyard loop mounted at the heel of the grip. Judging from photos, the finish was either a matte black lacquer or a Parkerized (phosphated) finish. Intended for military sales, this early version was limited in its success, with only about 4,000 such pistols produced. Later in the initial production run, which lasted until 1980, the short slide rails were retained, along with the resulting slab-sided forward portion of the frame and slide. Plastic grips, with their distinct pattern of raised dots, plus a spur hammer, became common. As commercial sales slowly picked up, a lustrous blued finish was also offered. The production of these short-slide CZ 75s lasted until 1979 and numbered perhaps 20,000 pieces.

In 1980, the Czechs greatly improved the Model 75 by adding a half-cock notch to the hammer and lengthening the slide rails by one inch to make a longer bearing surface. This last innovation improved both accuracy and durability to the point where the CZ 75 now in production is considered one of the strongest, most durable and reliable guns available. Thanks to its exceptional design, it has amassed an excellent service record, creating a band of loyalists who are almost fanatical in their affection for this pistol — and small wonder. Moreover, American shooters who long for one of these beauties need no longer pay a scalper's price to own one. Magnum Research (Minneapolis, MN) now imports the CZ 75 and its variants, including the CZ 75 Compact, CZ 85 and CZ 85 Combat.

Disadvantages. As for any problems or shortcomings connected with the CZ 75, they are very few indeed. The gun's narrow, recessed slide retraction grooves, for example, may cause difficulty for shooters with weak hands while trying to retract the slide. The disassembly procedure is virtually identical to that of the competing Smith & Wesson automatic pistols. It is also similar to that of FN's High Power; but unlike that earlier pistol the CZ 75's manual safety does not double as a disassembly latch. Thus fieldstripping the CZ 75 becomes a somewhat more difficult task. The CZ 75 also lacks ambidextrous controls (shooters who require this feature, however, can have it with Ceska Zbrojovka's nearly identical CZ 85). For a double-action first shot the trigger reach on the CZ 75 is rather long for shooters with small hands. In that case, one might consider carrying the pistol cocked and locked. Because it lacks a firing-pin lock, the CZ 75 relies on an inertial firing pin to exert backward pressure on the firing pin, thereby preventing accidental discharge. The M1911A1 and High Power use exactly the same sort of safety arrangement with little or no trouble. But if you must have a gun with the very latest safety devices, then the CZ 75 may not be for you.

Overall, the CZ 75 is an utterly dependable and reliable pistol suitable for all military, police and civilian defensive purposes. Whether it's an original or a clone, whether it's made in Czechoslovakia or elsewhere, the CZ 75 remains one of the finest handgun choices a shooter could possibly make.

CZ MODEL 75

Manufacturer	Years Produced	Caliber/Capacity	Dimensions
Ceska Zbrojovka Uhersky Brod, Czech Republic	1975–Present	9mm/up to 15 rounds	Barrel Length: 4.7" O.A. Length: 8.0" Height: 5.4" Width: 1.35" Weight: 35 oz. (unloaded); 42 oz. (loaded)

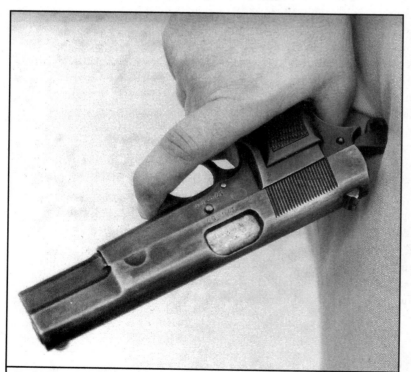

FN BROWNING HIGH POWER

The origins of this Browning-designed pistol date back to 1922–23, following a French request for test samples of an improved military pistol. This gave Fabrique Nationale the impetus to begin developing the design, although FN's Model 35 *Grande Puissance* (French for "High Power") did not enter series production (as the Model 1935) until November 1934. Ultimately the French were unwilling to order a foreign handgun for their armed forces, despite a series of test trials between 1923 and 1940 in which FN-designed pistols consistently outperformed their rivals. The more FN engineer Dieudonne Joseph Saive worked with the design, the more impressed FN was with it. Finally, the company decided to go ahead and produce it, with or without a French military order.

At first, FN wanted to introduce the gun in 1929, but the timing was not right. The collapse of the U.S. stock market late that year precipitated a worldwide depression that delayed the planned introduction. Although disappointing at first, the delay eventually proved beneficial to FN, for it enabled Saive to refine the design still further. As a result, by the time FN began series production in 1935, the High Power was a near-perfect design that has remained in continuous production—with very little modification—to this day.

Although the High Power is often touted as "John Browning's last pistol," much of the credit for developing it must rightfully be assigned to Saive. While Browning is properly credited with the underbarrel cam (to replace the link of the M1911), it was Saive who conceived the high-capacity magazine, which is the High Power's salient feature and indeed gave it its name. Saive's idea of stacking the slim 9mm Parabellum cartridges into a double column allowed the gun to hold nearly twice as many rounds as its competitors; and yet it measured no longer or higher and only a little thicker through the grip. Not until

Early FN High Power pistols featured a rounded hammer, which was easily cocked by hand against the leg or even against a horse's saddle, as advertised in early FN literature.

Smith & Wesson introduced its Model 59 (*see* separate listing) in 1971 did a gun exist that was even remotely competitive with the High Power in terms of its magazine capacity and handling.

Military Service. The High Power's performance in World War II was little short of extraordinary. It was the only pistol of the period that saw full-scale production by both the Axis—in the captured and occupied FN plant in Belgium—and by the Allies in the John Inglis plant in Toronto, Canada. It became the favorite pistol among the elite forces on both sides, especially Germany's SS and paratrooper units, and England's commandos and paratroopers. Later, during the postwar period, the use of High Power pistols increased steadily until its military and police issue had spread to over 90 countries. It remained the standard handgun of NATO for decades and was also distributed widely among civilian shooters. It saw heavy military service on both sides in the Vietnam War and contin-

The High Power — even one as old as this 50-year veteran — is capable of considerable accuracy, as demonstrated by this five-shot, 25-foot offhand group measuring 1.3 inches.

ues to prosper in the Middle East and in Central America. Although most countries now prefer a double-action pistol, it will be a long time indeed before all High Power pistols still in military service are phased out.

While best known as a 9mm pistol, the High Power is also available in 7.65mm (.30 Luger) caliber for export to countries that forbid civilian ownership of guns using military ammunition. In 1993, FN also introduced a .40 S&W caliber version of the High Power with a 10-round magazine; and several manufacturers have offered kits for converting the standard 9mm High Power to .22 LR or .41 Action Express.

Numerous copies of FN's standard High Power, both licensed and unlicensed, abound. Among the licensees are Argentina, Canada, Nigeria, Portugal and Venezuela. Unlicensed copies include those made in large numbers by established factories in Hungary, Israel and Indonesia, while others are produced in small workshops scattered throughout Afghanistan, Pakistan, Vietnam and elsewhere.

Despite the high capacity of the High Power magazine, the grip on this pistol has remained relatively compact; in fact, many people feel that the High Power has the best grip of any pistol made. Other positive characteristics include the High Power's slim, sleek slide. These features help to make it a surprisingly concealable firearm despite its great magazine capacity.

Shortcomings. The High Power is not entirely without its faults. The trigger pull is adequate at best, and its complicated trigger system does not lend itself to gunsmithing nearly as easily as its counterpart on the Colt M1911A1. The High Power's accuracy is adequate, although the new Mark IIIs seem to be extremely accurate. Until recently, the pistol's sights and manual safety were both considered too small on most models made by FN, shortcomings that still persist on most non-FN copies and clones. Also, the High Power's magazine does not release cleanly from the pistol; instead, it must be pulled loose by the shooter. The problem stems from a magazine disconnect safety feature, a device popular with FN but disliked by many shooters.

The High Power is also a fairly expensive weapon to produce, despite FN's continuous efforts to hold down costs by, among other things, assembling the guns in Portugal. Still, for what it costs to buy an FN High Power, one could buy any number of other competitive service pistols, many of which are more modern in design and include a double-action trigger.

The High Power, however, is without a doubt one of the best pistols ever made. Its success is no accident but represents instead the culmination of years of painstaking design improvements. As a result, more High Power pistols have been produced than any other automatic pistol. Today, more than 60 years after its introduction, the FN High Power remains the favorite pistol of numerous skilled shooters and elite forces throughout the world.

FN BROWNING HIGH POWER

Manufacturer	Years Produced	Caliber/Capacity	Dimensions
Fabrique Nationale d'Armes de Guerre (FN) Herstal, Belgium	1935–Present	9mm/13 rounds	Barrel Length: 4.7" O.A. Length: 7.8" Height: 5.6" Width: 1.3" Weight: 32 oz. (unloaded); 39 oz. (loaded)

FRENCH MODEL 1935A

Following World War I and after several years of trials in an effort to develop a new automatic pistol for the French Army, the Model 1935A was created. These trials also led to the development of what later became the world-famous High Power Pistol in 9mm Parabellum caliber (*see* previous listing).

Once the French armed forces had accepted the Model 1935A, production began in 1937 at the Société Alsacienne de Construction Mécanique (SACM). Production was well under way when the Germans captured the SACM factory in Alsace on June 23, 1940. The Germans kept the gun in production during the war, renaming it the "Pistole 625(f)." German production lasted until April 28, 1944, totalling 23,850 pistols. Production of the French Model 1935A resumed after the war and continued until 1950, by which time an estimated 85,000 had been made.

The pistol remained in service throughout World War II as well as France's colonial wars in Vietnam (1945–1954) and Algeria (1954–1962). Many Model 1935A pistols remained in use among Vietnamese forces during America's involvement in Vietnam. They were also issued to police units throughout France and remained in service as such until the late 1980s. In 1937, plans for the Model 1935A were sold to SIG of Switzerland, which used the handgun as a point of departure for the development of the world-famous pistol now known as the SIG P210 (*see* separate listing). The Swiss made many modifications and improvements to the French design, but the Model 1935A's influence is still plainly seen in the P210, which is widely regarded as the world's finest 9mm pistol.

The Model 1935A disassembles much like an FN High Power, but it also features a removable lock-work module inspired by the Russian-built Tokarev. In a pistol intended for heavy military use, this ability to field-strip so thoroughly is a definite asset.

Advantages. In addition to its high standard of materials, fit and finish, the Model 1935A had many fine features, attesting to the excellence of its ergonomic design. For example, its strong but simple manual safety positively blocked the hammer from reaching the firing pin. The safety lever pivoted

In this right-side view, the Model 1935A reveals its clean, simple lines. Its resemblance to the legendary SIG P210 is no accident, since SIG used the French pistol as its prototype in developing the world's most respected 9mm pistol. Note the loaded-chamber indicator protruding slightly from the top of the slide just behind the ejection port, and the safety standing straight up from the slide (shown in the safe position at rear end of barrel), making it easy to check whether the gun is on safe or ready to fire. Because of its single-action design, the hammer on this pistol must be at full cock, as shown, before it can be fired.

straight up to the safe setting; and when set on safe, the manual safety catch protruded above the plane of the slide, offering clear evidence that the pistol was on safe or ready to fire. To place the safety into its fire position, one simply thumbed it back and down, similar to cocking the hammer (which a right-handed shooter could do without breaking his grip on the pistol). A further benefit of this safety design was the manner in which the gun could be loaded and unloaded with the pistol on safe, a major advantage over Browning's designs. A magazine safety also helped avoid at least some careless accidental shootings, although this feature remains a controversial one disliked by many shooters.

Another safety feature was the Model 1935A's loaded-chamber indicator, located on top of the slide. When the firing chamber was unloaded, this indicator lay flat against the slide top; but should a round remain in the firing chamber, the indicator rose slightly, enough to give the shooter a clear warning. In addition, an exposed external hammer had to be cocked before the single-action pistol was ready to fire. Its lockwork came in a sturdy module that was removable as one complete unit. This clever and useful feature facilitated both routine disassembly in the field and more extensive maintenance procedures. The shape and size of the Model 1935A have also contributed to its excellent ergonomics. Its slim grip is well-shaped for rapid, instinctive pointing. Moreover, the gun is relatively small, light and flat—about the size of a Walther PP or an FN Model 1922—making it easy to carry and conceal. In addition, the 1935A is only slightly larger than the Makarov pistol (*see* COMPLETE GUIDE TO COMPACT HANDGUNS), yet it uses an advanced locked-breech design instead of the simple blowback mechanism employed in the Makarov and most other handgun designs of similar size.

Disadvantages. The French 1935A was not free of problems, however. Its sights are small, and the finish—black paint over parkerization—is not especially durable. The trigger pull is sometimes below par too, and the serrations on the slide are undersized, making it difficult to operate the slide quickly (despite a rather weak recoil spring). The magazine release is well-placed for rapid operation, but it lowers the magazine only a few millimeters, forcing the shooter to remove the empty magazine by hand, thus slowing down the reloading process.

Ammunition maker Old Western Scrounger loads the 7.65mm Longue in a cartridge with a 93-grain bullet driven at almost 1,000 fps. Having such a reliable source of quality ammunition makes the Model 1935A not only an interesting historical item, but also a useful handgun once again.

But the main problem with the Model 1935A concerns the power and availability of ammunition. The 7.65mm Longue cartridge—used only in the French Model 1935A and 1935S automatic pistols and the French Model 1938 submachine gun—propels an 87-grain (5.5 gram) bullet at a muzzle velocity of about 1100 feet per second (fps), comparable to that of the 8mm Nambu round once used by the Japanese and the .32 H&R Magnum, which is respected in many quarters as a good low-recoil round. The 7.65mm Longue may be no powerhouse, but it's definitely superior to the .32 ACP and .380 ACP rounds made popular by the Germans and Italians during World War II. The Model 1935A is no larger than many pistols that use those pocket-pistol rounds; furthermore, the 7.65mm Longue travels at well over 1,000 fps, which is widely regarded as conducive to reliable expansion. Loading the 7.65mm Longue in a hollowpoint format (or a Glaser- or MagSafe-type round) would definitely produce an effective self-defense cartridge.

Fortunately, Old Western Scrounger (Montague, CA) has come to the rescue of Model 1935A owners by offering the 7.65mm Longue in a cartridge with a 93-grain bullet—the same .308 bullet used in the .30 Luger pistol—driven at slightly less than 1,000 fps. This is a good round that doesn't exert undue wear and tear on such well-made but old pistols. Modest in power, the 7.65mm Longue gives the Model 1935A only a soft recoil, producing excellent accuracy. Our best five-shot offhand group fired from 25 feet measured a mere 0.7 inch across. At 50 feet, our best five-shot offhand group spanned just 2.2 inches. Considering the Model 1935A's tiny sights and heavy trigger pull, these are excellent results. Having a reliable source of quality, albeit expensive, ammunition raises the status of the Model 1935A from a mere oddity to that of a working pistol, thereby providing shooters a chance to learn firsthand what a good gun this is.

The Model 1935A is extremely accurate by handgun standards. This five-shot offhand group fired from 25 feet measured a fantastic .7 inch across.

Indeed, this pistol is a far better handgun than its critics would have us believe. The 1935A is well-designed, boasts excellent handling and, despite its low power for military purposes, is acceptable for self-defense use. What's more, its low esteem among many collectors notwithstanding, and with limited ammunition availability, prices for the 1935A tend to be low for a pistol with such fine materials and workmanship. The Model 1935A thus makes a useful handgun for both collector and shooter.

FRENCH MODEL 1935A

Manufacturer	Years Produced	Caliber/Capacity	Dimensions
Société Alsacienne de Constructions Mécaniques (SACM) Alsace, France	1937–1950	7.65mm Longue (.32 French Long)/ 8 rounds	Barrel Length: 4.3" O.A. Length: 7.6" Height: 4.9" Width: 1.15" Weight: 26 oz. (unloaded); 28.5 oz. (loaded)

LLAMA MODEL XI "ESPECIAL"

In 1931, Spain's Gabilondo Company introduced its line of Llama pistols based on Colt's Model 1911. That same line, which remains in production, replaced Gabilondo's earlier Ruby series of FN Model 1903 clones made from 1914–1918 (and the "Buffalo" and "Danton" pistols, both based on the FN Model 1910, produced from 1919 to 1931).

Typical of Gabilondo, the Model XI has an exposed pivoting extractor rather than the M1911's internal extractor, which is more likely to break. Also, unlike the Model 1911, the Llama Model XI has a curved backstrap without grip safety, a rounded hammer, and fires only the 9mm Parabellum cartridge. Similarities to the M1911 are strong, though. The locking mechanism is identical, although slightly downsized in keeping with the 9mm cartridge rather than the .45 ACP (for which John Browning designed the Model 1911).

This five-shot offhand group fired from 25 feet away from the target with the Llama "Especial" spans 1.4 inches.

Another five-shot offhand group fired from 50 feet away measures 2.2 inches across.

The most international of the early Llama pistols, the Model XI is similar in design to both the Tokarev and FN High Power pistols. It's strikingly attractive, with sleek contours and vertically ribbed walnut grips. Following its debut in 1936, the Model XI was used extensively in the Spanish Civil War, which began in July of that year and continued until February of 1939. Model XI pistols served initially in the Republican armed forces, but when the northern area of Spain fell into Nationalist hands in the spring of 1937, Model XI production went instead to Franco's pro-Fascist Nationalists. After the Civil War, the Model XI became well known in Europe and Asia, where its enduring design and popular 9mm Parabellum chambering were strong selling points. During World War II, the Model XI was used in limited numbers by various armed forces; and following the war it remained in production for another ten years, being exported both by Gabilonda and the Mugica firm.

The Model XI tested for this book showed excellent accuracy and flawless reliability—even with modern hollowpoint ammunition, which often fails to feed cleanly in older pistols not designed for it. Five-shot groups fired from a distance of 25 feet consistently produced bullet holes that practically touched one another, while 50-foot groups were limited only by the pistol's small sights, a problem found with virtually every automatic pistol made prior to the early 1980s.

In the opinion of British small arms authority Ian Hogg, the Model XI is perhaps the best combat pistol ever made in 9mm Parabellum. That's high praise indeed, given the many excellent designs made in this popular chambering. Sadly, the Model XI remains quite scarce in the United States, although other Llama pistols—particularly the earlier Model IX— abound. Compared to other major Spanish pistols produced by Star and Astra, the Llamas are held in low esteem by collectors but have proven excellent shooters and are less expensive than many competing pistols.

LLAMA MODEL XI "ESPECIAL"

Manufacturer	Years Produced	Caliber/Capacity	Dimensions
Llama Gabilondo y Cia. S.A., Vitoria, Spain	1936–1954	9mm Parabellum/ 9 rounds	Barrel Length: 4.9" O.A. Length: 7.6" Height: 5.2" Width: 1.3" Weight: 31 oz. (unloaded); 36 oz. (loaded)

LUGER (PARABELLUM) PISTOL

The Parabellum pistol—frequently referred to as the Luger after its inventor—is one of the most famous and widely recognized guns ever made. Soon after its introduction in 1900, the Luger was already considered a state-of-the-art automatic pistol. It went on to serve in the German armed forces through World Wars I and II. Numerous other armed forces—notably the Dutch and the Swiss—also used Lugers. But even in those countries that did not adopt the Luger, such as France, the U.S., Great Britain and the Soviet Union, small numbers were bought for testing and evaluation purposes. Their combined output among several different manufacturers exceeded two million units. The Swiss kept the Luger in service until the 1950s, and from 1970 on Mauser-Werke produced the pistol in limited quantities, chiefly for the collector market. Stoeger Industries introduced a brand-new stainless steel version of this ageless gun in 1994.

The heart of the Luger is its toggle-joint, a clever and rather intricate device that locks the breech at the moment of firing. Inspired by the mechanics of the human knee, the toggle is connected to a moving-barrel/barrel-extension assembly. Upon firing, this barrel and extension recoils rearward, pushing the toggle open. At the end of its upward travel, the toggle is forced forward by a mainspring housed in the rear of the pistol grip. During the recoil stroke, the toggle remains well above the sight plane, but the shooter hardly notices because the recoil stroke is so fast. After the shooter has expended all rounds in the magazine, the toggle remains up as a warning for the shooter to reload.

The 1900 (Old Pattern) Luger. Not surprisingly for a gun that has remained in production for so long and served in so many different armed forces, variations of the Luger abound. The original version, called the Model 1900 or "Old Pattern," had a leaf mainspring in the grip, a grip safety and a manual safety that moved forward and up to its safe setting. The caliber—7.65x22mm—was a high-speed, flat-shooting cartridge that remains in production. The Swiss adopted this model—often known as the .30 Luger—in 1900 as the *Ordonnanzpistole 1900*, making that country the first military force to take the Luger. The Swiss bought the initial batch of guns from DWM (Deutsche Waffen und Munitionsfabriken) and later arranged to have parts sent from Germany to be assembled and finished in Switzerland, an arrangement that lasted until 1917. The U.S. later purchased 1,000 for troop trials, and Bulgaria also ordered a large number.

The 1902 Luger. A major change in the Luger pistol in 1902 sent repercussions far beyond even the direct effects of this remarkable pistol: the creation of the 9mm Parabellum or Luger cartridge. This was accomplished by opening up the original .30 Luger case mouth so that it could accept a larger bullet (9mm in diameter) rather than the .30 Luger's 7.65mm. As a result, the weight of the bullet rose slightly, from 93 grains to 123 (approximately) and muzzle velocity dropped from about 1200 to 1100 feet per second. The 9mm case was shortened from 22mm to 19mm, causing the round to be known variously as the "9mm Luger," "9mm Parabellum" or "9x19mm." Whatever its name, this cartridge has become one of the few pistol rounds that has achieved nearly worldwide distribution. So many fine guns are now chambered for the 9mm Luger cartridge, in fact, that a whole section of this handgun series has been devoted to them.

The caliber change made in the Model 1902 required a few slight dimensional changes, particularly in the barrel. But with very few modifications, this 9mm pistol can be easily and quickly converted

The above illustrations compare cross-sections of the 7.65mm Old Model Luger (right) with the 9mm New Model Luger with 4-inch barrel (left).

to .30 Luger, or vice versa, often with only a barrel change. This has helped to ensure the continuing longevity of the .30 Luger round in countries that forbid civilian ownership of military-style weapons.

The Navy Model. The first official German purchase of the Luger was made in 1904 by the Imperial German Navy. This variant, now called the "Navy Model," retained the newly developed 9mm caliber. It had a 6-inch barrel, a grooved lug at the rear of the frame (for a shoulder stock that doubled as a holster), a grip safety and a loaded-chamber indicator on the extractor.

The 1906 New Model. The 1906 Luger, known as the "New Model," introduced a coil mainspring in the grip to replace the leaf spring of earlier models. Wisely, the direction in which the manual safety moved was reversed, so that now the shooter pushed the safety forward to fire and back to safe. This change greatly reduced the chances of accidental discharge, as had occurred in previous versions where hostering the gun caused shooters to move the safety inadvertently into its fire position. DWM produced this gun in both 7.65mm and 9mm calibers, and it proved quite popular in Germany and abroad. The German Navy took a large number, and in 1907 the U.S. also purchased a small test lot of a dozen or so pistols chambered in .45 caliber. DWM refused a U.S. Army request in 1908 for an additional 200 test pistols, but it did sell enough parts to the Swiss for that country to assemble just over 10,000 pistols in 7.65mm. The Swiss named those guns the *Ordonnanzpistole 1906,* replacing their *Ordonnanzpistole 1900.*

The Parabellum P08. Despite the success of the Models 1900 and 1906, the chief German Luger was the Model 1908, and it is this pistol which most people associate with the Luger. Adopted in 1908 by the Imperial German Army, the Parabellum P08, as it was known by the Germans, was produced in the greatest quantities of all Luger variants. It had a 9mm barrel measuring 4 inches (102mm) in length. It had all the features of the 1906-vintage New Model, except that it eliminated the grip safety. During World War I, tremendous quantities of the P08 were produced, with DWM's output supplemented by the government's Erfurt Arsenal in Prussia from 1911 on.

The Artillery Model. An 8-inch-barrel version—the Artillery Model—was produced in limited numbers beginning in 1914. Used by artillerymen, aviators and later by storm troopers, this model was issued from 1916 on with a unique 32-round rotary magazine. It never achieved the widespread distribution of the standard model, though, and is today an exceedingly rare and expensive item.

During World War I, Germany's armed forces never had enough P08s to go around. So great was the demand, in fact, that the German government ordered 150,000 Mauser C.96 pistols (*see* separate listing) in 1915, all rechambered for the 9mm cartridge. By 1917 the Germans, unable to supply their own troops adequately, quit sending Parabellum pistol parts to the Swiss, who then set up their own production facility in Bern. Between 1918 and 1928, this plant made over 12,000 Model 1906-style Parabellum pistols, mostly in 7.65mm caliber.

The German Parabellum or Luger pistol was popular almost from the moment of its inception and still attracts a wide following of shooters and collectors. This .30-caliber version, in its original chambering, was made to a commercial pattern popular from 1923 onward.

The 1923 Luger. After World War I, Germany's Luger production came under strict scrutiny by the victorious Allies. Among other things, manufacture of new Luger pistols in 9mm caliber with barrels over 100mm (3.9 inches) long was forbidden. In 1923, DWM resumed Luger manufacture with a Model 1923 pistol in 7.65mm caliber and a 90mm (3.86-inch) barrel. The Netherlands and Finland each ordered several thousand of these pistols for their armed forces. From that point on, the name "Luger" became the official name for this Parabellum pistol, although that had been its informal nickname in Great Britain and America at least since World War I. When the A.F. Stoeger Company of New York began importing these 1923-style guns into the U.S. in 1923, it shrewdly registered the Luger name with the U.S. Patent Office.

The decade immediately prior to World War II was a busy one in terms of Luger production. In Switzerland, the cost of making the *Ordonnanzpistole 1906* had reached an excessive level, so in 1928

Stoeger, which imported Lugers into the U.S. from Germany after World War I, purchased a U.S. Patent for the Luger name in 1923. Long after the company became Stoeger Industries, it introduced a stainless steel American Eagle Luger in 1994 (above), ensuring the longevity of this ageless gun.

Swiss engineers began considering ways to make the gun cheaper to produce. Their efforts led to the *Ordonnanzpistole 1906/29*, which remained in production until 1947. Almost 30,000 of these pistols were made, mostly for the Swiss armed forces, along with about 1,000 commercial pistols. With its straight front gripstrap and an enlarged grip safety on the rear gripstrap, this Luger was quite distinctive in appearance.

Meanwhile, in Germany, all of DWM's Luger-making machinery was sent in 1930 to Mauser-Werke in Oberndorf, near the Franco-German border. Mauser continued building Luger pistols until it phased out production in 1942 in favor of the newer P.38 designed by Walther. Also in Germany, Simson & Company of Suhl had been refurbishing and building Luger pistols since 1921 on production machinery transferred from the Erfurt factory. Simson sold this machinery around 1934 to Krieghoff, which then received a Luftwaffe contract for 10,000 pistols, built between 1935 and 1936. Before the war, the Germans sold Luger pistols to Persia (Iran), Turkey, the Netherlands, Latvia and Sweden, plus a large number—nearly 5,000—to Portugal in 1943.

By the time German P08 production ceased in 1942, over 2.8 million units had been made over a 38-year period for Germany's armed forces alone. Assembly of additional Luger pistols from existing parts and refurbishing of existing pistols went on until 1945, serving alongside later P.38s in German service until the end of the war. With the war's end, the production of Lugers for military use tapered off greatly. Today, most Lugers are collector's items; also, because an original, unaltered specimen will bring a good price, military forces wisely look toward other pistols with which to arm their troops.

From a shooter's perspective, the Luger is a pistol to enjoy and treasure. Despite its rather tiny sights, it is respectably accurate. And notwithstanding a reputation in some quarters as a fragile and temperamental gun, the Luger is probably one of the strongest handguns ever made. Its basic operating mechanism—the toggle—was used in Hiram Maxim's famous early machine gun from which, beginning in 1908, the German government developed the Parabellum machine gun. A similar toggle joint (inverted so that it broke downward rather than upward) was also used in the British Vickers machine gun. Far from being a problem, the toggle joint is in fact stronger than either the locking-block mechanism of the Walther P.38, which replaced the Luger in German service, or the tipping barrel used in the Browning-style locked-breech handguns.

The complaint that the Luger's mechanism was too sensitive for the type of ammunition it used does have some validity. A powerful round is needed for the mechanism to function properly. In addition, some Lugers will not feed hollowpoint ammunition or other short-bulleted ammunition. Moreover, the close tolerance and tight fit of its construction is not forgiving of mud or sand entering the mechanism. Another important disadvantage of the Luger is its high cost. It was always an expensive gun to produce, requiring many hundreds of machine steps and hand-finishing processes. It was this expense, more than anything else, that led to the Luger's replacement by later automatic pistols, including the P.38.

Untold thousands of Luger pistols came to the U.S. after World Wars I and II, and they are still good guns. Those who own one with matching parts and a good finish are advised to have an expert look it over to determine its collector value before firing it.

LUGER (PARABELLUM) PISTOL

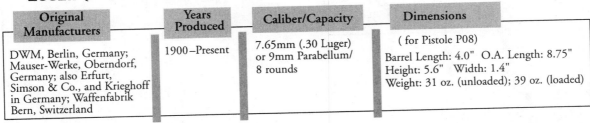

Original Manufacturers	Years Produced	Caliber/Capacity	Dimensions
DWM, Berlin, Germany; Mauser-Werke, Oberndorf, Germany; also Erfurt, Simson & Co., and Krieghoff in Germany; Waffenfabrik Bern, Switzerland	1900–Present	7.65mm (.30 Luger) or 9mm Parabellum/ 8 rounds	(for Pistole P08) Barrel Length: 4.0" O.A. Length: 8.75" Height: 5.6" Width: 1.4" Weight: 31 oz. (unloaded); 39 oz. (loaded)

MAUSER C.96 "BROOMHANDLE"

The world's first truly successful semiautomatic pistol was the German-made Mauser C.96. It pioneered this handgun type and was the first semiautomatic pistol to feature a bolt hold-open device once the last shot was fired.

Development of this pistol began around 1893 by three Mauser employees, the Federle brothers. Initially, the C.96 was the product of their spare time, until Paul Mauser decided that a self-loading pistol would be a good commercial product to compete with the Borchardt pistol that had appeared in 1893 (and later became the world-famous Parabellum or Luger). By March 1895, the Mauser pistol was ready for test-firing, and the following year permission was granted to enter series production.

When mass production began in April 1897, initial sales were slow. The world was apparently not ready for such a radical idea as the semiautomatic pistol. Then in 1899, the Italian navy ordered 5,000

Mauser's "Broomhandle" C.96 pistol was the first successful handgun with a device designed to hold open the firing mechanism, as shown, after the last round was expended. Note the broomhandle-shaped grip, which led to the pistol's common nickname.

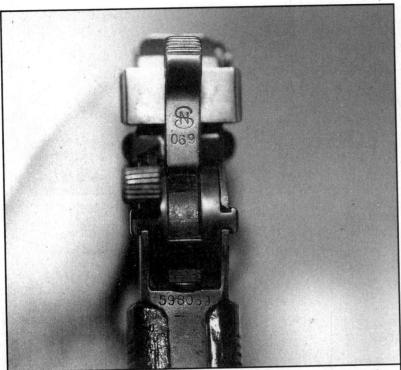

This rear view of the C.96 receiver reveals the pistol's hammer and safety mechanism. "NS" stands for the later variation, or "NewSafety." Note the high serial number on this Bolo Mauser pistol, which was exported to China.

pistols, and by 1902 some 7,000 C.96 pistols had been sold for military use and another 26,000 to commercial buyers. Most of the military buyers bought only small lots of the new pistol for testing and evaluation purposes, however, while they decided how best to incorporate the pistols into their own scheme of things. A more promising source of profit was sales to private individuals, many of them military officers who were expected to purchase and maintain their own handguns. Most prominent among the nonmilitary buyers was Winston Churchill, who, as a newspaper reporter in 1898, carried one of these weapons into Africa, later crediting it with saving his life.

As with most successful guns that enjoy a long production run, the Model C.96 was made in a variety of configurations. Some had a fixed rear sight—though a rifle-type tangent rear sight was more common—and most had a slot cut into the lower rear portion of the grip to accommodate a detachable wooden shoulder stock. Once removed, this stock could be

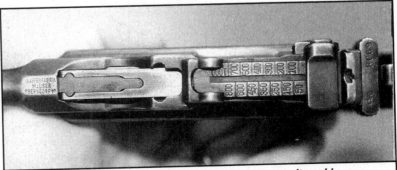

Most Mauser C.96-type pistols featured a long-range adjustable rear sight.

used as a holster, a dual-purpose feature that has since reappeared on a few other guns, notably the FN Model 1903, the Browning High Power and the Heckler & Koch VP-70.

From 1912 on, the "New Safety" design (marked "NS" on the rear of the hammer) could be set on safe by pulling it to the rear, and only after the shooter had cocked the hammer to bring it out of

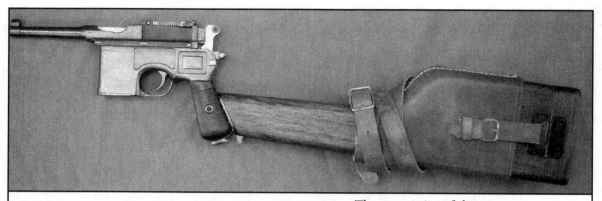

The rear portion of the grip on most Broomhandle Mauser pistols was slotted, as shown (inset), to accept a shoulder stock whose purpose was to steady the pistol for long-range shooting. With shoulder stock in place, the pistol is converted into a light-weight carbine. Such combinations were extremely popular in prewar China and in Germany during World War II.

contact with the firing pin. Later in the 1980s, Norinco copied this rather odd safety setup in its Model 213, one of the earliest Tokarev-type pistols to be offered in 9mm caliber, for export into the United States.

Model 1916 Pistols. From 1915 until the end of World War I, Mauser-Werke built approximately 138,000 Model C.96 pistols (out of a 150,000-gun order) chambered for 9mm Parabellum to supplement its P.08 Luger, then being issued to the German armed forces. These guns—officially called the Model 1916—are marked with a red (or sometimes black-stained) "9" in the grip to alert the shooter to the 9mm caliber. Today, they rank high among the many collector-grade C.96-type pistols available. A number of C.96 pistols that started out in 7.63mm (.30 Mauser) caliber have since been converted to the 9mm configuration.

The Bolo Mauser. The short-barreled C.96 pistols are popularly known as "Bolo" (a slang word for "Bolshevik," the early name applied to the Russian Communists, meaning "bigger" or "majority" party). Ironically, considering its name, the Bolo Mauser was actually the smallest C.96 pistol made. Its 3.9-inch (100mm) barrel barely conformed to restrictions on the manufacture of German firearms imposed by the Treaty of Versailles that officially ended World War I.

Model 712 Pistols. Perhaps the most interesting and glamorous variation of the C.96 pistol was the Model 712, introduced in 1932. Actually, it was a small submachine gun, a selective-fire weapon capable of either semiautomatic or fully automatic fire. Loaded with a detachable box magazine holding 20 to 40 rounds, the Model 712 (or *Schnellfeuerpistole*, meaning "rapid-fire pistol") could empty its magazine at a torrid rate of nearly 900 rounds per minute. Even when the holster was used as a shoulder stock to brace the weapon, this gun's controllability in automatic fire was quite poor, although the sheer volume of fire could compensate for the inaccuracy. On semiautomatic fire, however, the Model 712 was as accurate as any other C.96. Adding to its flexibility, the gun's detachable magazine could be kept on and the weapon reloaded through the top of the open action using standard 10-round stripper clips, the same as other C.96-type pistols. Because it was considered an unusual item, the Model 712 conferred considerable prestige to its owner, a factor that had as much to do with its popularity as with any military value. The Model 712 saw service in China, Yugoslavia, Nazi Germany and Argentina. In all, about 150,000 of this type were made.

Total production of all C.96-type pistols by Mauser alone was approximately 1.6 million. In addition, numerous copies were made, most notably the Astra 900 series built during the 1930s and the Chinese Type 80 machine pistol, which is still being made by Norinco. Virtually every armed force in the world bought C.96s, either as test and evaluation pieces or as substitute standard issue.

Interestingly, the 7.63 Mauser round introduced by Mauser with the C.96 was more widely distributed than even the pistol itself. It became, in slightly modified form, the standard pistol and submachine-gun round of the Soviet Union and China, including such famous weapons as the Tokarev TT-30/TT-33 pistol series and the PPSh-41 and PPS-43 submachine guns.

Ammunition aside, the C.96 is an amazing pistol even by modern standards. With its interlocking component pieces carefully fitted together without pins or screws, it is nothing less than artistic in its construction. By modern standards, though, the shooting characteristics of the C.96 are mixed at best. It has a terrible grip, its sights are undersized, and it tends to shoot high at reasonable pistol distances. Once the shooter compensates for that, however, the C.96 and its many variations can be very accurate. The trigger is spongy but its pull weight is very light—perhaps too light. Its recoil is not excessive, despite the light barrel and powerful ammunition it uses. By modern pistol standards, the .30 Mauser round itself has excellent penetration. Armed with a good expanding hollowpoint bullet, which it unfortunately lacks, this could be a truly formidable round. Reloading with the 10-round stripper clips is certainly less convenient than shoving a new magazine into the grip, as with most modern automatic pistols. On the other hand, there's no way the magazine can be separated from the gun and lost, as with most modern pistols.

Today, the C.96 is more a collector's item than a shooting pistol. A specimen in good original condition can fetch a high price, making it inadvisable to carry in one's coat pocket or automobile glove box. It can, however, serve reasonably well as a defensive handgun until something more suitable becomes available. Because many of the "Broomhandle"-type pistols now being imported into the U.S. are formerly Chinese in origin, their current owners are urged to have these pistols examined by a knowledgeable gunsmith before firing them—a warning that applies to all buyers of used guns.

MAUSER C.96 "BROOMHANDLE"

Manufacturer	Years Produced	Caliber/Capacity	Dimensions
Mauser-Werke Oberndorf, Germany	1896–1937	7.63mm/10 rounds	Barrel Length: 3.9" O.A. Length: 10" Height: 5.6" Width: 1.1" Weight: 37 oz. (unloaded); 42 oz. (loaded)

RADOM VIS-35 PISTOL

By 1929, the armed forces of a newly independent Poland were searching for a new standard handgun to replace their hodgepodge of foreign designs, including most notably the Russian M1895 Nagant revolver. The Polish government accordingly negotiated an expensive licensing arrangement with the Czechs to produce their vz 22 pistol. Before the agreement was finalized, however, two Polish engineers—Piotr Wilniewczyc and Jan Skrzypinski—submitted a design for an advanced locked-breech pistol that was far superior to the Czech gun. National pride undoubtedly played a part, too, but in any event the Czech contract was first postponed, then cancelled altogether.

By February 1931, a prototype of the new gun was ready for testing. It performed superbly and in March 1933 the Polish government bought the design from Wilniewczyc and Skrzypinski. The new handgun was named "Vis," but it is usually referred to by U.S. collectors as the "Radom," named after the arsenal where it was made.

Following troop trials, full-scale production of the Radom began in 1935. Several tens of thousands of these excellent handguns equipped the Polish armed forces at the time of the Nazi invasion in September 1939. Following their occupation of Poland, the Germans, recognizing the excellence of the Polish pistol's design, kept it in production throughout the war. Following the capture of the Radom factory by the Russians in late 1944, production was moved by the retreating Germans to Steyr in Austria.

The Radom was extremely popular with the Germans, who built over 310,000 for their armed forces during the war years. It became a common item used by SS and paratroop units, and it also saw naval service. Many thousands of Radom pistols were captured by American troops and brought to this country following the war. Total production is estimated at 385,000. The Polish arms industry, having switched over to Soviet designs, did not resume production. Radom pistols did see some postwar military use, though, notably with the East German armed forces.

The Polish Radom pistol (top), built from 1935 to 1945, strongly resembles the FN High Power (bottom). It also introduced some unique devices of its own, notably a decocking lever.

As a clever amalgamation of John Browning's M1911 design, the Radom offered some excellent original features. In general, it shares the M1911's rugged reliability. It also has a single-action trigger

As shown here, even disassembled the Radom pistol (left) is quite similar to the FN High Power (right). Despite these mechanical similarities, however, the Radom does not appear to be an exact copy.

mechanism and a grip safety. However, the Radom's locking system is more like that of the FN High Power (its underbarrel locking cam is subtly different in appearance, though, and may have been developed independently). The Radom also features a decocking lever for the hammer and has no manual safety catch. It was intended to be carried with the hammer down over a loaded firing chamber, then cocked before firing.

Even today, the Radom's innovative design makes it a viable choice for defensive shooting. Bear in mind that it was designed prior to the development of hollowpoint cartridges and will probably not feed them with complete reliability (although it performs well with standard military FMJ or ball ammunition). While the original Polish versions remain scarce, they are extremely well-made and expensive collector's items. Most of the Radom production was carried out under German/Austrian auspices, however, using inferior workmanship and materials; nor can outright sabotage be discounted. Consequently, a close and thorough examination by a gunsmith is definitely in order before one attempts to fire a war-era Radom pistol—or any gun made under the German occupation, for that matter.

RADOM VIS-35 PISTOL

Manufacturer	Years Produced	Caliber/Capacity	Dimensions
Fabryka Broni w Radomu Radom, Poland	1935–1945	9mm/8 rounds	Barrel Length: 4.8" O.A. Length: 8.1" Height: 5.3" Width: 1.3" Weight: 37 oz. (unloaded); 41 oz. (loaded)

SIG MODEL P210

As a neutral country during WWII, Switzerland was able to proceed leisurely in seeking a replacement for its 1929-vintage Parabellum pistol. In 1937, the Schweizerische Industrie Gesellschaft (SIG) purchased the patent rights of the Charles Petter-designed Model 1935 French service pistol. Between 1937 and 1940, SIG produced slightly modified experimental versions of this, some in 9mm Parabellum. As war raged, Switzerland began to test other pistols more aggressively. Several foreign designs were studied, including a U.S. Colt, the Walther Models HP/P.38 and PP from Germany, the Polish-made Radom, and the Astra 900 from Spain. The Swiss also rebarreled several of their own 06/29 Lugers to 9mm.

From 1944 to 1947, the Swiss military tested the much-improved Petter designs from SIG in both 8-shot and 16-shot versions, along with two guns from the Swiss government arsenal at Bern: the W+F 43 Browning, based on the FN High Power, and the W+F 47 *Gasolbensreaktion*. By 1948, the Swiss armed forces had settled on the 8-shot SIG— the SP 47/8—which went into service the following year as the Model 49. Since 1947, SIG's commercial designation for this pistol has been "P210," which still serves the Swiss armed forces despite the introduction in 1975 of the Model P220.

Advantages. An excellent pistol, the P210 is based on the best features of earlier automatic pistols, notably the Tokarev (from which it took its modular lockwork) and the FN High Power (*see* separate listings), which contributed the principle of breech locking. The P210 also incorporated numerous innovations which have made it one of the world's best service pistols. For example, it was the first production pistol with a slide that sat inside the frame, rather than surrounding the top of the frame as on most pistols. This reversed slide/frame arrangement, while expensive to manufacture, allows extraordinary support to the slide, which in turn makes the pistol both extremely accurate and durable. Several pistols, notably the Czech CZ 75 (*see* separate listing), have copied this arrangement. The P210 also introduced an enclosed lug underneath the barrel, rather than the shaped cam of the FN High Power. This improvement makes barrel unlocking more precise and controlled, hence improving accuracy. Still another improvement is the P210's extraordinarily smooth, light and crisp trigger pull.

Disadvantages. The P210 is a rather large gun, for one thing. The safety lever is not only hard to reach, it's difficult to put into the safe setting. And because the rear grip tang is small, many shooters risk being struck in the hand by the hammer as the slide recoils. The magazine release is stiff and tough to operate, too, making the reloading process unduly complicated. The P210's chief drawback, however, has been its high cost. Still, this gun remains a superb weapon—probably the most durable and accurate service automatic pistol ever built.

SIG MODEL P210

Manufacturer	Years Produced	Caliber/Capacity	Dimensions
SIG (Schweizerische Industrie Gesellschaft) Neuhausen, Switzerland	1947–Present	9mm/8 rounds	Barrel Length: 4.7" O.A. Length: 8.5" Height: 5.4" Width: 1.3" Weight: 38 oz.(unloaded); 42 oz. (loaded)

SMITH & WESSON MODEL 39

In the years immediately after World War II, Carl Hellstrom, then the visionary president of Smith & Wesson, foresaw a market for a modern double-action 9mm automatic pistol. This began a bold move forward for a company that was traditionally revolver-oriented—especially since its first automatic pistols, the prewar .35 and .32 automatics, had been dismal commercial failures compared to the successes of its arch rival, Colt.

The first prototype of this new S&W pistol was ready in October 1948. It combined an M1911-type barrel bushing and a breech-locking system (inspired by the FN High Power, discussed earlier) with a hammer-dropping manual safety lever and double-action trigger mechanism similar to the P.38. Smith & Wesson sent an early sample of the prototype to the U.S. Army for testing, which led to a request for a single-action version. The Army testing led nowhere, however, but Smith & Wesson continued to develop both double- and single-action pistols as a private venture, experimenting with steel as well as lightweight aluminum-alloy frames.

Smith & Wesson released its new 9mm pistol in December 1954 in both double- and single-action versions. When model numbers were assigned in 1957, the double-action pistol received the designation "Model 39" while the single-action configuration was called "Model 40." Interest in the latter never materialized—only ten were ever built, and they were used for testing by military and police agencies in hopes of landing a contract that never materialized.

This refined 1980s version of the Model 39 — the Model 639 — features an improved exposed extractor, stainless steel construction, ambidextrous safety levers, and an adjustable sight with large protective ears.

Meanwhile, the double-action Model 39, which also got off to a slow start, began attracting favorable notice in the late 1950s both in the U.S. and abroad. In 1967, the Illinois State Police became the first large police agency to buy Model 39s, beginning a police trend toward automatic pistols that has continued to this day. At the same time, the Model 39 was proving very popular with soldiers in Vietnam as mostly privately purchased weapons; the U.S. Navy also ordered small numbers of modified Model 39s. Made of stainless steel and equipped with a suppressor, they were known as the Pistol, Mark 22 Model 0, nicknamed the "Hush Puppy" (*see* S&W Model 59).

To utilize parts made during the development period of this pistol many years before, Smith & Wesson released a total of 927 steel-framed Model 39s in 1966 (the balance of Model 39 production had a lighter aluminum-alloy frame). Incidentally, the prototype Model 39 pictured above has a steel frame and "PAT'S PENDING" marking on the slide. Later in 1971, Smith & Wesson improved the extractor on the Model 39 to correct breakage problems that had occurred with earlier pistols. This pistol was given the designation Model 39-2.

Even by modern standards the Model 39 remains a passable defensive handgun. Reasonably small and light, its curved backstrap makes it a comfortable gun to hold. Its instinctive pointing qualities are also good, which is especially advantageous considering the guns mediocre sights. The reliability of early Model 39s with hollowpoint and other non-military ammunition is not always good, plus the extractors of original Model 39s have been known to break occasionally.

With a trigger pull better than that of the typical wartime P.38, the Model 39 became not only the first successful automatic pistol to be offered by Smith & Wesson, it also became the ancestor of what is today one of the world's largest and most successful lines of automatic pistols. Although the original Model 39 has been out of production since 1982, its successors include such highly acclaimed guns as the 14-shot Model 59 (introduced in 1971), the Model 439, the stainless steel Model 639 (introduced in 1982), the compact Model 469 (introduced in 1983), and the Model 3900 series (introduced beginning in 1989).

SMITH & WESSON MODEL 39

Manufacturer	Years Produced	Caliber/Capacity	Dimensions
Smith & Wesson Springfield, MA	1954–1980	9mm/8 rounds	Barrel Length: 4.0" O.A. Length: 7.4" Height: 5.2" Width: 1.2" Weight: 27 oz. (unloaded); 30 oz. (loaded)

SMITH & WESSON MODEL 59

In August 1964, Smith & Wesson began to explore the possibility of creating a pistol that would combine a double-action trigger mechanism with a high-capacity magazine. Smith & Wesson thought— correctly, as it later turned out— that such a pistol would have tremendous appeal among military and police forces.

Up to this time, only one high-capacity, military-type pistol had been commercially successful: FN's sensational High Power (*see* separate listing), a pistol that has sold in the millions over its 60-year production run. To compete against such a solidly established design was a daunting project, but Smith & Wesson set out gamely to do it. The Model 59 was simply a modified Model 39, made by combining a Model 39 upper half (slide assembly) with a new frame squared off and widened to accept a larger 14-round magazine. The grip on this modified pistol had a straight backstrap (instead of the Model 39's curved backstrap) and thin checkered plastic grips, instead of the wooden ones found on the Model 39.

A member of the "Third Generation" series introduced in the late 1980s, the 9mm Model 5904 is a direct descendant of the Model 59.

Ironically, after creating several prototype Model 59s (this name was not actually adopted until later), Smith & Wesson set them aside for several years to concentrate on other projects. Not until 1968, when the Navy SEALS sought a 9mm pistol for clandestine work, did the company revive the design. After experimenting with both modified Model 39s and experimental Model 59s under the project designation WOX-13A, the Navy requested that Smith & Wesson make a Model 59 in stainless steel and fitted for a silencer. The company complied with the Navy specifications to create in 1969 a pistol that became known officially as the Pistol, Mark 22 Mod 0, with the nickname of "Hush Puppy" (because one of its functions was to kill enemy watchdogs stealthily). Just 12.8 inches long with the bulky silencer attachment in place, and weighing just 34 ounces unloaded, the Mark 22 pistol remains in inventory. Thanks to special closures and gaskets, it can be carried underwater and still be used immediately upon the swimmer's resurfacing. It proved to be a highly successful handgun but was produced only in limited numbers because of its extremely specialized role.

Following this success, Smith & Wesson released a civilianized version of the 14-shot pistol in June 1971. Known as the Model 59, it did away with some of the more exotic features of the Navy pistol, such as the stainless steel finish and silencer attachments. Otherwise, it was substantially the same gun. With the Model 39 having already established Smith & Wesson as a serious manufacturer of automatic pistols, the Model 59 was an immediate success, especially among police departments.

The chief advantage of the Model 59 is its high-capacity magazine. It was the first high-capacity double-action 9mm pistol to reach production. The 18-shot Steyr GB was also under development in Austria at about the same time as the Model 59, but it did not achieve production status until almost a decade later. As such, the Model 59 was the first of the extraordinarily successful so-called "Wonder-nine" pistols. It has also been the design inspiration for the CZ 75, Beretta's Model 92, and many other pistols of similar design that have followed it.

The Model 59 was not without its weaknesses. Early issues had feeding and extraction problems, particularly with hollowpoint bullets, which had plagued the Model 39 as well. Smith & Wesson quickly corrected these difficulties, however. Compared to later, more refined designs, the Model 59's grip shape was boxy and clumsy. Several critics commented that it reminded them of holding a base-ball bat by the wrong end and other unflattering comparisons. Indeed, after holding a Model 39, with its exceptionally graceful and comfortable grip shape, the Model 59 was a great disappointment. On the other hand, it carries nearly twice as many rounds as the 39, and its grip has been greatly improved by Smith & Wesson in later variations of the basic Model 59 design.

Overall, the Model 59 proved to be an extremely successful gun, selling well both in the United States and overseas. Smith & Wesson kept the pistol in production in its original form until 1981, when the company introduced a slightly updated version: the Model 459. This pistol featured a firing-pin lock that could be deactivated only when the trigger was pulled back as far as possible, a feature now found on many automatic pistols. It was relatively new in pistols at that time, though common in revolvers.

The rear sight on the Model 459 was adjustable in some of its versions and was protected by pro-tective "ears" of the type often found on military rifles. Modifications were also made to the feed ramp of the Model 459, and its extractor was improved to increase reliability at the beginning and end of the firing cycle. Finally, some later Model 459s used a recurved trigger guard to facilitate two-handed shooting.

In 1982, Smith & Wesson began offering both the Model 59 and the Model 39 in stainless-steel versions, called the Models 659 and 639. Thus did the Model 59 design come full circle from its Navy origins. From 1981 to 1983, Smith & Wesson also offered an all-steel blued version, known as the Model 559, but this proved unprofitable. Customers who wanted a blued gun preferred the lighter weight of the alloy-framed Model 459, while those who were willing to tolerate a heavy all-steel gun wanted one made of stainless steel (a nickel-plated finish was also made available).

Smith & Wesson has continued to refine its line of automatic pistols to the point where they have become highly competitive with anything offered by other handgun manufacturers. In 1988, the company announced still another series of improvements to its Model 59 series. Called the "Third Generation," they include the Model 5904, a direct descendant of the Model 59. A significant pistol in its own right, the Model 59 represents a major milestone in handgun design. Today, even the oldest Model 59s are good, solid guns, still capable of protecting their owners with reliable performance.

SMITH & WESSON MODEL 59

Manufacturer	Years Produced	Caliber/Capacity	Dimensions
Smith & Wesson Springfield, MA	1970–1980	9mm/14 rounds	Barrel Length: 4.0" O.A. Length: 7.4" Height: 5.2" Width: 1.4" Weight: 29 oz. (unloaded); 36 oz. (loaded)

Star Model A

The adoption in 1921 by the Spanish Army of
Astra's Model 400 pistol did not sit well with many Spanish
officials. They preferred a Colt Model 1911-type pistol made by
Bonifacio Echeverria, called the Star Model A. Adopted in 1922 by the
Guardia Civil (Spain's paramilitary security force), the Model A enjoyed a long and
productive life. Its design differed from that of Colt's Model 1911 only in caliber and
its lack of a grip safety (which was added in 1924). The shape of its hammer was different too, along with the design of the trigger mechanism and mainspring, plus its use
of an exposed extractor rather than an internal one.

The Model A experienced a slight change in 1946, adding a loaded-chamber indicator and an
ingenious disassembly catch located on the right side of the frame. When rotated half a turn, this
catch, which was connected to a link underneath the barrel, rotated the link forward. This enabled the
slide to be drawn forward off the frame. The resulting pistol—called the Super A—stayed in production until 1989; but it never supplanted the standard Model A, which remained in production for several years after the Super A was discontinued.

*The Star Model A (bottom), like the Llama Model XI "Especial" (top) and many other Spanish handguns, is
based on the Colt Model 1911 pistol designed by John M. Browning.*

Shots touching a scoring ring
receive the higher value.
Shots outside of scoring ring
are recorded as misses.

Despite badly undersized sights, the well-made Model A can deliver good accuracy. This five-shot offhand group fired from 25 feet away measures only 1.6 inches across.

The Model A tested for this book proved completely reliable with every type of 9mm Largo ammunition fired. A well-made gun that is inherently accurate, its tiny sights make highly accurate shooting more difficult than it should be. Nevertheless, with its nice balance and weight, the gun is more than adequate for close combat distances. But for really accurate shooting in this caliber, Astra's Model 400 is a better choice. The Star Model is still recommended, though, for those who like the 9mm Largo round but who find the idiosyncrasies of the Astra Model 400 a bit too much to bear.

STAR MODEL A

Manufacturer	Years Produced	Caliber/Capacity	Dimensions
Star Bonifacio Echeverria SA Eibar, Spain	1922–Present	9mm Largo/8 rounds	Barrel Length: 5.0" O.A. Length: 8.5" Height: 5.2" Width: 1.3" Weight: 22 oz. (unloaded); 27 oz. (loaded)

STAR MODEL B SERIES

Inspired by the legendary M1911A1, Star's Model B became an extremely popular gun among many of the world's armed forces. Its evolution began in 1920, when Star introduced the Modelo Militar, an M1911-type pistol. Star gradually improved this gun with its Model A, Model B and Model B Super

variations. It has remained a popular military and police pistol in Spain, only recently being supplanted by more modern double-action pistols. During World War II, the British and Germans both bought quantities of the Model B from Spain; and it was popular in many other countries as well, notably South Africa, as a substitute standard pistol for military and police forces. Production lasted from about 1933 (the exact starting date is in dispute) until 1984, while the highly successful Model B Super was made from 1946 to 1983.

Mechanically, the Model B strongly resembles the Colt M1911A1 without that gun's grip safety. In outward appearance, the Model B Super resembles the Model B, but with a fixed underbarrel cam for breech locking and unlocking (instead of the Model B's underbarrel swinging link). Noticeably slimmer and more graceful than the Colt M1911A1 which inspired it, the Model B is usually chambered for the 9mm Parabellum cartridge, which is appreciably smaller than the .45 ACP round. An even smaller and handier version, the Model BKM, appeared in the early 1970s and lasted until the early 1990s when Star decided to concentrate on the Firestar pistol.

All of Star's M1911-type variants are made to high standards of workmanship, using first-rate materials to assure decent performance. They are appreciably less expensive than a Colt pistol and represent a good buy. Star offered a number of caliber variations, however, and not all of them are winners in terms of performance or availability, so be wary. Your best choice is probably 9mm Parabellum or .45 ACP.

STAR MODEL B SERIES

Manufacturer	Years Produced	Caliber/Capacity	Dimensions (Model B)
Star-Bonifacio Echeverria Eibar, Spain	1933–1984	9mm/9 rounds	Barrel Length: 4.8" O.A. Length: 8.5" Height: 5.5" Width: 1.1" Weight: 38 oz. (unloaded); 47 oz. (loaded)

TOKAREV TT-30/33

For many years, the handgun needs of Soviet Russia were served well by the Model 1895 Nagant revolver. In the early years of the Soviet regime, though, the Red Army decided to follow the lead of its competitor nations and adopt a semiautomatic pistol. The result—the Tokarev TT-33 —has been extremely successful, with total production in the Soviet Union alone exceeding 1.7 milion. The

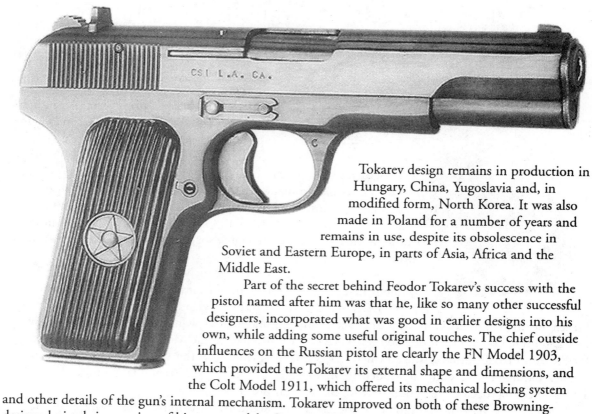

Tokarev design remains in production in Hungary, China, Yugoslavia and, in modified form, North Korea. It was also made in Poland for a number of years and remains in use, despite its obsolescence in Soviet and Eastern Europe, in parts of Asia, Africa and the Middle East.

Part of the secret behind Feodor Tokarev's success with the pistol named after him was that he, like so many other successful designers, incorporated what was good in earlier designs into his own, while adding some useful original touches. The chief outside influences on the Russian pistol are clearly the FN Model 1903, which provided the Tokarev its external shape and dimensions, and the Colt Model 1911, which offered its mechanical locking system and other details of the gun's internal mechanism. Tokarev improved on both of these Browning-designed pistols in creation of his own model. One original touch was the clever way in which Tokarev mounted the hammer mechanism on a separate module. Another was the retention of the slide stop by a simple clip rather than the plunger and spring found on the M1911. Still another improvement was Tokarev's stronger muzzle bushing.

The original TT-30 (introduced in 1930, as its designation indicated) competed favorably in extensive tests against foreign handguns, including Walthers, Lugers and the Browning-designed Colt and FN pistol. An improved version went into production in 1933 with, among other improvements, its locking lugs machined all the way around the barrel. This allowed the job to be performed more easily and less expensively on a lathe. Moreover, the backstrap of the TT-33 frame was included as part of the frame forging, instead of being machined separately. Production of the TT-30 probably did not exceed 93,000 pieces, and it is a rare item today, having been almost wholly supplanted by the simpler Model TT-33.

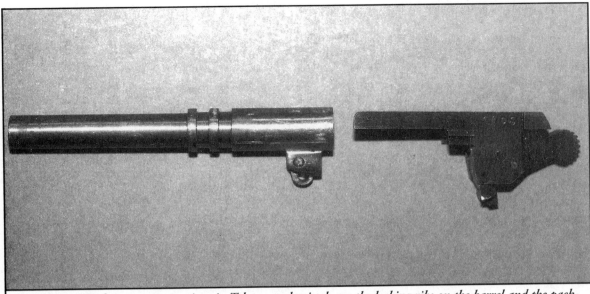

Two clever manufacturing innovations in Tokarev-style pistols are the locking ribs on the barrel and the packaged hammer mechanism, which is removable.

For all of its clever features, these Tokarev models were not very popular at first among Soviet troops. Their magazine release springs were weak, causing the magazine to fall inadvertently, and the trigger spring was weak as well. In addition, the barrel design made the Tokarev poorly suited for firing from inside armored vehicles. As a result of these shortcomings, the Soviets kept their Model 1895 revolver in production well into the war years, meanwhile commencing a search in 1938 for a new automatic pistol. Then, in April 1941, just eight weeks before Germany invaded Russia, the Red Army adopted a new pistol invented by P.V. Voyevodin, but its manufacture was halted by the Nazi invasion. Still, the Soviets did quite well with the Tokarev, which in the crucible of war proved itself a good pistol after all.

The main problem with the Tokarev is its poor safety system, which features a half-cock notch on the hammer. Even most of the postwar Tokarev versions made in foreign countries have either no manual safety at all or an undersized and awkward safety catch. In addition, the shape of the grip, which closely follows that of Browning's FN Model 1903, is too straight for most people's tastes. And the Tokarev's sights — particularly the front sight — are undersized.

Conversely, its strong points include good accuracy, extreme simplicity and ruggedness, all traits typical of Soviet weapons designs. The pistol is also pleasingly compact for its level of power, and it's a pleasure to shoot, whether in 7.62mm or 9mm calibers.

TOKAREV TT-30/33

Manufacturer	Years Produced	Caliber/Capacity	Dimensions
Soviet State Factories East Bloc/Third World Countries	1930–1954 in USSR; still in production in Red China & Hungary	7.62mm/8 rounds	Barrel Length: 4.5" O.A. Length: 7.7" Height: 5.2" Width: 1.15" Weight: 36 oz. (unloaded); 40 oz. (loaded)

WALTHER P.38

Since its introduction in the late 1930s, Walther's Model P.38 has proven one of history's most successful handguns, finding wide use among military, police and civilians worldwide. Not only was it the first military-caliber automatic pistol with a double-action capability, its durability, reliability and accessibility have combined to make the P.38 one of the world's most important and influential handguns.

Following its acceptance by Germany's armed forces during the Nazi era as a replacement for the Luger pistol, the P.38 saw extensive service throughout World War II. Despite its designation, which suggests a service beginning in 1938, initial acceptance of this pistol by German troops was slow. It was quite a radical gun for its time, and some design details still remained to be ironed out. Then, in early 1939, anxious to secure good relations with neutral Sweden, the Germans sold that country about 1,500 of the brand-new pistols, making Sweden the first country to adopt a large-caliber, double-action automatic pistol for military use. In Germany, meanwhile, official issue didn't begin until April 1940.

The Walther P.38 was the first successful military-caliber pistol with a double-action trigger mechanism to achieve series production. Disassembled, it reveals its rugged construction. The underbarrel locking block, similar to the mechanism used in Mauser's C.96 pistol, has been copied by Beretta and Gabilondo.

A few years earlier, Walther had advertised the P.38 for commercial sale as the "Model HP," or *Heeres Pistole,* meaning "Army Pistol." Prewar commercial sales were extremely limited, however, mostly because the German military was expanding rapidly and needed the pistols. Although Walther, which had designed and developed the pistol, was its prime producer, accounting for about half the total production, other companies in Germany and Occupied Europe also participated. Mauser-Werke began production of the P.38 in 1942, as did Spreewerke. In addition, Fabrique Nationale (Belgium) and Czeska Zbrojovka (Czechoslovakia) among others, produced P.38 components to assist the three prime contractors. In all, wartime production of this handgun exceeded a million pistols.

With war's end, a vast number of P.38s had fallen into Allied hands. American soldiers brought these war-trophy pistols home and began to circulate them almost immediately. (The Russians, on the other hand, held most of their P.38s in storage until 1993, when they began to release large quantities to the American market). Thus did the P.38 become very popular in America; this eventually led to a demand for 9mm double-action pistols made in the U.S., a need first filled in 1954 with Smith & Wesson's Model 39 (*see* separate listing).

As mentioned earlier, the French continued to operate Mauser-Werke's Oberndorf facility for a year after the war ended. During this period, the French assembled about 50,000 P.38s from wartime parts stockpiled by the Germans. These P.38s, often called "Gray Ghosts" (because of their gray phosphate finish) served the French army and police into the 1980s.

In Germany, interest in the P.38 remained high. A refurbishing facility was maintained in Suhl, near Walther's original home in Zella-Mehlis (at that time, East Germany). At about the same time, the Walther company relocated to the city of Ulm on the banks of the Danube River in West Germany. By 1955, the Western Allies—Britain, France and the U.S.—realized that a strong West Germany would serve as an excellent buffer against Soviet expansion in Western Europe. Thus, after a

The P.38 is surprisingly accurate despite the heavy double-action trigger pull, a feature inherent in Walther pistol designs. The **Heeres Pistole** *shown is a prewar and wartime-era version of the P.38 intended for civilian sale.*

The Walther P.38 service pistol (top) outsizes the earlier Model 4 (center), a medium-frame pistol, and the tiny Model 5 vest-pocket pistol (bottom). A durable, reliable design with numerous clever features and innovative refinements, the excellent P.38 remains in production and service today.

10-year period of producing calculators, adding machines, air rifles and other nonmilitary goods, Walther was given permission to retool for P.38 production. Since all wartime-era P.38 production machinery had been lost to the Soviet zone, Walther had to recreate the appropriate machinery, and inspection gauges with which to mass-produce the pistols once again. By May 1957, new-production P.38s were again serving the German armed forces.

Although it was out of production for 10 years after the war, surplus P. 38s continued to serve in every major conflict from 1945 on, including the Arab-Israeli War of 1948, the Algerian War (for independence from France), and Vietnam. The P.38 also started a widespread interest in double-action pistols that led eventually to the Smith & Wesson Model 39, the CZ 75, the Beretta Model 92 and, in fact, most other modern double-action 9mm pistols. In all, since the P.38 was revived in the mid-1950s, the pistol has served police and military organizations in over 60 countries. Incidentally, many of the P.38-type service pistols made in Germany since 1963 were known officially as the "P 1" and were so marked.

Mechanically, the P.38 has the same features as the smaller PP and PPK pistols, notably in the design of the double-action trigger mechanism and the hammer-dropping safety. Due to the increased power levels of the 9mm cartridge, however, the P.38 requires a breech locking system, a feature not required on the simple blowback PP and PPK with their low-powered .32 and .380 cartridges. The P.38 uses a clever and innovative breech lock in which, upon firing, the barrel recoils straight to the rear, stopping when a block located under the barrel makes contact with an abutment in the frame. One advantage of this locking system over the more common tipping barrel mechanism designed by Browning is that the Walther barrel recoils in a straight line, allowing greater accuracy; also, it's easier to fit with a silencer. One disadvantage of the Walther system is that a wide slide is required to accommodate the locking block. Another is that the Walther pistol is, theoretically, not quite as durable as Browning's short-recoil setup.

Postwar P.38s. The chief difference between wartime and postwar P.38s is the change in weight—about 6 ounces—from the all-steel construction of the wartime guns to the lighter aluminum alloy- framed postwar guns. In the late 1960s, Walther added more metal (about half an ounce) to the slide, while at the same time increasing the number of cocking serrations at the rear of the slide. More recently, larger sights have been added to the P.38, and a steel pin with a hexagonal shape has been let into the frame (for reinforcement where the underbarrel locking block stops following recoil). Nearly all P.38s built since 1957 have alloy frames, but in the 1980s Walther briefly introduced a steel-framed version of the P.38, the All Steel Classic. Primarily a collector's item, rather than an issue pistol, it went out of production within two years.

Another major change in the postwar P.38s is its rounded firing pin, as opposed to one with the square center section found on wartime models. This change meant that several small parts in the postwar slide, such as the safety lever, could not be interchanged with wartime models. Fortunately, the entire slide assembly of a wartime model will fit and function well on the frame of a postwar model, and vice versa.

The P.38, with its slim, comfortable grip and good balance, is set up ideally for defensive shooting. Both versions—all-steel and alloy-framed —carry enough weight to dampen recoil but not enough to slow down handling. Some may find the exposed barrel undesirable for concealed carry, however, not to mention its muzzle rise upon firing. Not only is the P.38 extremely rugged and reliable, it's capable of feeding even hollowpoint ammunition without malfunction, even under the most atrocious conditions.

On the other hand, the P.38 is pricey (it was designed in an era when skilled labor was much cheaper), and its magazine capacity (8 rounds) is low. Many American shooters also dislike the P.38's heel-mounted magazine release. Still, it is an excellent gun and remains widely available. Despite its age, it still ranks high as a first-class combat handgun, one that compares favorably with any other 9mm pistol.

WALTHER P.38

Manufacturer	Years Produced	Caliber/Capacity	Dimensions
*Waffenfabrik Walther (Orig.) Zella-Mehlis, Germany, and others	1939–1945 (Orig.); 1957–present	9mm/8 rounds	(Steel-framed WW II Model) Barrel Length: 5.0" O.A. Length: 8.5" Height: 5.25" Width: 1.45" Weight: 34 oz. (unloaded); 38 oz. (loaded)

* post-war by Carl Walther Waffenfabrik, Ulm (Donau), Germany, and others

WALTHER MODEL PP

After making a series of high quality but unimagina-
tively designed pistols, Walther introduced the *Polizei Pistole* or
PP in 1929. A pistol of such advanced design, it has been copied by
literally scores of manufacturers. The PP's rugged construction, its
fixed barrel pinned to the frame, its recoil spring surrounding the barrel, and its
double-action trigger mechanism, all have for nearly 70 years stood as the standard
against which medium-frame automatic pistols have been judged.

Among the Model PP's features is a manual safety that is easily accessible to the
right thumb. It can be left down in the safe position and pushed up to the fire position before shooting, although many shooters leave it in the fire setting all the time, relying upon the
stiff double-action trigger pull for safe carrying. That way, the shooter has only to pull the trigger to
fire the gun.

Sensing that a more concealable version of the PP would sell well, Walther unveiled a shortened
version in 1931 called the PPK, which caught on immediately. Its advanced features, combined with a
wider choice of calibers (.22 LR, .25 ACP, .32 ACP and .380 ACP— the PP was not available in .25
ACP), its rugged construction and the famous Walther quality all contributed to its immediate and
enduring success. (*See* COMPLETE GUIDE TO COMPACT HANDGUNS for a more detailed discussion.)
This was especially true in European police and military circles prior to World War II. Its appearance
coincided with the rise to power of the Nazis in Germany, becoming one of their top pistols, dubbed
Ehrenwaffe, or "Honor Weapon."

During wartime, Germany's armed forces used both the PP and the PPK in large quantities, making them highly desired captured items among Allied troops. By 1945, the German government and

*The Walther PP is available with an extra magazine with fin-
ger-rest extension, which provides a comfortable fit for large-
handed shooters.*

Nazi Party had purchased more than
200,000 PPs and more than 150,000
PPKs. After the war, when the Allies
halted German armaments production, manufacture of these pistols
continued in other countries, notably
France, Turkey, the U.S. and possibly
China. The PP remains a top police
pistol throughout much of Western
Europe, Asia and Africa, although it
has been largely supplanted in its
native Germany by 9mm handguns.
The PPK is still widely used as a concealable police pistol, especially in
Europe, while both guns serve in several military establishments as aircrew
pistols and as armament for off-duty
officers.

Variants of the PP/PPK series

include the rare KPK, a slightly modified PPK from the late wartime years. The PPK/S was introduced in 1969 to appeal to the U.S. market, which had just been closed to the PPK by the Gun Control Act of 1968.

Despite the age of the basic design, the PP remains a good service handgun by modern standards. It competes primarily with such short-barreled .38 Special revolvers as Colt's Detective Special and Smith & Wesson's J-frame series. Using a modern .380 cartridge of advanced design, the PP offers a level of stopping power competitive with that of a .38 Special cartridge fired from a short barrel (such as the 1.9-inch barrel of Smith & Wesson's Chiefs Special). In addition, the PP pistol is more comfortable to shoot than a .38 Special revolver, because its recoil levels are milder than the .38 Special's and therefore more easily mastered. The sleek, smooth lines and compact dimensions of the PP are also suited to concealed carry.

There remains room for improvement in the PP design however. As other double-action pistols made by Walther, the PP has a heavy double-action trigger pull. The typical double-action trigger pull, for example, may run from 18 to 20 rounds, making first-round hits difficult. Single-action follow-up shots, though, have a much lighter trigger. With practice, a skilled shooter with a PP can achieve good accuracy up to 50 feet.

The PP series also has a propensity for hammer bite, a painful condition that results when the hammer or slide pinches the shooter's hand (especially left-handers) with the slide in full recoil. Unwary shooters have been known to be injured.

Despite its heavy double-action trigger pull for the first shot, Walther's PP can be quite accurate. This five-shot, 25-foot offhand group measures 1.9 inches.

The PP pistol, like the P.38, features a loaded-chamber indicator. When a round is in the firing chamber, the pin protrudes slightly (shown just above the hammer), providing a more advanced feature than the simple-cocked-striker indicator on Walther's earlier Model 9.

Despite these shortcomings, the tremendously successful PP/PPK series pistols are well designed and beautifully made, sparking a revolution in compact pistol design that continues to this day. The PP's double-action feature, its method of construction, and even its attractive appearance, all have inspired numerous imitators over the years; it remains the standard by which knowledgeable shooters judge compact automatic pistols.

WALTHER MODEL PP

Manufacturer	Years Produced	Caliber/Capacity	Dimensions
*Originally Waffenfabrik Walther Zella-Mehlis, Germany	1929–1945 (Orig.); 1952–Present	.22 LR, .32 ACP or .380 ACP/7–8 rounds	Barrel Length: 3.8" O.A. Length: 6.7" Height: 3.9" Width: 1.1" Weight: 22 oz. (unloaded); 25 oz. (loaded)

*Post-war under license by Manurhin (France) and Interarms (U.S.), and others; postwar home factory is Carl Walther Waffenfabrik, Ulm (Donau), Germany

5. SERVICE PISTOLS
9MM, .40 AND .45 CALIBER

CONTENTS

American Arms Spectre 161
Astra Model A-100 163
Auto-Ordnance 1911A1 Government 166
Beretta M9/92F/92FS 167
   Model 92D/92DS 170
   Model 92G 172
   Model 96 173
Bren Ten (formerly Dornaus & Dixon) 176
Browning BDM 177
Colt Double Eagle 181
   "Enhanced" Government Model 185
   Model 2000 All American 188
CZ Model 85/85 Combat 191
Daewoo DP51 193
European American Arms
   FAB-92 196
   Witness 197
FÉG Models FP9/PJK-9HP 201
   Model GKK-45/P9R 205
F.I.E. Model TZ 75 208
FM Hi-Power (Argentina) 210
FN Browning
   High Power (.40 S&W) 211
   High Power Mark II 212
   High Power Mark III 214
Glock Model 20 217
   Model 21 218
Heckler & Koch
   Model P7M10 220
   Model P7M13 223
   Model P9S 225

H&K Model SP89 227
   Model USP 229
Hi-Point Model JC 231
Israel Arms Kareen 232
Israel Military Industries
   Baby Eagle 234
   UZI 237
Norinco Model of the 1911 239
   Model TU-90 241
Para-Ordnance Model P14 244
Ruger Model P85/P89 246
   Model P90 248
   Model P91 250
SIG P220 Series 252
Smith & Wesson Model 411 255
   Model 915 256
   Model 1000 Series 258
   Model 4506 259
   Sigma (SW40) 262
Springfield Armory
   Model 1911-A1 264
   Omega 265
   P9 Pistol 267
Star Megastar 269
   Model 31P/31PK 271
Steyr Model GB 274
   Model SPP 276
Taurus Model PT-92 Series 277
Walther Model P4 281
   Model P5 285
   Model P88 287

Although the 9mm Parabellum is today the world's most prolific handgun and submachine-gun cartridge, that was not always the case. The 9mm Parabellum cartridge was originally created in Germany to make the small 7.65mm Luger more attractive to prospective military buyers. Despite its extensive use by German forces in World War I, the 9mm Parabellum took a long time to become accepted worldwide. And not until the 1930s and the onset of World War II (with the Belgian FN Browning High Power and the Polish Radom pistols, for example) did other nations take a serious look at and adopt 9mm Parabellum pistols and submachine guns.

After the war France, Italy, Switzerland and Austria all began converting their military pistol and submachine-gun armories to 9mm Parabellum weapons. Soon the 9mm round became a standard cartridge in practically all of Western Europe. From their factories came weapons that reached near-worldwide distribution and use.

In the U.S., the Vietnam War and the military's desire to find a high-capacity replacement for the .45 ACP Colt M1911 eventually led to the 9mm pistol trials of the 1970s and '80s. After years of testing among Beretta's Model 92SB and 92SB-F (92F), the FN High Power and FN DA double-action pistols, the Heckler & Koch P9S, VP-70 and P7M13, SIG's P226, Smith & Wesson's Model 459, the Steyr GB and the Walther P88, the Beretta 92F (M9) emerged as the victor. [A detailed account of U.S. testing of 9mm pistols from 1979–1989 can be found in MODERN BERETTA FIREARMS by Gene Gangarosa Jr., Stoeger Publishing Company, 1994.]

The decision by the U.S. to adopt the Beretta pistol opened wide the floodgates to acceptance by U.S. civilians of the 9mm Parabellum cartridge and the pistols that fired it. Prior to 1985 many shooters were skeptical about 9mm pistols, and in some circles they still are. But the military's acceptance of the 9mm has led to a greatly improved selection of 9mm pistols now available to American buyers.

Equally significant have been the improvements during the past two decades in the performance of the 9mm round. The 9mm Parabellum or Luger cartridge is a high-pressure, high-intensity round that packs an impressive amount of energy into a small space, making it very efficient. However, it fires a small bullet, a fact that has always handicapped it when compared with the larger and heavier .45 ACP pistol round. Modern developments, beginning with Winchester's introduction of the Silvertip round in the 1970s, have concentrated on harnessing the 9mm's inherent energy levels, giving it a wider, flatter shape upon hitting the target—in effect, making a big bullet out of a small one. Some modern hollowpoint designs, including improved versions of the original Silvertip, have proven significantly more effective than standard 9mm fully jacketed, military-style ball ammunition.

The .45 ACP—Still Going Strong

Despite the worldwide proliferation and success of 9mm pistols, the traditional bastion represented by the pistols and revolvers in .45 caliber remains popular. Manufacturers continue to make automatic pistols in .45 caliber, while the classic .45-caliber revolver, led by Colt's Single Action Army (SAA) dating from 1873, remains alive and well. Both it and Colt's Model 1911 pistol served the armed forces of dozens of foreign countries. These outstanding handguns continue to attract legions of admirers and are still in production by Colt.

Generally speaking, the .45 ACP round, which dates from 1905, is designated for use in automatic pistols, while the .45 Colt or .45 Long Colt (LC) is used in revolvers (there's also a .45 ACP round with an added rim, or flange, called a .45 Auto Rim round, for chambering in revolvers). While no automatic pistols are chambered for .45 LC, the .45 ACP round may appear in revolvers as well; in fact, some revolvers are offered with dual cylinders, allowing the same gun to accept either .45 LC or .45 ACP.

To many people, the M1911-type pistol is the ultimate defensive handgun, one that has saved the lives of untold numbers of people who've owned them. Because of this and the widespread manufacture of competing designs, sales of M1911-type pistols remain very strong.

The .40 Caliber—Something for Everybody

In recent years, the ambition of many gun and ammo makers—to combine the high velocity of the 9mm with the big bullet of the .45 ACP—has led to two successful handgun cartridges: the 10mm auto (including the related "10mm FBI" or "10mm Lite") and the .40 S&W. Because the two rounds use true .40 caliber (.401 inch diameter) bullets, they are covered together in this discussion.

The 10mm auto's origins are tied to those of the Bren Ten pistol, made by Dornaus & Dixon between 1983 and 1985. Following the failure of that project, the 10mm auto round lay dormant and on the verge of extinction for two more years until 1987, when Colt began to market its Delta Elite, a 1911-type pistol chambered in 10mm. With a major gun company like Colt supporting it, the 10mm was literally rescued from oblivion. Smith & Wesson was next to offer a 10mm pistol with its Model 1066, which appeared in 1990 and was followed a few months later by Glock's Model 20. Springfield Armory also offered a 10mm caliber as part of its Omega series, along with a "Linkless" M1911-type pistol.

Ballistics for the 10mm Auto are impressive, with bullet weights varying from 155 to 200 grains and muzzle velocities topping 1300 feet per second. Even at 100 yards, a 10mm round can produce more power than a 9mm+P round at the muzzle. With this power, of course, come such penalties as increased recoil, muzzle flash and possibly over-penetration. This leads many experts to conclude that the full-power 10mm cartridge is simply too much of a good thing.

Indeed, the 10mm auto cartridge and the pistols made for it have only a restricted following and distribution, due largely to their great power and size. As SWAT team weapons in the hands of skilled professionals, however, 10mm pistols have a great potential.

The so-called "10mm FBI" round (often referred to as the "10mm Lite") is actually a less powerful loading of the original 10mm Auto round designed to offer 10mm ballistics in a milder, more controllable package. The 10mm Lite round enjoyed a brief surge of popularity in 1989 when the FBI adopted it—along with Smith & Wesson's M1076 pistol—as a standard firearm for its agents. Muzzle velocities for the 10mm Lite come in at around 950 feet per second with a 180-grain bullet. Critics of this round complain that it offers little or no improvement over the well-tested .45 ACP; and that, since the pistols made for this round can also chamber full-power 10mm loads, they must be big and strong enough to withstand such use. Consequently, it's impossible to make a truly compact 10mm Lite pistol.

Much more successful has been the .40 S&W cartridge, which can be used in a 9mm-sized pistol. That's because it uses a small pistol primer and a rebated rim to operate with 9mm-sized extractors, ejectors and breech faces. The chief design advantage of the .40 S&W over the 9mm, therefore, is that the newer round offers big-bore performance in a medium-sized pistol.

The .40 S&W cartridge was unveiled as a joint venture in 1990 by Winchester (creator of the cartridge) and Smith & Wesson (maker of the Model 1006, which was chambered to fire it). Within only a few short years, this impressive round has caught on with almost all major gun manufacturers, including Astra (A-80, A-75, A-100), Beretta (Model 96 Centurion), Browning (High Power), Colt (Government Model), EAA (Witness and others), Glock (Models 22, 23, 24 and 27), Heckler & Koch (P7M10 and USP), IMI (Baby Desert Eagle), Llama (Large Frame,

Model 82), Ruger (P91), SIG (P229), Smith & Wesson (Models 411, 4006, 4013, 4014, 4053, 4026), Sphinx (AT-2000), Star (Firestar M-40) and Taurus (PT-100/101).

While many .40 S&W guns—including the Ruger P91, Glock 22 and Smith & Wesson's Model 4006—are full-sized duty sidearms, others (the Glock 23, SIG P229, Smith & Wesson Model 4013, Star Firestar M-40, *et al*) are compact guns. What the .40 S&W round offers in a gun like the Firestar or Glock 23 is a major-caliber loading in a compact 9mm-sized pistol. (*See* COMPLETE GUIDE TO COMPACT HANDGUNS, the companion volume, by Gene Gangarosa Jr.)

The .40 S&W offers impressive performance and does an excellent job of splitting the difference between the 9mm on the low end and the .45 ACP on the high end. A .40 S&W round with a 180-grain jacketed hollowpoint bullet produces muzzle velocities around 950–980 feet per second. The lighter 155-grain bullets, which many favor in this caliber, are considerably faster—around 1100 to 1200 fps at the muzzle. The .40 S&W, particularly in its lighter bullet weights, should generally outperform both the 9mm Parabellum and the .45 ACP cartridges.

In addition to its high performance as a pistol round, the .40 S&W, unlike the .45 ACP, can be fitted into a high-capacity magazine with comparative ease. In fact, most .40 S&W pistols now in production are based on 9mm platforms and give up only a few rounds of ammunition capacity. As a result, the most compact .40 S&W pistols have a smaller frame and grip size than do the .45-caliber or 10mm pistols. The smallest .40 S&W pistols arguably represent the most likely prospects in the ongoing effort to achieve "maximum power in a minimally sized package."

For those who are interested in the high-powered 9mm, the traditional .45 ACP or the middle-ground .40 S&W (10mm), the following listings include all three caliber offerings with complete details, photos and specs.

AMERICAN ARMS SPECTRE

The Italian-made Spectre is available in two versions: a large pistol version that fires semiautomatically and a selective-fire submachine-gun version firing at a cyclic rate of 850 rounds per minute. The submachine gun is available only to authorized police agencies, but the pistol has been available to civilians since 1984 (although importation from Italy was banned in late 1993).

The Spectre has excellent credentials. Italy is, after all, the home of the submachine gun; indeed, its *Vilar Perosa* of World War I fame is widely regarded as the first true submachine gun. With excellent submachine guns emerging from Italy ever since, most notably from Beretta, the Spectre is not "just another Italian submachine gun." In fact, it boasts several unique features, including a double-action-only mechanism. That means it has no separate manual safety device, nor any need of one, and it can be carried safely, ready to fire instantly merely by pulling through on the trigger.

To help the barrel cool off between bursts, most submachine guns fire from an open bolt. The disadvantage here is that the bolt slams forward at the beginning of each burst, causing an abrupt change

The Spectre pistol, derived from a highly regarded Italian-design submachine gun, will outshoot most 9mm automatic pistols. This five-shot offhand group fired from 50 feet measures 2.5 inches.

in the center of gravity that's tough on accuracy. The Spectre's designers wisely decided to have the gun fire from a closed bolt, rearranging the mechanism so that the bolt forced cooling air through the barrel during firing. Also, in its submachine-gun version a 50-round magazine was made available in a package not much longer than a pistol magazine, thanks to the designer's decision to stack the rounds in a clever four-column configuration.

The Spectre is now used by security forces worldwide and has gained an excellent reputation as a safe and reliable weapon, ready to fire instantly. For our purposes, however, the pistol version, which fires only one shot for each pull of the trigger, was tested. Not surprisingly, the Spectre is larger than the typical automatic pistol, including Iver Johnson's Enforcer, Intratec's TEC-9/TEC-9M, and the Heckler & Koch Model SP89 (*see* separate listing). Sometimes called a "heavy pistol" or an "assault pistol," this type of handgun functions mechanically in much the same manner as a typical automatic pistol, except that it uses a massive bolt assembly rather than a slide.

In range testing, the Spectre proved quite accurate. Our best five-shot offhand group at 25 feet measured just over an inch, while at 50 feet, a similar group measured 2.5 inches. The gun's sights are easy to pick up in rapid shooting and are rugged enough to withstand tremendous damage.

The sole weak point of the Spectre, aside from the limitations imposed by its size, is an extraordinarily heavy trigger pull of 20 pounds, made necessary by its double-action-only trigger mechanism. Eventually, the shooter's trigger finger is going to lose its ability to exert that kind of pressure. Nevertheless, this is a reliable and rugged handgun that seems ideal for defensive purposes. Indeed, its extremely intimidating appearance alone could prove enough to dissuade a would-be attacker without having to fire a shot.

AMERICAN ARMS SPECTRE

Manufacturer	Years Produced	Caliber/Capacity	Dimensions

SITES SpA
Gardone Valtrompia, Italy
Imported by:
  American Arms
  No. Kansas City, MO
	1984–Present	9mm or .40 S&W/ 30 rounds	Barrel Length: 6" O.A. Length: 13.75"
			Height: 8.1" Width: 2.5"
			Weight: 72 oz. (unloaded); 87 oz. (loaded)

ASTRA

ASTRA A-100

Astra was one of three major Spanish pistol-making firms to compete in Spain's 9mm service pistol trials of the late 1970s (Star and Gabilondo's Llama were the other two). The Astra pistol did not win, but it showed great promise. It was also one of the earliest automatic pistols to utilize a good firing-pin safety lock linked to the trigger.

In 1982, a few years after the trial, Astra introduced an improved version of its previous contender for the military contract. Dubbed the A-80, it was followed in 1987 by the A-90, which was essentially the same gun with slightly altered controls and a magazine release mounted on its trigger guard. The A-90 also supplemented its decocking lever with an ambidextrous safety mounted on the slide. Later, after many complaints about the A-90's controls, which seemed excessive and confusing, Astra created the A-100, combining the best features of the A-80 and A-90 models, including the A-80's clean slide and the A-90's magazine release. Interarms briefly imported the refined A-100 until European American Armory (EAA) took over importation of the entire Astra pistol line in 1993.

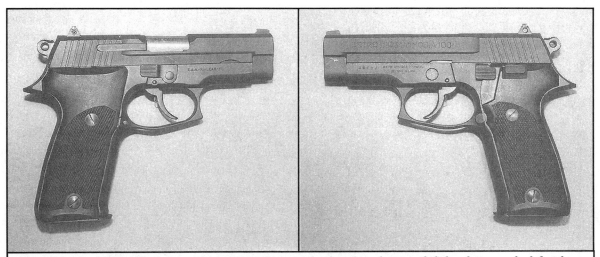

Inspired by the SIG P220 design, Astra's A-100 features the decocking lever and slide release on the left side (right photo). The disassembly latch, located just above the trigger, is on the right side (left photo), although the SIG's is on the left.

The A-80, A-90 and A-100 models represent Astra's second series of modern pistol designs (the Constable being the first). For the A-80 series, Astra chose as its inspiration the excellent SIG P220 (*see* separate listing), with its modified Browning short-recoil, breech-locking mechanism, and decocking lever on the left grip. In this system, the rear end of the barrel meshes with the forward edge of the large ejection port located on the slide. Upon recoil, a cam draws the rear end of the barrel down out of engagement with the slide. When the decocking lever is depressed, the cocked hammer is automati-

Disassembled, the Astra A-100 includes (top to bottom): slide, barrel, recoil spring/guide assembly, frame and magazine. Considering its high-capacity clip, the A-100's grip is remarkably slim (only 1.4 inches).

cally lowered onto a notch on the sear, just short of the firing pin. Once the decocking lever is released, it pops back into its rest position, leaving the gun ready for a double-action first shot. The only major differences between the A-80 series pistols and the SIG P220 series actually favor the Astras: they cost less, and their all-steel construction makes them more durable than the lighter, alloy-framed SIGs.

The A-100 (imported by EAA) comes in three calibers: 9mm (17-shot), .40 S&W (13-shot), and .45 ACP (9-shot). Considering its impressive ammunition capacity, the A-100 is remarkably compact and has a surprisingly slim (1.4") grip. This is not a large, clumsy pistol, however. The decocking lever is a relatively small and well-contoured piece that must by necessity protrude from the grip slightly so that the shooter's thumb can get a firm hold on the lever. In fact, the A-100 is one of the slimmer, more compact guns of its type; moreover, its barrel, being relatively short, gives the gun excellent balance without hurting accuracy.

Using the .45-ACP version from 25 feet, this five-shot offhand group fired with Federal Classic 185-grain jacketed hollowpoints measures only 1.7 inches across.

The recoil experienced with the .40-caliber version of the A-100 approaches the level of its .45 ACP cousin, not the more gentle 9mm. Still, it is certainly manageable. The optional satin nickel finish is recommended, mostly because the front sight, highlighted with a bright red dot, shows up clearly, making the gun easy to aim quickly. The double-action trigger pull is long and heavy, but smooth, and the single-action's has nearly 10mm of slack before enough pressure is generated to fire the pistol.

With its excellent sights and decent trigger, both the .40 S&W and .45 ACP versions of the A-100 proved quite accurate. Our smallest five-shot offhand group with the .40 S&W fired from a distance of 25 feet measured 1.8 inches across, using Federal Hi-Shok 180-grain jacketed hollowpoints. At 50 feet, the test group measured 3.6 inches, using the same brand of ammunition. With Winchester "Deep Penetrator" 180-grain jacketed hollowpoints, the A-100 proved less accurate, but no malfunctions were experienced with either load. Our best five-shot offhand group with the .45 ACP version measured 1.7 inches across, using Federal Classic 185-grain jacketed hollowpoints.

In summary, the Astra A-100 is a well-made, accurate and reliable pistol. It offers a level of performance comparable to the SIG P220 and at a lower price (although it's hardly inexpensive).

Astra A-100

Manufacturer	Years Produced	Caliber/Capacity	Dimensions
Astra-Unceta y Cia. Guernica, Spain Imported by: European American Armory, Hialeah, FL	1991–Present	9mm/17 rounds .40 S&W/13 rounds .45 ACP/9 rounds	Barrel Length: 3.9" O.A. Length: 7.1" Height: 5.6" Width: 1.4" Weight: 29 oz. (unloaded); 39 oz. (loaded)

AUTO-ORDNANCE 1911A1 GOVERNMENT

Chambered in .45 ACP, the popular Colt 1911Al service pistol is "copied" by Auto-Ordnance complete with matte blued finish and checkered plastic grips. In .45 ACP this gun is fully interchangeable with the stock military gun. Auto-Ordnance also makes several variations on the basic pistol, including 9mm and .38 Super, 10mm (with enlarged sights and wrap-around rubber grips), a Colt Commander-sized "General Model," a "Duo Tone" (with nickel frame and blued slide), the Pit Bull, featuring a 3.5-inch barrel and shortened slide, and a Custom High Polish version with 5-inch barrel.

The Auto-Ordnance 1911A1 line may be worth considering for shooters who like the basic Government Model system (*see* separate listings, page 109, and later in this section for a fuller discussion of the Government Model), but who find a new Colt too expensive.

Two variations of the 1911Al pistol offered by Auto-Ordnance are the Pit Bull (left) with 3.5-inch barrel and the Custom High Polish (right) with 5-inch barrel and wood grips. Both are considerably lower in price than the Colt-manufactured models.

AUTO-ORDNANCE 1911A1 GOVERNMENT

Manufacturer	Years Produced	Caliber/Capacity	Dimensions
Auto-Ordnance West Hurley, NY	Late 1980's–Present	9mm, 10mm, .38 Super/ 9 rounds .45 ACP/7 rounds	Barrel Length: 5.0" O.A. Length: 8.5" Height: 5.4" Width: 1.3" Weight: 39 oz. (unloaded); 46 oz. (loaded)

BERETTA MODEL M9/92F/92FS

After Beretta introduced its Model 92 double-action pistol around 1976 (*see* page 106), the company changed the original design considerably because of the handgun testing going on in several countries, particularly the U.S. When the second XM9 pistol trial took place in 1984, the Beretta Model 92 was already a mature, proven design, with several hundred thousand pistols having been produced and marketed as the result of a growing worldwide acceptance by military, police and civilian shooters. The changes made in the Model 92SB to satisfy U.S. service requirements included improved sights, a more durable finish, a chrome-lined bore, and ambidextrous operating controls. All these improvements served to make a good gun even better. The adoption by the U.S. Armed Forces of Model 92SB-F in January 1985 as the "Pistol, M9" firmly established it as a handgun to be reckoned with. It went into production for the police and civilian markets as the

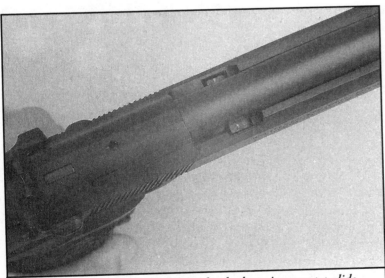

This top view of Beretta's Model 92 clearly shows its open-top slide design and P.38-type locking system.

Model 92F and has since garnered laurels wherever it has been used.

However, when three dozen or so slide breakages occurred during U.S. military testing and active service in 1989, Beretta was forced to redesign the M9/92F slightly to include a slide retention device. Rather than redesign the slide completely, as many experts demanded, Beretta's engineers chose a simpler remedy that involved minimal retooling. First, they increased the diameter of the hammer axis pin, so that it mated with a groove cut into the bottom left rear portion of the slide. To facilitate this change, they relieved the inside portion of the left grip to accommodate the enlarged axis pin. With this change, the possibility of a slide flying off the rear of the pistol was eliminated. The exact causes of the earlier slide breakages, and the likelihood of further slide separations in the future, are still hotly disputed by all interested parties. Nevertheless, it hasn't stopped Beretta's sales.

In common with other modern Beretta pistols, the Models 92F and 92FS are generously supplied with safety features. For example, thumbing the ambidextrous safety lever down (up for firing position) automatically decocks the hammer. The safety lever can then be left down as additional security against accidental discharge, or it can be pushed up to ready the pistol for firing. Since the

Beretta's Model 92 pistol handles well even when the shooter wears heavy gloves.

Model 92SB was introduced in 1981, Beretta has added a firing-pin lock as an added safety feature on all its 9mm pistols. A loaded chamber indicator on the extractor lets the shooter know if a round is in the firing chamber. Unlike the FN High Power, most competing Smith & Wesson pistols, and even some of Beretta's own designs, there is no magazine safety on the Model 92SB.

Due in part to its Walther-style, straight-recoiling barrel, the Model 92F is capable of excellent accuracy. The sights are also quite good, although some shooters dislike the front-dot/rear-hemisphere white markings. Apparently in response to consumer preference in the U.S., the latest 92F models now use the more common three-dot configuration on their sights.

In testing a Model 92F and two Model 92FS pistols for an extended period, all three operated smoothly, with excellent, responsive controls (except for a rather heavy military-style trigger pull). They are also slightly muzzle heavy, but there is minimal recoil and all are well set up for accurate rapid fire. In testing an Italian-made Model 92F, a five-shot offhand group measured 1.5 inches at 25 feet, using Federal 9BP, a potent combat round with 115-grain jacketed hollowpoints. Another group fired at 25 feet using Federal 9BP measured 2 inches across. The best five-shot group at 50 feet measured just 2.3 inches across, using Federal's 9BP 115-grain jacketed hollowpoint once again. With the more recent Model 92FS, it was much the same story. The best five-shot, 25-foot group measured only 1.25 inches across, while at 50 feet an offhand group came in at 2.9 inches. The best accuracy in these later guns was attained when using Winchester Silvertip 115-grain hollowpoints.

The Beretta Model 92 was without doubt one of the most accurate handguns tested for this book. All results referred to on these pages were from offhand groups, mostly because defensive shoot-

The Model 92FSS by Beretta is available with stainless steel slide and barrel and anodized silver frame to match.

ings almost always develop in a hurry. There's no time to set up behind a rest when you're in the act of defending your life.

Another strong point with the Model 92F/92FS is its utter reliability. Having fired most of the Beretta pistols made during World War II and later, we have never experienced a single jam with any of them. No doubt the much-maligned open slide is part of the reason for this reliability, since there's no place for a spent cartridge case to hang up and create a jam.

Beretta's Model 92F is extremely accurate, as clearly shown by this tight 1.5-inch offhand group.

Despite its great accuracy and smooth operation, the Model 92 is larger than it needs to be, making it difficult for small-handed shooters to hold the pistol. Granted, Beretta has done an excellent job in making the Model 92 more manageable, but other excellent 9mm pistols—notably the High Power and the CZ 75—are equally capable yet noticeably smaller. The astute grip design and excellent checkered stocks on this pistol make it a more user-friendly gun for shooters with medium-sized hands than the almost identical Taurus PT-92 (*see* separate listing), which has thicker and smoother wooden stocks.

The Beretta's weak open-slide design and aluminum-alloy frame are other detractors. An alloy frame on a pistol that fires a high-pressure round like the 9mm is, in the author's opinion, a mistake. It's like using a "space-saver" spare tire instead of a heavy-duty, full-sized spare on an automobile. Other top-quality guns with all-steel construction—the FN High Power, CZ 75 and Steyr GB—weigh no more than the Model 92. If Beretta must use a metal lighter than steel, titanium is a better choice by far than aluminum. In Beretta's defense, though, its alloy frame does seem especially durable as alloy frames go. After some frame-cracking problems early in the production run of its M9s for the U.S. military, Beretta U.S.A. made a slight change in the design and manufacture of the Model 92FS frame and has had no further problems. Meanwhile, SIG and Walther have both experienced frame cracking on some of their pistols.

Despite the shortcomings of Beretta's aluminum-alloy frames, the Model 92FS is still highly regarded as a superb defensive pistol. Its widespread use and fine reputation make it a gun worthy of respect and consideration. Moreover, its acceptance by the U.S. military and many police forces means that spare parts and reliable gunsmithing will be widely available for years to come.

BERETTA MODEL M9/92F/92FS

Manufacturer	Years Produced	Caliber/Capacity	Dimensions
Pietro Beretta SpA Gardone, V.T., Italy Beretta U.S.A. Accokeek, MD	1984–Present	9mm/15 rounds	Barrel Length: 4.9" O.A. Length: 8.7" Height: 5.5" Width: 1.5" Weight: 34 oz. (unloaded); 41 oz. (loaded)

BERETTA MODEL 92D/92DS

Introduced in 1992, the Model 92D is identical to the Model 92FS except that the single-action feature has been eliminated in favor of a double-action-only trigger mechanism. This new model is exactly the same size as a Model 92FS, but it boasts a smoother slide contour. That's because there's no manual safety, and the hammer is bobbed and flush with the frame. The hammer has no full-cock settings, either, and it cannot be cocked with the thumb. When the shooter pulls the trigger, the hammer moves back and, as it falls, the round is fired. As the slide recoils, it pushes the hammer back as in a standard single-action or double-action pistol. But once the recoil spring has pushed the slide forward, the hammer, with no cocking notch to hold it back in a cocked position, follows the slide down to its rest position. The pistol is then ready for another double-action shot. Aside from eliminating the manual safety lever, all other safety features on

Although the trigger pull of the Model 92D is somewhat lighter and smoother than the double-action first shot of the 92F, the Model 92D definitely gives the shooter's trigger finger a workout. One five-shot offhand group with the 92D from 25 feet measured a solid 1.4 inches, but that was achieved only after much practice. At longer distances, the double-action-only trigger of the Model 92D produced a five-shot group measuring an unacceptable 5.9 inches across (right).

the Model 92D are identical to those found on the Model 92F/FS. The Model 92DS is the same as a 92D but is supplied with the 92F/FS-style ambidextrous safety lever.

Even though it has the same accurate barrel lockup and prominent sights of the Model 92FS, the Model 92D, which fires in double action for every single shot, is a different animal where accuracy is concerned. The trigger pull of the Model 92D is somewhat lighter and smoother than the double-action first shot of the 92F, but the Model 92D definitely gives the shooter's trigger finger a workout. One five-shot offhand group with the 92D measured only 1.4 inches across at 25 feet, but that was achieved only after much practice. Typically, groups at this distance ran 3 inches across during the tests, due mostly to the considerable effort required in cycling the trigger. At longer distances, the double-action-only trigger of the Model 92D produced a five-shot group measuring an unacceptable 5.9 inches across. On the positive side, the Model 92D is completely reliable, as are the other Model 92 series pistols. It also produces slightly better double-taps than other double-action Beretta pistols.

The only real purpose of a double-action-trigger in a pistol is to give it a revolver-like feel, making it more appealing to tradition-minded police departments and those civilians who still distrust automatic pistols. Forjas Taurus has made an almost identical gun, which is restricted to police sales only, and Smith & Wesson makes numerous double-action-only pistols. Pistols made by Glock and Colt's Model 2000 All-American are similar in concept. The double-action first shot of many modern automatic pistols is certainly a useful safety adjunct. It is, after all, the one most likely to be discharged accidentally, so it makes sense to require a longer, heavier trigger pull. That way, the shooter really has to want it and work a little harder for it. Once firing has commenced, though, why handicap the shooter with an unnecessarily heavy trigger pull? Some also argue that the shooter should have a consistent trigger pull from shot to shot. This point is usually advanced as an argument in favor of single-action pistols over conventional double-action models, however, rather than a defense of the double-action-only automatic pistol. The argument loses its force when the double-action-only trigger pull is consistently poor from shot to shot. Unless the double-action-only trigger is extraordinarily smooth and light, as in the S&W Model 3953, for example, there seems little use for it. Thus, while numerous police departments have accepted the Model 92D or 92DS for service, readers are advised to approach it with skepticism.

BERETTA MODEL 92D/92DS

Manufacturer	Years Produced	Caliber/Capacity	Dimensions
Pietro Beretta SpA Gardone, V.T., Italy Beretta U.S.A. Accokeek, MD	1992–Present	9mm/15 rounds	Barrel Length: 4.9" O.A. Length: 8.5" Height: 5.4" Width: 1.5" Weight: 34 oz. (unloaded); 41 oz. (loaded)

BERETTA MODEL 92G

Except for an ambidextrous manual safety lever that's been replaced by a spring-loaded decocking lever, the Model 92G is identical to the Model 92FS. After the pistol is loaded and the decocking lever lowered, thereby dropping the hammer, the lever automatically springs back up to the firing position. All other Beretta safety features of the Model 92FS series, including the firing-pin lock and the loaded-chamber indicator, are retained on the Model 92G.

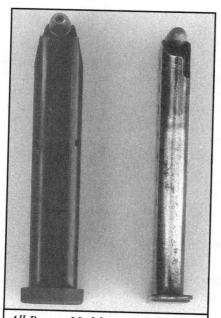

All Beretta Model 92s (except the 8-shot Type M) use a thick double-column magazine (left). This requires a much wider grip than the single-column magazine of the classic Walther P.38, whose 8-shot single-column magazine is shown at right.

The story behind this model began in 1985, when Beretta submitted its Model 92F for a French police pistol competition against other foreign pistols, including the SIG P226 and Walther P88. The French liked Beretta's Model 92, however, and its price was lower than the other competitors. As a result, in July 1987 the French National Police ordered 110,000 Beretta pistols, in return demanding the substitution of a decocking lever for a hammer-dropping safety that could—by leaving it in the down or safe position—prevent the pistol from firing immediately. Once this change was made, the pistol went into production, with 110,000 units going to the French police. In 1990 the French Air Force followed the lead of the police by ordering 35,000 92Gs. Since then, several major police departments in the U.S. have also ordered the 92G.

The accuracy of this model is comparable to the 92FS, with a five-shot offhand effort from 25 feet measuring 1.8 inches, and another five-shot group from 50 feet measuring 4.2 inches across.

Other features that help make this model the best of the full-sized Berettas include a decocking lever that allows safe loading while leaving the pistol ready to fire immediately. After all, a gun that cannot shoot when it's needed is not worth much. By contrast, the Walther-style hammer-dropping safety levers used on many Beretta and Smith & Wesson pistols are awkward to operate; they also move in the opposite direction—up to fire, down to safe—instead of the more natural down-to-fire Colt M1911 and Browning High Power-type safety levers. The decocking lever on the Model 92G places this Beretta in the same league as the Colt Double Eagle, SIG and Steyr GB.

BERETTA MODEL 92G

Manufacturer	Years Produced	Caliber/Capacity	Dimensions
Pietro Beretta SpA Gardone, V.T., Italy Beretta U.S.A. Accokeek, MD & GIAT, France	1987–Present	9mm/15 rounds	Barrel Length: 4.9" O.A. Length: 8.7" Height: 5.5" Width: 1.5" Weight: 34 oz. (unloaded); 41 oz. (loaded)

BERETTA MODEL 96

In its usual meticulous, painstaking way, Beretta took its time introducing a pistol chambered for the .40 S&W cartridge. Ironically, the Model 96 is virtually identical in

dimensions and operating characteristics to the well-tried Beretta Model 92. For that reason, it could probably have been rushed into production; but instead Beretta wisely chose to get it right the first time.

The Model 96 differs from Beretta's classic 9mm double-action Model 92 only in its barrel, in the slide parts necessary to accept the larger cartridge, and in its magazine. It comes in a standard

Beretta's 9mm Model 92 (top) has met serious competition from the Brazilian-made Taurus PT-92 (bottom). Taurus also made a .40 S&W version, the PT-100, to compete with the Beretta Model 96.

The .40-caliber Model 96 comes in the 96 "Stock" version for competition shooting (left). With 4.9-inch barrel and three interchangeable front sights, this single/double-action model has a half-cock notch and can be carried in the cocked-and-locked position. Another variation is the Combat model (right), five ounces heavier (40 oz.) than the Stock model, in single action only, with 5.9-inch barrel, competition-tuned trigger, adjustable rear target sight and tool set.

model, a Model 96D double-action-only variant, a "Centurion" version whose full-sized grip is allied with a compact-size barrel and slide, a "Stock" version for competition, and a heavier single-action-only Combat version. The double-action-only 96D tested for this book had a vestigial hammer that was bobbed to make it flush with the slide and could not be cocked except by trigger action. Elimination of the half-cock notch found on standard double-action/single-action Beretta pistols gives the 96D a smoother, lighter trigger pull than is usual, although it could be lighter and smoother still. Also, because it has no ambidextrous manual safety levers, the Model 96D is slightly thinner across the slide area than the standard version, a welcome change from the thick Model 92.

Due to its double-action-only trigger, the standard Model 96 is not especially accurate. From 25 feet, our best five-shot offhand group measured 2.7 inches across, while from 50 feet the group spanned 4.1 inches. Still, this is a reliable, well-made gun, although many shooters prefer the standard Beretta 92, whose recoiling slide cocks the hammer after the first shot.

The standard Beretta Model 96, with its double-action-only trigger, is less accurate than the company's 9mm pistols. This five-shot offhand group fired from 25 feet measures 2.7 inches.

Taurus International of Miami, Florida, imports a .40 S&W caliber version of its Model PT-92 from Brazil. Called the PT-100, it has a fixed rear sight (the PT-101's is adjustable) and most of the Beretta features. The three-position ambidextrous manual safety now standard on all Taurus Model PT-92-type pistols allows safe and easy decocking of the hammer; it also provides shooters with a choice of carrying the pistol cocked and locked (for a single-action first shot) or double- action carry after decocking the hammer.

BERETTA MODEL 96

Manufacturer	Years Produced	Caliber/Capacity	Dimensions
Pietro Beretta SpA Gardone, V.T., Italy Imported by: Beretta U.S.A. Accokeek, MD	1992–Present	.40 S&W/10 rounds	Barrel Length: 4.9" O.A. Length: 8.5" Height: 5.4" Width: 1.4" Weight: 33 oz. (unloaded); 41 oz. (loaded)

BREN TEN PISTOL

Although it was an interesting concept that attracted a great deal of attention, the Bren Ten pistol was plagued with difficulties. The idea behind it was the creation of a pistol that combined the excellent handling and features of the legendary CZ 75 pistol with the more powerful 10mm cartridge. Initial production by Dornaus & Dixon of Huntington Beach, California, began in 1983, with Norma (Sweden) providing the ammunition for the initial run.

The new pistol was offered in at least four major variations: the standard Military & Police; a slightly smaller Pocket Model; a Dual-Master (offering easy interchangeability of 10mm and .45 ACP calibers); and a commemorative model. Unfortunately, Dornaus & Dixon badly overextended itself, often selling guns in advance that weren't delivered on time—or sometimes not at all. Some guns were sold with only a single magazine, or even no magazine. Another problem arose because the initial run of Norma ammunition was loaded too hot for the Bren Ten, causing breakage of parts. As a result, Dornaus & Dixon quickly wilted and failed in 1985 after producing only some 1,500 pistols.

The Bren Ten is well-shaped to the hand, albeit heavy, with handling qualities that are good if not exceptional. Had the gun been made in quantity and marketed with more panache, it might have been successful. In 1990, sports equipment mogul and gun enthusiast Richard Voight attempted to revive the Bren Ten as the "Peregrine Falcon." The project foundered when banks refused to loan Voight the capital needed for tooling up.

Dornaus & Dixon's ill-fated Bren Ten was an attractive pistol that failed to catch on in the marketplace. Note the cross-bolt safety in the slide, which acts upon the firing pin to supplement the standard frame-mounted manual safety.

BREN TEN PISTOL

Manufacturer	Years Produced	Caliber/Capacity	Dimensions
Dornaus & Dixon Huntington Beach, CA	1983–1985	10mm/11 rounds (Military & Police) 9 rounds (Pocket)	Barrel Length: 5.0" (M&P); 3.75" (Pocket) O.A. Length: 8.75" (M&P); 6.9" (Pocket) Height: 5.8" (M&P); 5.3" (Pocket) Width: 1.4" Weight: (M&P) 39 oz. (unloaded); 50 oz. (loaded) (Pocket) 28 oz. (unloaded); 37 oz. (loaded)

BROWNING BDM

In 1952 and again in the period 1979 to 1988, Fabrique Nationale (FN) made several attempts to introduce a modern double-action pistol to supplement (and eventually replace) their legendary but aging High Power (P-35) single-action pistol. Unfortunately, these attempts were unsuccessful. Finally, in 1992, FN's North American distributor, Browning Arms Company of Morgan, Utah, succeeded in creating the BDM (for Browning Double Mode), which combines much of the High Power's elegant lines with a modern double-action trigger mechanism. Actually, Browning has taken the traditional double-action trigger several steps further. Now the shooter can choose between a double-action first shot followed quickly by single-action follow-up shots ("pistol mode"); all shots fired in double action (or "revolver mode").

The BDM is not simply a High Power pistol modified to fire double action. In fact, except for the experimental pistol of 1952, none of FN's double-action pistols, or this Browning, were ever modified High Powers; rather, they were completely new designs. When Browning introduced the BDM in early 1991, it had to withdraw the pistol almost immediately, because it had to be beefed up to handle +P+ ammunition according to a Secret Service order. Release of this pistol to the civilian market took a back seat, therefore, until the gun had been strengthened. Ironically, this delay of more than a year caused Browning to lose its government order for the BDM; but the improvements made during that year produced a better gun.

Aside from its choice of operating modes, the BDM is unusually slim for a 15-shot pistol. In fact, it's no thicker through the grip than many 8-round 9mm pistols, due partly to the BDM's unique grip design. The one-piece grip is well-checkered to ensure a secure yet comfortable hold. Among all high-capacity 9mm pistols, only the Glock pistols have

The BDM (top) is about the same size as the High Power (bottom) and bears a faint resemblance to it; yet no parts are interchangeable between the two guns.

The BDM (top) is highly competitive in price, performance and features with other popular 9mm pistols, such as the Glock 19 (center) and Smith & Wesson's Model 3914 (bottom). Inset: The BDM's grip (left) is notice-ably slimmer than that of Glock's Model 19 (center), and barely wider than the Smith & Wesson Model 3914 (right), which holds more than half as many rounds.

grips as thin as the BDM (which has a slimmer and narrower slide than the Glock). The BDM also features all-steel construction throughout, yet weighs only 31 ounces unloaded.

The BDM sights are well-rounded, virtually snag-free and good-sized. For a pistol designed in the late 1980s, perhaps it was inevitable that the BDM's sights would employ the popular three-dot sighting system. The rear sight somewhat resembles a Novak-type sight—the type found on the latest Smith & Wesson pistols. Also, the front sight is pinned in place, rather than dovetailed onto the slide, to prevent its coming off accidentally under heavy recoil.

Among the BDM's other well-conceived features are its nonreflective matte black finish and a trigger that's narrow and smooth—ideal for rapid double-action revolver-style shooting. The BDM also has the SIG-style variation of Browning's time-tested short-recoil locking system. The magazine release is intelligently shielded from accidental release by slightly raised thumbrests on each grip. The magazine well is beveled for the smooth, rapid insertion of fresh magazines. The magazine bottoms are shielded to minimize damage when the empty magazine pops out (as it should on a combat pistol). A lanyard loop is positioned ambidextrously in the center rear of the grip, but higher than the bottom of the magazine, so that it can't interfere with rapid reloading. To reduce manufacturing costs, the frame is made by investment casting and the slide is formed by stamping. And as in the latest SIG pistols, the separate breechblock is pinned into place.

Another feature is the BDM's passive firing-pin safety, which can be deactivated only when the trigger is pulled all the way to the rear. A decocking lever (which doubles as a manual safety when desired) is located on both sides of the frame to suit both right- and left-handed shooters. Unfortunately, the lever must be moved up to fire and down to safe, but at least the movement required to deactivate the gun is only 30° or so, compared to the 60°— or even 90°— required to arm most competing double-action pistols. Unlike the Browning High Power, the BDM does not have a magazine safety, which means it can still be fired even if the magazine is lost or accidentally released. Like many modern pistols, the BDM is well set up for ambidextrous operation.

Despite the BDM's "revolver mode," with its double-action pull for every shot, its performance is, with a little practice, more comfortable and generally more accurate than one finds in the "pistol mode." Gun experts Jeff Cooper and Chuck Taylor both agree that a single-action pistol, an all-double-action (double-action-only) automatic pistol, or a double-action revolver are all inherently more accurate than a pistol that switches from double action to single action. They may have a point. The BDM's recoil is mild, even with +P ammunition, and its sights are good. The trigger is smooth in all configurations, although several millimeters of initial slack are noticeable in its single-action trigger pull. Even the double-action trigger pull, whether in revolver or pistol mode, is surprisingly light and easy to operate. All of these factors contribute to the BDM's accuracy and shooting comfort.

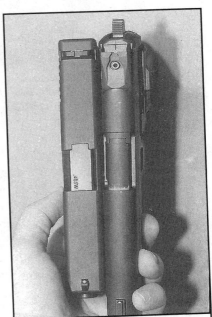

Viewed from above, the BDM (right) has the same SIG-type modified Browning breech-locking mechanism as the Glock Model 23 pistol (left).

The two BDMs tested for this book functioned almost flawlessly with a variety of ammunition types. Ironically, the only jam occurred because the Federal 124-grain Nyclad nylon-coated hollowpoint— usually one of the smoothest functioning of all rounds— failed to feed. This jam took place early on in the breaking-in process, however, and was never repeated. In addition to feeding well, the BDM has an ejection port large enough so that stovepipe jams are next to impossible.

While it's not exceptionally accurate, the BDM performs acceptably. One five-shot, 25-foot offhand group fired with Samson 115-grain FMJ measured 1.5 inches across. Using Federal 124-grain Hydra-Shok hollowpoint rounds, a 1.6-inch group was recorded at the same distance. Both groups were fired in the pistol mode, with a double-action first shot and single-action follow-up shots. In the revolver mode, the best group was fired with Hansen Combat 115-grain JHPs and measured 1.8 inches across. All other groups fired from 25 feet spanned more than two inches. Opening the distance to 50 feet, a five-shot offhand group in pistol mode, using Hansen Combat 115-grain

A five-shot group fired offhand with the Browning BDM from 25 feet measures 1.6 inches across (above). Another five-shot offhand group fired from 50 feet measured 2.6 inches.

JHPs, measured 3.6 inches across. This was followed by a revolver-mode group using Samson 115-grain FMJs that came in at 4.7 inches.

Browning's impressive BDM pistol makes an excellent choice—particularly in its revolver mode—for police forces. Shooters with small hands will finally discover in the BDM an ideal high-capacity 9mm pistol, one that is comfortable to handle and fire. Moreover, it's appreciably slimmer and smaller than any of the other high-capacity 9mm's, including the Glocks. Mechanically, the BDM shares many of the features found in the SIG pistols, but it uses stronger all-steel construction and has trimmer lines. In short, this Browning pistol is an excellent handgun, one of the best now available.

BROWNING BDM

Manufacturer	Years Produced	Caliber/Capacity	Dimensions
Browning Arms Co. Morgan, UT	1991–Present	9mm/15 rounds	Barrel Length: 4.73" O.A. Length: 7.85" Height: 5.45" Width: 1.3" Weight: 31 oz. (unloaded); 38 oz. (loaded)

COLT DOUBLE EAGLE

The immediate and enduring success of its Government Model (for a complete discussion of the Colt 1911A1/Government Model, *see* pages 109–114) caused Colt Industries to become rather complacent about the need to develop an improved, modernized pistol— one that appealed to a new generation of shooters who'd been brought up to expect such refinements as a double-action trigger and high-capacity magazine. The first wake-up call rang in 1979 when Colt realized that the U.S. military was about to replace the trusty M1911A1 pistol with a new automatic model. The company then rushed—too hastily, as it turned out—to submit its experimental Stainless Steel Pistol, or SSP. This promising and innovative design simply failed to perform well in military testing, unfortunately, whereupon Colt went back to sleep and Beretta won the military M9 pistol contract. During the 1980s, Colt's lead in automatic pistol design continued to slip away, while its competitors, led by Smith & Wesson, quickly developed modern pistols with all the features that appealed to new shooters. Finally, by the late 1980s, Colt realized the urgent need for a new pistol design. The result: the unveiling in 1989 of their first new handgun in years: the Double Eagle.

After the initial flurry of congratulations over this new gun, Colt encountered difficulties. Some critics felt that the Double Eagle was too much like the Government Model, while others complained that the Double Eagle didn't have enough of the Government Model's good qualities. A more serious problem was the Double Eagle's trigger, which pinched trigger fingers and sometimes failed to return all the way forward, thus preventing the pistol from firing a second shot. Moreover, a spring necessary to operate the mechanism properly kept getting lost or misplaced by curious owners. Finally, Colt was forced to take the Double Eagle back to the drawing board, where eventually the company managed to rework the new gun and correct its faults.

The corrected "Mark II" version of the Double Eagle is an excellent, debugged pistol that has sold in 9mm, .38 Super, .40 S&W and 10mm calibers as well as .45 ACP. Still, the

Colt experimented with double-action pistols for many years before actually putting one on the market. The company's famous Stainless Steel Pistol, or SSP, was briefly tested by the U.S. Armed Forces in 1981 but was never adopted.

Double Eagle line has not done especially well in the marketplace and production continues on a limited basis, particularly in non-.45 caliber. As of mid-1995 Colt had made only a little over 10,000 Double Eagle-type pistols.

In designing the Double Eagle, Colt sensibly used many of the same parts found in the Government Model. The slides, for example, are almost identical, as is the Series '80 firing-pin safety (which blocks the firing pin until the trigger has been pulled all the way to the rear after firing). Unlike the traditional Government Model, though, the Double Eagle has a double-action

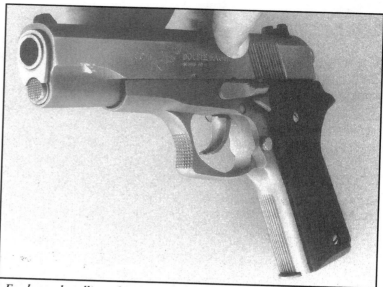

For better handling, the Double Eagle features a checkered trigger guard and gripping striations on the front gripstrap.

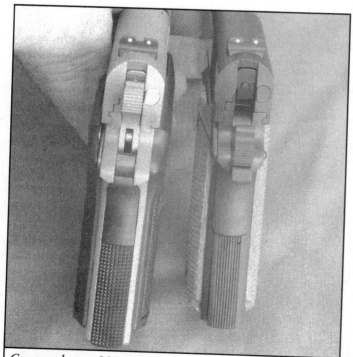

Compared to an M1911-type pistol (right), the Colt Double Eagle (left) is only slightly wider, despite a double-action trigger mechanism that tends to bulk up a handgun.

trigger and, instead of a manual safety, a decocking lever has been added to the front edge of the left grip panel. When depressed, this lever safely lowers the hammer and, upon being released, returns to its fire position.

Although the operating controls on the Double Eagle are not ambidextrous, left-handed users can properly work the magazine release, slide stop and decocking lever with the trigger finger of the left hand. Unfortunately, from a left-hander's standpoint, the stiff magazine release is hard to operate with the trigger finger. Interestingly, the decocking lever and slide stop are so close together that a right-hander can have trouble gaining the proper control.

The Double Eagle's workmanship is excellent. Its grips are made of checkered Xenoy, an ultra-tough synthetic material (also used by Ruger in its P85-series pistols). In an unusual touch, the right grip plate of the Double Eagle has an extension covering the trigger drawbar, which remains exposed on many double-action pistols. This feature may look ugly and awkward, but it makes sense to protect the drawbar, one of the most delicate parts of a double-action pistol.

The box magazine on the Double Eagle holds eight rounds—instead of only seven—thus becoming the first of the M1911-type pistols to have this feature. Another major improvement—one that has benefited all large Colt automatic pistols—is the relieved area beneath the trigger guard. This feature causes the gun to sit lower in the hand and as a result helps to reduce the level of recoil. Modifying the frame in this fashion was necessary to give shooters the same amount of grip area as with an M1911, in which the double-action trigger, with its enlarged guard, sits lower on the frame. In addition to eliminating the Government Model's grip safety, the Double Eagle has a long grip tang and a rounded, Commander-style hammer to reduce the chances of hammer bite.

The double-action trigger mechanism of the Double Eagle, though odd-looking, has proved durable and reliable in service.

The Double Eagle shoots extremely well, and its double-action trigger pull is surprisingly smooth. To test the transition from double-action to single-action shooting, a series of rapid double taps were test-fired. With a double-action trigger mechanism like the Double Eagle's, the first shot of a double tap necessarily involves a double-action trigger pull, with the follow-up shot employing the shorter and lighter single-action trigger pull. For a pistol with a double-action trigger pull significantly more difficult than its single-action trigger pull, one would expect the two shots of the double tap to land at least several inches apart. In firing the Double Eagle, though, double taps landed as close as one inch apart. Moreover, there is hardly any recoil sensation.

In testing two full-sized Double Eagle pistols—an early one and a later one—our best five-shot offhand effort with the early model at 25 feet measured 2.8 inches, while a five-shot offhand group at 50 feet patterned a rather wide 5.2 inches. With the more recent version, our best five-shot offhand efforts at 25 feet measured 2.6, 2.7, and 2.8 inches, using Winchester 185-grain Silvertip hollow-points, Remington 185-grain +P jacketed hollowpoints, and Winchester U.S.A. 230-grain FMJ ammunition, respectively. With the newer Double Eagle, the best five-shot offhand group at 50 feet measured a much-reduced 3.6 inches (but the four single-action shots made a tight 2.2-inch pattern). This kind of consistency using different ammunition types says a lot for an automatic pistol's quality.

From 25 feet, the Colt Double Eagle fired this five-shot offhand group, which measures 2.6 inches.

Clearly, the accuracy potential of the Double Eagle is there. Its double-action trigger pull is very smooth and easy to adjust to, while its single-action trigger pull is light.

As for reliability, both the old and new Double Eagles proved flawless with all varieties of ammunition tested, including half a dozen or so popular brands in JHP and FMJ configuration and 185-grain and 230-grain bullet weights. In all, the Double Eagle's excellent design combines with great skill what is good in the Government Model with a modern double-action trigger and safety mechanism.

COLT DOUBLE EAGLE

Manufacturer	Years Produced	Caliber/Capacity	Dimensions
Colt Industries Firearms Division Hartford, CT	1989–1996	.45 ACP/8 rounds (also 9mm, .38 Super, .40 S&W, 10mm)	Barrel Length: 5.0" O.A. Length: 8.5" Height: 5.5" Width: 1.3" Weight: 38 oz. (unloaded); 46 oz. (loaded)

COLT "ENHANCED" GOVERNMENT

When people think of .45-caliber handguns, they think of Colt. That's because Colt created the fantastically successful .45 Long Colt caliber Single Action Army revolver (1873, *see* page 32) and the .45 ACP Model 1911 automatic pistol (1911, *see* page 109). Both handguns have enjoyed phenomenally successful careers and have been widely copied. As a natural consequence, some of Colt's most successful modern handguns are variations on the old M1911 series. These include the "civilianized" M1911, called the "Government Model," and its reduced-size variants, the Commander and the even smaller Officer's and Lightweight Officer's Models. There is also a double-action .45-caliber pistol—the Double Eagle (*see* previous listing), which is available in smaller versions, including the Double Eagle Commander. (For discussions on the compact versions, please consult the companion volume, COMPLETE GUIDE TO COMPACT HANDGUNS.)

Since its introduction in 1911, the Colt Government Model has set the world standard in automatic pistols. The crowning achievement of John M. Browning, this .45-ACP pistol has been copied probably more than any other handgun. Even now, almost exact copies abound. Indeed, many experienced handgunners insist there's no room for improvement, and that John Browning got it right the first time. Others maintain that, while Browning's basic design is certainly sound, improvements are not only possible but desirable.

As the original manufacturer of the M1911, Colt of course realized that improvements were certainly possible, and introduced in 1992 its "Enhanced Models" of the Government Model series. Naturally, the firing-pin block of Colt's Series '80 has been retained, but other changes to the basic design have been made as part of the Enhanced program. These include a widened beavertail grip safety (which many, including the author, would like to eliminate altogether), a flat-topped slide, enlarged sights with a 3-dot aiming system, forward-angled cocking serrations on the slide, a slightly relieved ejection port, a rounded and lightened hammer, a relief cut at the bottom of the trigger guard (so the pistol sits lower in the shooter's hand), a longer trigger than the M1911A1, and a beveled magazine well for faster reloading.

These changes may be the most radical made to Colt's fac-

The ejection port on Colt's Enhanced Government Model is relieved at the rear to prevent the brass from being damaged and to reduce the possibility of stovepipe jams. Note also the Commander-style hammer instead of a spur.

tory pistol since the U.S. Army accepted the M1911A1 in 1926, but actually they represent what custom gunsmiths have been doing to many privately-owned M1911-series guns for decades.

The workmanship found in Colt's Enhanced pistol line is, as one would expect, flawless. The two Government Model pistols tested for this book were a matte stainless GM and a Government Model with a blued finish. Colt also offers the Government Model with an attractive, more expensive

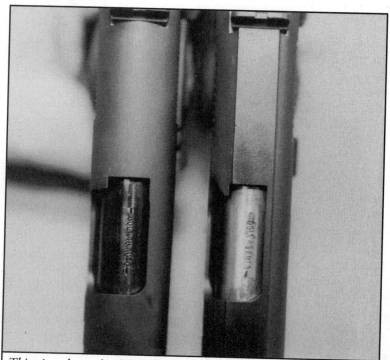

This view shows the difference between the ejection port of a new Enhanced Colt Government Model (right) and an older one (left). Note also that the newer version has a flattened area across the sighting plane.

"Ultimate" bright stainless finish. Fit and finish were excellent on both pistols, although some dislike the pebbled neoprene grips, which have gradually become standard on most Colt Government Model-type pistols (try instead a set of Bill Wilson's checkered wooden grips and his extended ambidextrous safety). Another accessory worth buying is a set of Wilson's Shok-Buffs, which are washers that attach to the recoil spring (without gunsmithing) and cushion the recoil of the slide.

Among the improvements introduced earlier with the Double Eagle series are an 8-round magazine (instead of 7) and a relieved area beneath the trigger guard. Some will doubtless prefer to top up the magazine with 8 rounds, load the first round into the pistol, remove the magazine, place another round into the magazine and replace it in the pistol, for a total of 9 (8+1) rounds. Many people have carried the M1911 for years as an 8-shot pistol even though it had only a 7-shot magazine for most of its existence.

The Enhanced Government Model, in whatever finish and despite its size, is an excellent shooter. The enlarged upper rear portion of its grip safety practically eliminates any possibility of hammer bite, and the rounded hammer is not likely to catch on clothing the way earlier spur hammers could. Because the gun sits low in the hand with grips that have a lot of give to them, felt recoil—especially for a .45-caliber pistol—is light.

Despite being tested hard with a wide variety of ammunition, both Enhanced Government Models we used had flawless reliability. The stainless steel model fired offhand from 25 feet measured 1.5 inches, while from 50 feet the best five-shot offhand group measured 3.0 inches. Firing the blued Enhanced Government Model at 50 feet produced still another 1.8-inch group, our best-ever performance with any Government Model. Except for the 1.8-inch 50-footer, all shots placed in the black zone

This five-shot group was fired offhand with a stainless steel Colt Government Model pistol from 25 feet. The pattern shown measures 1.5 inches across.

of the target; what's more, most of the groups put one or more rounds square in the bull's-eye. There's a slight amount of creep in the trigger pull, but for those who insist on a match-tuned trigger this is an easy problem for a qualified gunsmith to fix.

The Government Model is still a superb weapon whose various changes implemented by Colt have made a great gun even greater. It may not be for everybody, but the Government Model certainly rewards those who are willing to spend the time and effort learning to master it.

COLT "ENHANCED" GOVERNMENT

Manufacturer	Years Produced	Caliber/Capacity	Dimensions
Colt's Manufacturing Co. Hartford, CT	1992-Present	.45 ACP/8 rounds	Barrel Length: 5.0" O.A. Length: 8.5" Height: 5.4" Width: 1.3" Weight: 39 oz. (unloaded); 46 oz. (loaded)

COLT MODEL 2000 ALL AMERICAN

When Colt introduced its Model 2000 All American in 1991, it took some time before the pistol became available in quantity. By the mid-1990s, though, the gun on which America's oldest gunmaker had pinned its hopes in the fiercely competitive high-capacity 9mm police and civilian pistol market was flourishing. Interestingly, the Model 2000 is not, strictly speaking, a Colt product at all. Rather, it was created by Knight's Armament Company (Vero Beach, Florida), whose engineering know-how had made it a favorite among police and military buyers. Between 1985 and 1987, Reed Knight, owner of the company, together with Eugene Stoner, creator of the M16 Rifle, designed a series of prototypes of what became the Model 2000. Their first prototype was a small, 10-shot 9mm pistol only a little larger than an AMT Backup (*see* the companion volume, COMPLETE GUIDE TO COMPACT HANDGUNS). When Knight showed this gun to Colt in mid-1987, they expressed great interest in the project. A year later, Knight introduced a second, larger prototype at the International Association of Chiefs of Police. The third prototype, which looks very much like the current production model, was completed in December 1988, and on June 15, 1989, Colt bought an option for the rights to Knight's design, which it executed in April 1990.

In size and magazine capacity, the Model 2000 resembles most other 9mm high-capacity pistols, but it is quite different internally. For one thing, the Model 2000 is an "all-double-action" or "double-action-only" automatic pistol. This means that the striker remains at rest until the trigger is pulled. This action automatically resets the striker and allows multiple hits on the primer of a defective cartridge without having to draw back the slide to reset the hammer or striker (as with Smith & Wesson and Glock pistols). The trigger/sear

This right-hand view shows the sleek lines and unusual-shaped grip of the Model 2000 All American. The disassembled view (inset) reveals its unique components.

Like the Taurus Model PT-99 (top), the standard Model 2000 All American has a 5-inch barrel and is essentially a full-sized 9mm service pistol.

assembly of the Model 2000 is mounted on rollers, giving the trigger an exceptionally smooth, revolver-like pull. The entire firing mechanism, except for the trigger/sear assembly, is contained within the slide.

The Model 2000 also features an unusual locking mechanism. Upon firing, the barrel not only recoils to the rear, it rotates into grooves that have been cut into a steel cam block in the frame. This barrel rotation unlocks the barrel from the slide, which in standard automatic pistol fashion reciprocates. The rotating barrel is not new, having been used previously in Steyr's Hahn Model of 1912, the MAB PA-15, and the new Steyr TMP/SPP. But the Model 2000 has an unusually strong lockup that allows the pistol to be adapted, if desirable, to different calibers.

The frame of the Model 2000 is of tough polymer, not unlike that used on the Glock pistols. An alloy-framed model is also available, adding four ounces to the weight of this pistol. The polymer version has a matte blue finish, while the fancier alloy-framed model sports a high-polish blued slide. The sights, featuring the popular 3-dot configuration, offer a good sight picture.

The safety mechanisms on the Model 2000 resemble those found on a revolver more than an automatic pistol. To fire a chambered cartridge, the striker is released only by pressing the trigger all the way through its travel. Thus, there's no need for a manual safety (the long lever on the left rear portion of the frame is actually a slide lock). Thanks to its design, the Model 2000 has a very slim,

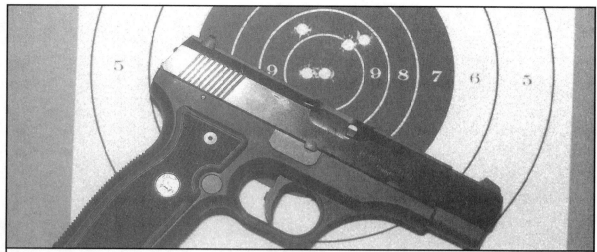

Colt's Model 2000 All American pistol boasts an innovative design with many positive qualities. As shown here, accuracy is more than acceptable.

ergonomic grip that fits the hand much more comfortably than that of a typical 15-shot 9mm pistol. Indeed, the Model 2000 is competitive with any high-capacity 9mm pistol where grip size and shape are concerned, even with any of the Glock pistols or the Browning BDM.

As for accuracy, the Model 2000's performance depends greatly on when the gun was made. One test firing produced a 1.3-inch five-shot, offhand group from 25 feet using Cor-Bon 115-grain JHP, while a 1.8- inch group from the same distance was achieved with Winchester Silvertip 115-grain hollowpoints. The trigger pull was long and rather spongy, but recoil was soft and manageable.

Some feeding troubles have arisen with the Model 2000 when firing Cor-Bon +P jacketed hollowpoints. This round uses a blunt-tipped Sierra bullet with excellent expansion, but it also produces difficult feeding in some pistols. Otherwise, the Model 2000 performed with perfect reliability using all other ammunition types, including Silvertip hollowpoints and several brands of full-metal-jacketed ammunition.

As with its Double Eagle pistols, Colt experienced some trouble getting the Model 2000 right the first time around. Later on, its accuracy problems were cleared up, but still Colt decided to discontinue production in the fall of 1993. Nevertheless, the Model 2000 is an interesting gun and should prove serviceable enough for police and civilians alike. Colt would be well advised to make a truly compact version of this gun. The company did try offering a two-for-one package by selling the standard Model 2000 with a 5-inch barrel along with an extra 3.75-inch barrel, but that was not a true compact pistol

COLT MODEL 2000 ALL AMERICAN

Manufacturer	Years Produced	Caliber/Capacity	Dimensions
Colt's Manufacturing Co. Hartford, CT	1991–1993	9mm/15 rounds	Barrel Length: 4.5" O.A. Length: 7.5" Height: 5.4" Width: 1.3" Weight: 29 oz. (unloaded); 36 oz. (loaded)

CZ MODEL 85/85 COMBAT

The Model 85 was originally introduced in 1985 by Ceska Zbrojovka, Europe's second largest firearms manufacturer, but only after close assessment of its attraction to Western design trends and informal testing by the U.S. armed forces. In the latter case, the 9mm Model 85 bested the M9 Beretta and SIG P226 pistols in all aspects except in its safety configurations.

The CZ 85 is nearly identical to the excellent Model CZ 75 (*see* pages 117–119). Magnum Research, its current distributor (Action Arms imported the CZ guns until 1994), sells both models in a variety of finishes, including blued, nickel, matte black lacquer and chrome. Among its differences are an ambidextrous slide stop and safety lever, ribbing across the sight plane, flat rather than recessed slide-retraction grooves, and a squared, serrated trigger guard. Oddly enough, considering all the other ambidextrous controls, the magazine release on the CZ 85 is the same non-ambidextrous type as the CZ 75. The fully checkered grips are also the same type used in CZ 75 pistols built since 1987 (earlier CZ 75s used the distinctive waffle pattern). Internally, some (but not all) Model 85s feature a firing-pin lock as an added safety feature; aside from that, though, the manual safety lever on the CZ 85 works the same as that on the CZ 75.

The standard CZ 85 (top) differs from the original CZ 75 primarily in its ambidextrous controls and recurved trigger guard. The Model 85 Combat (bottom) features a number of changes from the original CZ 75, including ambidextrous controls, a matte finish, wooden grips and adjustable rear sights.

For a combat pistol, accuracy was acceptable. A five-shot off-hand effort from 25 feet measured 1.3 inches using Winchester 115-grain Silvertip hollowpoints; from 50 feet the group measured 5.1 inches. The double-action trigger pull on the Model 85 is slightly rougher and heavier than the 75, but its single-action pull is equal to that of the original pistol.

Overall, the CZ 85 is a superb service pistol suitable for military, police or civilian defensive purposes. It retains most of the excellent features of the CZ 75—arguably the world's best double-action 9mm service pistol—while offering improved ambidextrous handling not found in the earlier classic handgun.

The CZ 85 Combat put five shots, fired offhand at a range of 25 feet, into a 1.1-inch group (above). From 50 feet, the same pistol produced a five-shot offhand group measuring 3.9 inches.

CZ 85 Combat. In late 1992, Action Arms began importing the Model 85 in a modified configuration meant to appeal to American shooters. Called the CZ 85 Combat, this pistol is identical to the regular CZ 85 except that its spur hammer has been replaced with a rounded one, and it has wooden grips instead of plastic ones. It also features an adjustable overtravel stop on the trigger, a removable front sight and a sturdy adjustable rear sight.

Most, if not all, of these changes are improvements on the basic gun; for example, the spur hammer of a CZ 75 can occasionally hang up on a holster when drawing, which makes this new configuration a positive move. Unlike the CZ 75, moreover, the sights on the Combat model can be easily removed and replaced with tritium-illuminated ones. The wooden grips are somewhat thicker than the plastic type used on other CZ 9mm pistols, but they are still easily manageable. The Combat model is available in a variety of finishes, including matte, black lacquer, blue, nickel and chrome.

In terms of accuracy, the CZ 85 Combat proved slightly better than the standard CZ 85. The best of a five-shot offhand group measured 1.1 inches from 25 feet using Norinco-made 124-grain FMJs, while another group fired from the same distance with Winchester 115-grain Silvertip hollow-points went into 1.5 inches. The best offhand shots fired from 50 feet measured 3.9 inches. Like the standard CZ 85, the double-action trigger pull on this smaller version is inferior to that of the Model 75 (although its single-action pull is equal to that of the original pistol). No jams were experienced in test-firing a variety of hollowpoint and FMJ ammunition.

CZ MODEL 85/85 COMBAT

Manufacturer	Years Produced	Caliber/Capacity	Dimensions
Ceska Zbrojovka Uhersky Brod, Czechoslovakia	1985–Present (85) 1992–Present (Combat)	9mm/15 rounds	Barrel Length: 4.7" O.A. Length: 8.0" Height: 5.4" Width: 1.35" Weight: 36 oz. (unloaded); 43 oz. (loaded)

DAEWOO DP51

In 1992 Daewoo Precision Industries, a huge
South Korean industrial conglomerate, introduced
the DP51, a 13-shot 9mm pistol of advanced design. Daewoo's
short history of gun production includes a domestic version of the
M16A1 (under license from Colt), a .223-caliber K1A1 carbine, a .223
rifle called the K2, and a .223-caliber light machine gun. With its growing experience in building top-quality military weapons, Daewoo felt confident enough to
offer a high-capacity 9mm pistol, despite the many fine 9mm pistols already on the
market.

The result of Daewoo's efforts—the DP51—is a locked-breech pistol with a
modified Browning short-recoil mechanism. Its locking lugs, located on the upper rear portion of the
barrel, fit into grooves
machined inside the slide.
Another lug at the bottom
rear of the barrel then forces
the slide down into an abutment in the frame, much like
FN's High Power model. To
hold down its weight, the
DP51 utilizes an alloy frame.

*Daewoo's DP51 shows considerable influence of the FN High Power pis-
tol, especially in its "Fast-Action" trigger mechanism. Like many other
modern pistols, it also caters to the needs of left-handed shooters by
including an ambidextrous safety lever on the right side of the frame
(above).*

Although the DP51 has
a double-action trigger, it
also includes a "fast-action"
mechanism, a device first
developed by Fabrique
Nationale in an experimental
pistol tested in the late 1970s
but not adopted at the time.
With this fast-action mechanism, the hammer is first
cocked (by loading the pistol) and then pushed forward
to its uncocked position,
thus compressing a return
spring. The pistol, it now appears, is ready for a regular double-action first shot requiring a long,
heavy pull on the trigger. With the fast-action mechanism, however, once the trigger has been pulled
the hammer is forced by the spring back to its fully cocked position, then immediately falls again, firing the chambered cartridge. The advantage of this system over double action is that the trigger pull is
much lighter—more like a single-action pull—despite a long travel similar to the double-action trigger. The DP51's design thus allows the shooter to choose a variety of carrying and operating modes,
for in addition to the fast action, the shooter can now elect to leave the hammer cocked and push the

safety up into its safe position. The gun is now ready for a single-action first shot as soon as the safety lever has been pushed down.

In addition to its passive firing-pin block, the DP51 features an ambidextrous manual safety lever, which we found difficult to put back on safe without shifting our grip on the pistol. This problem is much less serious, however, than a safety that's hard to release before firing. Left-handed shooters should also know that the right-side safety lever is slightly smaller than the one on the left side. Another useful feature borrowed from FN's High Power is that the ambidextrous safety lever moves down to fire and up to safe. However, the safety on the DP51, when it's in the "on" position, does not lock the slide. This means that loading and unloading operations can proceed with the safety "on," a

Using the Daewoo DP51 pistol, this five-shot offhand group from 25 feet measures 2.4 inches. Note how the first two shots made a single large bullet hole right in the center of the target.

useful feature not possible with the Colt M1911A1 and FN High Power pistols. The safety lever on a DP51 can also be left either on or off in the fast-action and double-action modes.

When neither a fast-action nor a single-action first shot is chosen, conventional double-action shooting is also possible. Since the DP51 has not been equipped with a hammer-dropping lever, the only way to prepare for a double-action first shot is to lower the cocked hammer very carefully with the thumb while at the same time pulling the trigger. This can be a dangerous process because it makes an accidental shooting quite possible should the thumb slip while the shooter is decocking the hammer. Whether the first shot is made in fast-action, single-action or double-action mode, all subsequent shots are single action, because the slide automatically recocks the hammer upon recoil.

The DP51 used for our testing had comfortable checkered plastic grips. Both front and rear gripstraps used vertical grooving to prevent slippage, although the grip seemed to fit people of different hand sizes effectively. The gun as a whole handles and shoots very well, and despite its light weight, recoil is reasonable with only a slight muzzle flip. The rear sight needs to be a little wider for rapid acquisition, and the white dots—two on the rear sight and one on the front— are too large and distracting (the front sight is also too low).

In range testing, the DP51 proved capable of reasonably good accuracy at 25 feet. Our best five-shot offhand groups measured 1.4 inches using Federal 124-grain Hydra-Shok JHP. Offhand at 50 feet, a five-shot group with Winchester 115-grain Silvertips measured 4.5 inches. When a fast-action first shot was compared to a double-action first shot, accuracy did not seem to be affected. The test pistol never malfunctioned while handling a wide variety of ammunition, including Remington and Cor-Bon +P loads, nor were there any failures to feed or eject. The DP51 owner's manual instructs shooters not to use +P+ ammunition, a limitation that could affect police sales adversely.

How the DP51 holds up in rugged use remains to be seen, although South Korea's armed forces have adopted it. National pride no doubt played a part in the decision, but presumably the pistol passed some rigorous testing as well. Still, neither alloy frames nor the fast-action mechanism have much of a reputation for durability. Aside from these objections, the DP51 is an excellent gun—a good choice.

DAEWOO DP51

Manufacturer	Years Produced	Caliber/Capacity	Dimensions
Daewoo Precision Industries Pusan, South Korea Imported by: Kimber of America Clackamas, Oregon	1992–Present	9mm/13 rounds	Barrel Length: 4.0" O.A. Length: 7.5" Height: 5.1" Width: 1.4" Weight: 28 oz. (unloaded); 34 oz. (loaded)

EAA FAB-92

In addition to the Astra line, European American Armory (EAA) imports the FAB ("Foreign American Brand") and Witness pistols made by Tanfoglio in Italy. These CZ 75-inspired pistols include guns made in 9mm, .38 Super, .40 S&W and .45 ACP cartridges. Tanfoglio/EAA offers a variety of safety arrangements, including ambidextrous units and a FAB-92 version with a slide-mounted, hammer-dropping safety (usually ambidextrous) similar to the Walther pistols. The ambidextrous slide-mounted safety lever, when pushed down to the safe setting, also decocks the hammer. By contrast, the CZ-type manual safety found on the Witness pistols blocks the sear but does not decock the hammer. Otherwise, the FAB-92 is identical to the Witness, including its handling capability. EAA also imports compact models of the Witness and FAB pistols (*see* the companion volume, COMPLETE GUIDE TO COMPACT HANDGUNS).

   The FAB-92 in .40 S&W caliber handles well and boasts excellent natural pointing qualities

Available in 9mm, .40 S&W and .45 ACP, the FAB-92 is comfortable to hold and accurate at close ranges. This five-shot group fired offhand from 25 feet measures 1.5 inches across.

and balance. The trigger pull is acceptable in both single- and double-action modes, although reaching the double-action trigger may be difficult for small-handed shooters (the smooth wooden grips, while attractive, could also present problems for small-handed shooters). Even in rapid fire, the recoil of this pistol was manageable. It was easy, therefore, to achieve rapid-fire offhand groups as small as 1.5 inches from 25 feet away. Moreover, reliability was perfect with a variety of loads and bullet weights.

Perhaps the least desirable features of the FAB are its sights, which are poorly regulated and seem unnecessarily large and likely to snag. Although it was quite accurate at 25 feet, the test pistol fired 5 inches below point-of-aim at 50 feet. The controls were acceptable, but the safety lever was stiff and difficult to move up to its firing position. For safety reasons, some shooters would also prefer the slide-retraction grooves to be located at the rear of the slide, around the safety levers, rather than at the front near the muzzle.

Magnum Research (Minneapolis, MN) imports an Israeli-made version of the Tanfoglio CZ 75 pistol called the Baby Eagle, which is available in .40 S&W caliber and 9mm. And aside from Smith & Wesson, which co-developed the .40 S&W round, EAA boasts one of the world's best .40-caliber handgun lines. Considering that it handles both Astra and Tanfoglio pistols, this single company offers a wide variety of full-sized, single-action and double-action, compact and subcompact pistols, all at competitive prices.

EAA FAB-92

Manufacturer	Years Produced	Caliber/Capacity	Dimensions
Fabbrica d'Armi Fratelli Tanfoglio SpA Gardone, V.T., Italy Imported by: European American Armory, Hialeah, FL	1992–Present	9mm, .40 S&W, .45 ACP/10 rounds	Barrel Length: 4.7" O.A. Length: 8.1" Height: 5.4" Width: 1.4" Weight: 35 oz. (unloaded); 44 oz. (loaded)

EAA WITNESS

The Tanfoglio company, which has been involved in firearms manufacture since the late 1940s, is best known for its small-caliber pistols, but it has also been producing good copies of the famed Czech CZ 75 pistol for more than a decade. These pistols have been imported under different names by various companies. Until recently, most of Tanfoglio's production of CZ clones has been in 9mm Parabellum caliber, with some interchangeability to .41 AE caliber; but in 1992–1993, European American Armory (EAA), in an effort to round out its line of 9mm Witness pistols, began importing Tanfoglio pistols in .38 Super, .40 S&W and .45 ACP calibers.

Like the CZ 75, the Witness is a large-frame, locked-breech, double-action automatic pistol. Construction is all steel and the workmanship is very good. Fit and finish (blued, chrome, Duo-tone or "Wonder") are also excellent. The trigger guard is rounded, rather than squared-off or recurved,

The resemblance between the EAA Witness (top) and the CZ 75 (bottom) is more than coincidental. The Witness has obviously borrowed heavily from the classic Czech design. However, the Witness's hammer can be put on safe even in its uncocked (lowered) position, a departure from the CZ 75 design. Note also the large, upswept grip tang that protects the shooter's hand from contact with the slide or hammer during recoil.

and large enough to accommodate a gloved trigger finger with ease.

The breech-locking mechanism on the Witness features a modified Browning short-recoil system in which, upon recoil, an enclosed lug beneath the barrel locks up with a cam set in the frame. Another feature borrowed from the CZ 75 (which in turn borrowed from SIG's P210 design) is the manner in which the slide sits inside the frame, not surrounding it. This allows for exceptional slide support and also helps create a relatively thin, low-profile slide, causing the pistol to sit lower in the hand than is normally the case with an automatic pistol. Interestingly, the slide on the Witness has serrations at both the rear end, in the conventional manner, and at the front around the muzzle, as in a competition pistol.

Although the box magazine on a .45-caliber Witness has an advertised capacity of 10 rounds, it's difficult to load because of its sharp lips and stiff spring (9 rounds is more like it, but even that takes some doing). The sights feature the popular 3-dot configuration, with a slightly larger dot on the front sight. The rear sight is also quite tall and could conceivably snag on clothing.

The safety mechanisms on the Witness include an automatic internal firing-pin block, which is released only when the trigger is pulled all the way to the rear immediately upon firing. A half-cock notch on the hammer helps lower the risk of accidental firing should the shooter's thumb slip while cocking the hammer. A manual safety lever, located on the left side of the frame, pushes up to safe and down to fire. In its safe setting, the manual safety locks the sear lever, trigger, hammer and slide.

When the safety is in its fire position, a red dot on the frame indicates that the weapon is off its safe setting and can be fired with a pull on the trigger. The safety lever, unlike many others found on this type of gun, can be placed on safe whether the hammer is cocked or uncocked. Again, unlike the safeties on many Tanfoglio CZ copies, applying the manual safety lever on the Witness does not decock the hammer.

When electing to lower the hammer after loading—in order to fire the first shot "double action"—the shooter must first place his thumb on the hammer, then gently squeeze the trigger while slowly and carefully lowering the hammer to its rest position. This is a potentially risky procedure, for if the thumb should accidentally slip off the hammer before it is fully down, the gun could easily fire. Always remember to carry out this procedure with the muzzle pointing in a safe direction.

When disassembled, the EAA Witness breaks down into the following components (top to bottom): slide, barrel, slide stop, recoil spring with guide rod, frame and magazine.

Despite its size, the .45-caliber Witness fits well in the hand and is comfortable to hold. The rear grip tang is generously sized to prevent hammer bite, and the hammer itself is rounded. And because of its low-lying slide assembly and overall weight, felt recoil with this gun is light. As for accuracy, our best five-shot offhand effort from 25 feet went inside 1.6 inches, and from 50 feet the group measured 3.0 inches. Reliability was flawless with every brand of ammunition tested, including Federal Hydra-Shok 230-grain hollowpoints, Remington 185-grain +P hollowpoints, Federal "American Eagle" 230-grain FMJs, and Winchester "USA" 230-grain FMJs.

The EAA Witness fired this five-shot offhand group measuring 3.0 inches from 50 feet away.

Overall, the Witness handles superbly and is well contoured for comfortable carry—even concealed carry, if necessary. Its only weaknesses are the rear sight and difficulties encountered when loading the magazine. But the gun's assets far outweigh any shortcomings it may have. For those who find the full-size gun too big, EAA also imports a compact Witness that also performed well in our testing (*see* COMPLETE GUIDE TO COMPACT HANDGUNS, the companion volume).

EAA WITNESS

Manufacturer	Years Produced	Caliber/Capacity	Dimensions
Fabbrica d'Armi Fratelli Tanfoglio SpA Gardone, V.T., Italy Imported by: European American Armory, Hialeah, FL	1991–Present	9mm/15 rounds .40 S&W, .45 ACP/ 10 rounds .38 Super/19 rounds	Barrel Length: 4.5" O.A. Length: 8.2" Height: 5.6" Width: 1.3" Weight: 35 oz. (unloaded); 45 oz. (loaded)

FÉG

FÉG MODELS FP9/PJK-9HP

In 1982, the Hungarian company FÉG introduced a close copy of Fabrique Nationale's (FN) High
Power pistol (*see* separate listing). It is now imported into the U.S. by
two companies: Century International Arms of St. Albans, VT, which
imports the FP9; and K.B.I., Inc., of Harrisburg, PA, which brings in the PJK-9HP.
Both copies are based on FN's post-1962 version of the High Power pistol, with its
pivoting external extractor, and all parts between the Hungarian copies and the
Belgian originals are interchangeable. Since FN had been producing the High Power
for nearly 50 years, no patent infringement was involved in Hungary's appropriation
of the design, which enabled it to offer a high-quality copy at a much lower price.

FÉG's version of the High Power, originally introduced in 1982 as the FPg, features an attractive
ventilated rib atop the slide, similar to the Colt Python and other deluxe revolvers. The front and rear
sights are carried atop this rib, which has intricate cross-hatching on its upper surface to deflect glare.
It also has a slab-sided slide with no taper all the way to the muzzle. Originally equipped with a spur
hammer, current FP9s use the rounded hammer of the original High Powers (until FN introduced the
spur hammer in 1973). The current version imported by K.B.I., called the PJK-9HP, has FN's old
stepped slide, which narrows near the muzzle. The top of the slide, like the original High Power, has

*FÉG's Model FP9 differs from the PJK-9HP shown above primarily in its prominent ventilated rib located
atop the slide (on which its sights are mounted).*

slightly undersized front and rear sights; otherwise, the FP9 and PJK-9HP are the same and can be considered together.

Basically, it's a single-action automatic pistol with a 13-shot magazine that uses a short-recoil locking system with a lug underneath the barrel (rather than a link as in the M1911). This locking system, first developed for the High Power, has been thoroughly tested over the years in a number of pistol designs and is quite capable of handling the powerful pressures of the 9mm cartridge.

Even though FN has updated the old High Power design with ambidextrous safety levers and

FÉG's PJK-9HP (top), shown here with a World War II-era FN High Power, is an excellent low-cost alternative to the Browning-designed classic.

enlarged sights, the FP9/PJK-9HP still resembles the older model, especiallly the FP9, which has its muzzle bushing flush with the muzzle. The PJK-9HP, in comparison, uses an extended muzzle bushing that protects the crown of the muzzle from damage. Safety features on the FP9/PJK-9HP are typical of the High Power's original design, including its badly undersized manual safety. This small lever goes down to fire and up to safe, with a half-cock notch on the hammer to prevent an accidental shooting should the thumb slip while the hammer is being cocked. FÉG has also retained the High Power's controversial magazine safety, which prevents the pistol from firing once the magazine has been removed.

Externally, the FP9/PJK-9HP is a most attractive, well-made pistol. Its polished blued finish is a dark glossy black, with the magazine Parkerized a dull gray, like current FN magazines made in Italy. The grips, made of hand-checkered hardwood, are usually colored a lighter blond than the dark grips found on the FN. The FP9/PJK-9HP also handles much like the High Power. It comes easily to hand, and the safety, despite being small and rather stiff in operation, wipes down quickly into the fire position. Its sights, although small by modern standards, are acceptable as well.

In testing, the gun reacts well under recoil and comes back onto target easily after each shot. The PJK-9HP performed with complete reliability and excellent accuracy using both FMJ and jacketed

The FP9's prominent sight rib (right) gives it a slightly higher profile than the PJK-9HP.

hollowpoint ammunition. In rapid fire, a loaded magazine (13 rounds) at 15 feet measured only 1.7 inches across. A double-tap (two shots fired as fast as possible) from the same distance went into .9 inch. At 25 feet, another group measured 1.7 inches with Samson 115-grain FMJs. The best 50-foot offhand group measured 2.5 inches, using Federal 9BP 115-grain jacketed hollowpoints. The FP9 tested even better, with one five-shot 25-foot group measuring 1.2 inches and another five-shot 50-foot group measuring 1.9 inches, both with Federal 9BP 115-grain JHPs.

The only real shortcoming of the PJK-9HP is its overly heavy trigger, which requires about 11 pounds before it will release to fire the pistol. This is 3 to 4 pounds heavier than a typical out-of-the-box High Power made by FN.

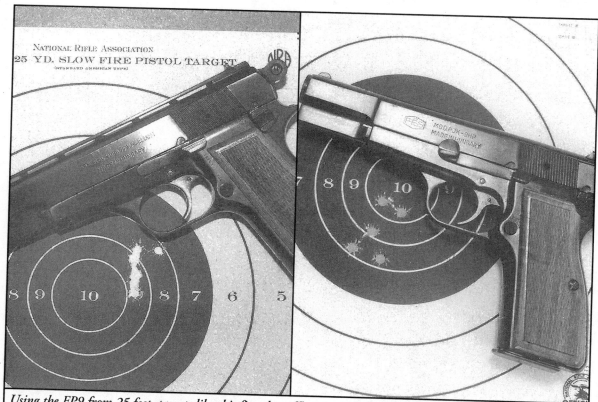

Using the FP9 from 25 feet, targets like this five-shot offhand group measuring 1.2 inches come with ease (left). Similarly, the PJK-9HP from 25 feet produced a five-shot offhand group of 1.3 inches (right), showing they are both comparably accurate.

Both pistols cost significantly less than even the least expensive version of FN's High Power pistol. The FP9/PJK-9HP is an attractive and functional pistol, one that faithfully replicates what many consider the best 9mm pistol design of all time. Those who like the classic FN High Power pistol will most assuredly like the Hungarian versions of this gun as well.

FÉG FP9 AND PJK-9HP

Manufacturer	Years Produced	Caliber/Capacity	Dimensions
FÉG* Budapest, Hungary Imported by: Century International St. Albans, VT & K.B.I. Harrisburg, PA	1982–Present	9mm/10 or13 rounds	Barrel Length: 4.75" O.A. Length: 8" Height: 5.1" Width: 1.3" Weight: 32 oz. (unloaded); 38 oz. (loaded)

* Fégyver es Gazkeszuelekgyara

FÉG GKK-45/P9R

Hungary's armsmakers have a knack for taking established Western handgun designs and modifying them to suit their own export needs. In 1984, for example, FÉG brought out its 9mm Model P9R, and ever since then it has gained increasing respect. The P9R has an interesting history, full of the exciting political events of our times. In 1985, during a slight relaxation of Cold War tensions, two importers — Kassnar and Interarms — were allowed to bring into the U.S. some Eastern European firearms. Included among them was FÉG's new double-action pistol (known as the MBK-9 when imported by Kassnar, and R9 when imported by Interarms). This opportunity lasted only about a year, but during that time the Hungarian pistol attracted much favorable notice from U.S. firearms journals.

By late 1991, with the collapse of the Warsaw Pact and a reduced Russian presence in Eastern Europe, conditions were right for a resumption of trade between the U.S. and the various Eastern European nations, including Hungary. Impor- tation of FÉG's double-action pistol resumed, first by KBI (as the MBK-9HP in 9mm and the GKK-45 in .45 ACP, then in .40 S&W), and later by Century International Arms (as the P9R). As a result, depending on when one of these guns was bought, almost half a dozen names could be used to identify the same pistol.

The P9R in 9mm combines the double-action trigger and decocking lever/manual safety found on Smith & Wesson's Model 39 with the outward appearance, locking system and magazine of Browning's High Power. Although the basic P9R is made completely from steel, a lighter alloy-framed version, the P9RA, is also available. In its fit, finish and workmanship, the P9R is an excellent and extremely attractive pistol, with its dark blue-black finish and honey-colored, checkered hardwood grips. Its slide is milled from solid bar stock, while the frame is an investment casting. To ensure a good hold on the pistol, the frame features a ribbed area — actually a separate piece of black-anodized aluminum alloy — at the lower rear of the gripstrap.

At the front of the grip — in the "toe" posi-

The FÉG GKK-45 (left) is only slightly taller and thinner than FÉG's P9R (right), the 9mm version of the same pistol. The .45-caliber version has a narrow magazine holding 8 rounds in a single column, while the 9mm magazine hold up to 14 rounds stacked in a double-width column.

tion—a small relief has been cut to facilitate magazine removal. In true High Power fashion, this useful feature does not fully eject magazines from the grip, which means the shooter must reach in to draw out the partially ejected magazine. The sights, which are a carryover from an earlier era, are too small for an acceptable sight picture, representing one area in which FÉG lags behind U.S. and Western European armsmakers.

The P9R uses an inertial firing pin instead of an automatic firing-pin safety, and its hammer wears a half-cock notch. The pistol's manual safety lever—down to safe and up to fire—appears only on the left side of the slide. Unlike the High Power and Model 39, which jointly inspired the design of this gun, the P9R does not include a magazine disconnect safety. Its slide is slim and graceful, as on

Reliable and accurate, the GKK-45 produced a five-shot offhand group from 25 feet measuring just 1.4 inches (left). The group on the right, fired from 50 feet, measures a mere 1.8 inches across.

the High Power, but it has a wide grip. Compared to Beretta's Model 92, its grip is shorter and a little wider. It's well-checkered, though, and doesn't require an enormous hand to hold and control it.

The .45 ACP-caliber Model GKK-45 is only slightly taller and thinner than the 9mm version P9R. The GKK-45 has a narrow magazine holding 8 rounds in a single column, while the 9mm magazine holds up to 14 rounds stacked in a double-width column. Otherwise, it combines the graceful external appearance of the High Power with the internal features of S&W's double-action pistols.

Both the GKK-45 and P9R exhibit flawless reliability and excellent accuracy. In test-firing the GKK-45 from 25 feet, results showed a five-shot offhand group measuring just 1.4 inches; from 50 feet another group measured only 1.8 inches. With the P9R, one five-shot offhand effort from 25 feet

FÉG

Like the GKK-45, FÉG's double-action P9R combines features of the High Power with Smith & Wesson's Model 39. Equally accurate from 25 feet, the P9R shot this five-round offhand group, measuring 1.4 inches.

using IMI Samson 115-grain FMJs measured 1.4 inches; from 50 feet using Cor-Bon +P 115-grain JHPs another group covered 4.1 inches And while the double-action trigger pull starts out rough and heavy, it becomes quite smooth just before firing. Overall, it's a superb pistol and much less expensive than the average double-action high-capacity model. Yet it offers performance that is competitive with guns costing hundreds of dollars more.

FÉG GKK-45/P9R

Manufacturer	Years Produced	Caliber/Capacity	Dimensions
FÉG* Budapest, Hungary Imported by: Century International St. Albans, VT & K.B.I. Harrisburg, PA	1984–Present	.40 S&W/9 rounds .45 ACP/8 rounds 9mm/14 rounds (P9R)	Barrel Length: 4.66" O.A. Length: 8.0" Height: 5.4" Width: 1.4" Weight: 36 oz. (unloaded); 43 oz. (loaded)

* Fégyver es Gazkeszuelekgyara

F.I.E. MODEL TZ 75

During the early 1980s, when the demand for CZ's popular Model 75 pistol grew well beyond the point where the small supply of genuine Czech-made pistols could satisfy it, several Western European companies sought to copy this outstanding handgun. The first of these was ITM in Switzerland, which sought at first a licensing arrangement with the Czech firm of Ceska Zbrojovka. By 1984, the Swiss had produced a pistol virtually identical to the Czech Model 75. But when CZ attempted to import its Model 75 pistols directly into the U.S. (via Bauska Arms of Kalispell, Montana), ITM severed its relationship with Ceska Zbrojovka and began making its own version of the pistol, which it first called the AT-84 and later the AT-88. ITM's limited production never approached that of Ceska Zbrojovka, but the Swiss firm's manufacture of Model 75 copies was subsequently revived by the Sphinx Corporation.

After watching the Swiss begin their production of this pistol, Fratelli Tanfoglio of Italy decided to manufacture its own "Model 75," and they've been considerably more successful at making and selling these pistols than have the Swiss. "TZ 75" was the trade name given the Tanfoglio CZ 75 copy imported to the U.S. by the Firearms Import and Export Corporation (F.I.E.) of Florida, before it went out of business. Essentially the same pistol has since appeared under other names and imported by different companies, including Springfield Armory's Model P9 and European American Armory's Witness (*see* separate listings). Even the Jericho and Baby Desert Eagle pistols imported from Israel are Tanfoglio CZ 75 clones, despite their radically altered styling.

Like the Swiss copy, the Tanfoglio model differs from the Czech original. The TZ 75 has appeared in a variety of finishes and with slight stylistic variations, but from a mechanical and operational standpoint two major versions stand out. The first of these had a slide-mounted safety lever that also functioned as a hammer decocker. Some of these had ambidextrous safeties with the lever

The Series '88 was a response to consumer demand that the TZ 75 be more similar in design to the original Czech CZ 75 after which it was patterned. Note the frame-mounted manual safety and the redesigned checkered grips compared to the early-production TZ 75 above.

on both sides of the slide. Then, in the late 1980s, in response to consumer demand that F.I.E. offer a version closer to the original CZ 75, the TZ 75 Series '88 was introduced with a frame-mounted manual safety lever which, when applied, locked the slide, hammer and sear.

Functionally, the TZ 75 is much like any other CZ clone. The only objections to it seem to be the smooth wooden stocks usually found on the pistol, which add noticeably to the width of the grip, and the full-length guide rails, which are more likely to carry dirt into the mechanism (the guide rails of the Czech original are sealed). The fact that Ceska Zbrojovka has absolutely no trouble selling its original CZ 75, which remains in full production at their home factory in Uhersky Brod, suggests that many thousands of satisfied customers feel that any deviation from the original design is probably a step in the wrong direction.

The fit and finish of TZ 75s are usually quite good, and among the variations in finish are blue, satin chrome, and even casehardened and engraved models. The TZ 75 can now be found in gun shops and at gun shows as a used pistol. Due to slight changes in manufacturing techniques, parts for Tanfoglio pistols currently in production, including the EAA Witness and Baby Desert Eagle, may or may not fit perfectly in the older guns imported by F.I.E.

F.I.E. MODEL TZ 75

Manufacturer	Years Produced	Caliber/Capacity	Dimensions
Armi Fratelli Tanfoglio Gardone, V.T., Italy Former Importer: F.I.E. (Firearms Import/Export Corp.) Miami, FL	1980's-1990	9mm/15 rounds	Barrel Length: 4.75" O.A. Length: 8.0" Height: 5.5" Width: 1.45" Weight: 35 oz. (unloaded); 42 oz. (loaded)

FM HI-POWER (ARGENTINA)

In 1970, Argentina arranged to manufacture the FN Browning High Power pistol under license from Fabrique Nationale (FN) of Belgium, the original manufacturer. Since then, this "FM Hi-Power" (nicknamed after its South American acronym) has established a reputation as a solid, well-made and reliable copy of the FN original. During the conflict with Argentina over the Falkland Islands in 1982 the British, ironically, used the exact same pistol; except that theirs—called the L9A1—was made in Belgium.

Several changes have been made to the FM Hi-Power since its introduction. Until the early 1980s, the models had a rounded hammer; but in the late 1980s FM finally went to the spur hammer found on all Belgian-made originals since 1973. The grips on the early Argentine pistols were made of the same checkered hardwood (as in the Belgian High Power) but are now made of more comfortable checkered rubber.

Argentina's FM Hi-Power is an excellent low-cost understudy to FN's original High Power, including interchangeability of parts with the Belgian version. Equally accurate, this 1.3-inch five-shot offhand group was fired with an FM Hi-Power from 25 feet, while a 50-foot group measured only 2.0 inches across.

The FM Hi-Power is a sensational shooter with outstanding accuracy. In testing, our best 25-foot offhand group, using Winchester Silvertip hollowpoints (115-grain bullets), placed five shots in a 1.3-inch pattern. Another five-shot 25-foot offhand group, this time using Norinco 124-grain FMJs, measured 1.4 inches across. Our best five-shot offhand group fired from 50 feet measured only 2 inches.

The FM Hi-Power is a very smooth, good-shooting gun, with a much better trigger than the competing FÉG High Power copy. Moreover, because Argentina set up its factory with FN's help, FM Rosario is a genuine FN licensee, eliminating any question about whether Belgian-made parts will fit its pistols.

FM HI-POWER (ARGENTINA)

Manufacturer	Years Produced	Caliber/Capacity	Dimensions
DGFM* Rosario, Argentina Imported by: Century Int'l Arms St. Albans, VT	1970–Present	9mm/13 rounds	Barrel Length: 4.7" O.A. Length: 7.8" Height: 5.0" Width: 1.2" Weight: 32 oz. (unloaded); 37 oz. (loaded)

* Direccion General de Fabricaciones Militares

FN BROWNING HIGH POWER (.40 S&W)

One of the most exciting handgun developments in years was the marriage of the .40 S&W cartridge and the world-famous FN Browning High Power pistol—a true classic considered by many to be the best handgun available.

Although slightly thicker and higher in the slide—and thus three ounces heavier—the .40-caliber High Power is identical in size to the standard 9mm model. Holding up to 10 rounds—a loss of only three rounds from the 9mm model— its magazine includes an extra spring at the bottom designed to eject rounds forcefully from the magazine well, thus eliminating one of the few negative features of the standard High Power, which required two hands for rapid magazine exchange. Furthermore, Browning's .40-caliber High Power has a heavy trigger pull (approx. 11 pounds), but otherwise it's a sturdy, reliable and reasonably accurate pistol.

Note in the photos that the guns are marked "Browning Arms Company" even though the parts are made in Belgium by Fabrique Nationale.

Ever accurate even in .40 S&W caliber, the FN Browning High Power fired this five-shot offhand group from 25 feet; it measures only 1.2 inches across.

FN BROWNING HIGH POWER (.40 S&W)

Manufacturer	Years Produced	Caliber/Capacity	Dimensions
Fabrique Nationale (FN) Herstal, Belgium Imported by: Browning Morgan, Utah	1993–Present	.40 S&W/10 rounds	Barrel Length: 4.8" O.A. Length: 7.8" Height: 5.1" Width: 1.3" Weight: 35 oz. (unloaded); 41 oz. (loaded)

FN BROWNING HIGH POWER MARK II

The High Power Mark II—an updated version of the High Power—first appeared in 1982. At the time, the venerable FN single-action pistol was rapidly losing market share to a host of more modern 9mm service pistols, many of which offered a double-action trigger mechanism at a considerably lower cost. Thus did FN conceive of the High Power Mark II as a stopgap measure designed to keep FN in the 9mm handgun business until it could develop a more advanced double-action pistol.

In the end, the High Power Mark II outlasted the double-action FN pistol; and although it soon went out of production itself, FN's Mark II introduced a number of improvements that the company still uses on its High Power model. Among them are the Mark II's sights. Earlier High Powers had either tiny fixed sights or adjustable tangent sights. Neither system produced anything close to an adequate sight picture. By contrast, the sights on the High Power Mark II consisted of a large square notch in the rear and a good-sized square post in front, making a sight picture large enough for serious combat use.

From the outset, FN's goal was to adapt the High Power Mark II to allow it to be operated ambidextrously. To do this, FN developed a two-sided safety lever far superior to the tiny manual safety used previously on the High Power. With this ambidextrous safety, the excellent High Power finally

FN Browning's High Power Mark II was an attempt to update the basic High Power design and make it more competitive in the 1980s. The new model featured improved ambidextrous safeties and better sights. Here it is shown disassembled (left) beside the standard .40 S&W High Power.

This five-shot offhand group, measuring 1.4 inches across, was fired with a High Power Mark II pistol from 25 feet. A follow-up five-shot offhand group from 50 feet measured only 1.9 inches across.

became a pistol for left-handers to use as well. Its safety lever is so good that even right-handed shooters swear by it. To augment this improved safety lever, FN developed a new set of ambidextrous thumbrest grips made of thin, checkered black plastic. Although some prefer the earlier thin, checkered hardwood grips, many shooters find that the thumbrest on the grip of a High Power Mark II helps position the thumb near the safety levers—an important consideration for a single-action pistol. The Mark II's plastic grips are also much less expensive than the wooden ones.

To further reduce costs, FN changed the way it built the Mark II pistols. The parts were still made in Belgium, but the pistols were assembled at a new plant in Vianna, Portugal, for much less cost. In addition, a matte phosphate-type finish replaced the polished blued finish of earlier High Powers. The duller finish was less expensive and more preferable for combat use. As a result of these and other cost reductions, FN was able to sell the Mark II for significantly less than their top-of-the-line High Power model.

The Mark II sold fairly well to military forces, but complaints were raised concerning its manufacturing quality. As a result, it could not compete against Beretta, SIG and other manufacturers of advanced new double-action 9mm pistols that were coming on line. Ironically, civilian shooters preferred the fancier standard model, with its more attractive finish and grips, despite the higher price. Disappointed in sales, FN discontinued the Mark II in 1988 and introduced the Mark III the following year.

Despite its lack of commercial success, the Mark II, because of its improved safety and sights, made a significant contribution to the long history of the High Power line. Moreover, serious collectors of High Power pistols will want to own a Mark II. Those who desire a High Power for self-defense only should not consider a Mark II unless and until it's been test-fired first and the price is right. In general, the Mark III (*see* next listing), with all the Mark II improvements and high standard of workmanship, is a better choice.

FN BROWNING HIGH POWER MARK II

Manufacturer	Years Produced	Caliber/Capacity	Dimensions
Fabrique Nationale (FN) Herstal, Belgium Imported by: Browning Morgan, Utah	1982–1988	9mm/13 rounds	Barrel Length: 4.66" O.A. Length: 7.8" Height: 5.0" Width: 1.3" Weight: 32 oz. (unloaded); 37 oz. (loaded)

FN BROWNING HIGH POWER MARK III

The High Power Mark III, which made its debut in January 1989, is the latest version of the High Power line. Basically, it continues where the Mark II left off. All of the Mark II improvements, including an ambidextrous safety, have been retained on the new model, as has the "Made in Belgium—Assembled in Portugal" method of production. Finish options include service matte blue and polished blue, while the grips are either the Mark II's checkered plastic thumbrest style or the original thin checkered wood. A newer version—the "Mark IIIS"—features a firing-pin lock deactivated by the trigger, tritium-illuminated sights for low-light shooting (optional), and a lanyard loop on the lower left rear corner of the frame. Most of the Mark III pistols imported into the U.S. are, for safety and liability reasons, made according to the configuration of the Mark IIIS.

The sights on all Mark IIIs are even better than those found on the Mark II, which were themselves a big improvement over the undersized sights on early High Powers. Both front and rear sights on the Mark III are mounted in dovetails on the slide, from which they can be drifted out, if need be, and replaced. The fixed and adjustable patterns fit the same dovetails, offering a degree of flexibility in sight selection never before available in the High Power line. Quality control on the Mark III, which translates into better fit and finish, plus accuracy, is also an improvement.

Two versions of the Mark III were tested for this book: a standard service Mark III with matte finish, checkered plastic grips and fixed sights; and a Sport Model, with high-polish finish, wood grips and adjustable Millett sights. Both guns handled well, as all High Powers do, but the triggers were only fair. A lot of slack had to be taken up initially before the trigger would break at about 7 or 8 pounds. Unfortunately, the High Power's trigger pull is not especially amenable to improvement, so shooters are best advised to accustom themselves to the standard unaltered trigger. It is, after all, considerably better than those found on earlier High Power pistols or even the modern FÉG High Power copies made in Hungary. It is not a good idea, as some have suggested, to improve trigger pull by removing the magazine safety. Deactivating a safety device on a handgun could lead to real trouble in court should its owner ever need to shoot in self-defense.

In terms of accuracy, a five-shot offhand effort from 25 feet, using fixed sights and Federal 9BP 115-grain JHP ammunition, measured just 1 inch. From 50 feet, a five-shot group expanded to 5.3

The Mark III version of the FN High Power features improved dovetailed sights and better quality control over the Mark II, resulting in better fit, finish and accuracy. To reduce costs and pass the savings along to buyers, the Mark III also offers plastic stocks and a matte finish.

inches with Norinco 124-grain FMJs. Not surprisingly, a model equipped with adjustable sights shot better. One five-shot offhand effort from 25 feet measured 1.4 inches, while another offhand group from 50 feet came in at an outstanding 1.9 inches. Both groups used Winchester Silvertip 115-grain hollowpoint rounds. To ensure that they will feed hollowpoint ammunition reliably, FN has throated the feed ramps of all High Power pistols made since the Mark II model was introduced in 1982.

When all is said and done, the High Power is still the gun to beat among automatic pistols. Slim

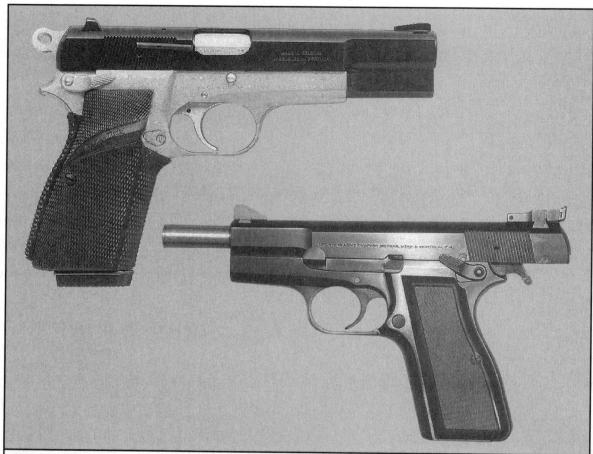

Other variations of the "new" High Power include the HP Practical (left) with fixed or adjustable sights, checkered Pachmayr wraparound grips and duo-tone finish. The Deluxe High Power (right) retains the fancy wooden grips and polished blued finish of the original, but features extended barrel/slide and Millett adjustable sights. Both models are considerably higher in price than the standard Mark III.

and elegant, it handles at least as well or better than most other high-capacity 9mm pistols. The only other 9mm pistol that compares favorably with it is the Czech-made CZ 75, several variants of which are discussed in this volume.

FN BROWNING HIGH POWER MARK III

Manufacturer	Years Produced	Caliber/Capacity	Dimensions
Fabrique Nationale (FN) Herstal, Belgium Imported by: Browning Morgan, Utah	1989–Present	9mm/13 rounds	Barrel Length: 4.66" O.A. Length: 7.8" Height: 5.0" Width: 1.3" Weight: 32 oz. (unloaded); 37 oz. (loaded)

GLOCK

GLOCK MODEL 20

In 1990, after offering it to the
FBI as a possible replacement for
the 9mm Smith & Wesson
Model 469, Glock introduced
the 10mm Model 20. Identical in
design to the tough polymer-frame
Model 17, the Model 20 was enlarged to
handle the bigger, higher-pressure 10mm cartridge. As
other Glock pistols, this one is accurate, reliable and comfortable to

Glock's 10mm Model 20 is available with a "Plus 2" magazine extension that offers two extra shots and a slightly longer gripping surface for large-handed shooters. Note the two-piece trigger; only when the trigger is properly pulled all the way through its travel will the gun fire.

shoot with either a standard full-power load or an attenuated load, i.e. the "10mm FBI" or "10mm Lite." Recoil, even with full-power loads, is not excessive or uncomfortable.

The chief drawback of the Model 20 is its size. Unless the shooter has really large hands, he will probably have difficulty getting a comfortable grip on this pistol. Otherwise, its a relatively light handgun— especially considering its caliber and ammunition capacity— with excellent accuracy in its favor.

GLOCK MODEL 20

Manufacturer	Years Produced	Caliber/Capacity	Dimensions
Glock GmbH Deutsch-Wagram, Austria Imported by: Glock, Inc. Smyrna, GA	1990–Present	10mm/10 or 15 rounds	Barrel Length: 4.6" O.A. Length: 7.6" Height: 5.5" Width: 1.3" Weight: 28.4 oz. (unloaded); 40 oz. (loaded)

GLOCK MODEL 21

In early 1990, Glock brought a prototype of its
.45-caliber Model 21 pistol to the S.H.O.T. show.
But the highly publicized introduction of the Smith &
Wesson/Winchester .40 S&W round at that same show caused
Glock to delay production of the Model 21 until its Models 22 and 23
in .40 S&W could be developed, whereupon Glock turned its attention to production of the Model 21.

Built like all Glock pistols, it has the same safety features and construction
methods. Its chief distinguishing feature, however, is its large 13-round magazine available to law-enforcement personnel. Being chambered for the popular .45-ACP cartridge
has made Glock's pistol a hot seller, especially in the United States. One might think that with such a
large magazine the Glock 21 would be difficult to handle and shoot—but it is not. Like other large

*The Glock .45-ACP Model 21 has the distinctive appearance of this company's other pistols, but it has a con-
siderably larger grip than the 9mm Models 17 and 19. Note the ribbed trigger guard and inner grip designed
for assured handling.*

The .40 S&W Model 22 actually saw production before the Model 21 because of the instant popularity of the .40 S&W caliber that debuted in 1990. Like other Glock pistols, the Model 22 Service is hammerless and features double-action (Safe Action) trigger pull and matte non-glare finish that is 99% salt-water corrosion resistant. For law enforcement, it is supplied with an extra 15-round magazine and accessories.

guns covered in this book, it is well-shaped to enhance its handling qualities as much as possible.

The Model 21 sits low in the hand and has a recoil-dampening polymer frame, making recoil surprisingly gentle despite the gun's relatively low weight. In rapid-fire tests from 15 feet using full 13-round magazines, our best efforts put 13 rounds into groups of 3.6 inches and 2.4 inches, respectively. The highest accuracy was attained with Federal "American Eagle" 230-grain FMJ, but all other FMJ rounds and hollowpoints tested without incident.

GLOCK MODEL 21

Manufacturer	Years Produced	Caliber/Capacity	Dimensions
Glock GmbH Deutsch-Wagram, Austria Imported by: Glock, Inc. Smyrna, GA	1990–Present	.45 ACP/10 or 13 rounds	Barrel Length: 4.6" O.A. Length: 7.6" Height: 5.5" Width: 1.3" Weight: 27 oz. (unloaded); 39 oz. (loaded)

HECKLER & KOCH MODEL P7M10

Although the Heckler & Koch P7 series is best known as a 9mm Parabellum caliber handgun, the company has over the years experimented with alternate calibers. In 1987, it began work on the P7M45, a version of the basic P7 designed to fire .45 ACP ammunition. Unlike the gas-locked P7M8 and P7M13, the P7M45 used an oil-filled buffer to hold the slide shut until gas pressures had died down enough to permit safe opening of the breech. H&K later developed this idea into its small-caliber P7K3 series. Although the P7M45 project proved too expensive, the prototype pistols worked well enough to prove that a P7-type pistol in a heavy caliber could succeed. The introduction of the .40 S&W cartridge in 1992 was just what H&K needed, and soon the company began marketing the .40 S&W version of its P7 as the P7M10 (designating a 10-round magazine).

The construction of this large-frame, gas-locked automatic pistol is all steel, which enhances its durability. The workmanship of the P7M10, moreover, is virtually flawless. Practically the same size as the P7M13 (*see* next listing), its slide is noticeably taller to accommodate the larger .40 S&W cartridge. Despite its size, the P7M10 has clean, simple lines and smooth contours, making it unlikely to snag or catch in one's holster or clothing.

Since H&K was one of the first companies to develop 3-dot sight markings on a production pistol, it comes as no surprise that the Model P710 uses this configuration as well. The heart of its safety mechanisms, meanwhile, is the squeeze-cocking lever, an ingenious mechanism located at the front of the frame (*see* the photo on page 221 for details of this). The .40-caliber P7M10 shoots extremely well. Whereas its P7M13-sized grip is quite large, the roughened grip plates, rear gripstrap and squeeze-cocking lever help make this pistol easy to grasp, even for a medium-sized hand. Felt recoil is light, due to the barrel's position just above the frame, the gun's overall weight and its gas system, which bleeds

In this photo of a disassembled Heckler & Koch Model P7M10, note the remarkably low positioning of the barrel, which helps minimize felt recoil and muzzle jump.

off some of the propellant gas for operating the slide. All H&K pistols tested proved extremely effective in rapid follow-up shots—a valuable asset in any combat pistol.

With all of these positive factors working for it, the P7M10 offers excellent accuracy. Our best five-shot effort from 25 feet measured a remarkable 1.5 inches, using Winchester's "Deep Penetrator"

Heckler & Koch's P7-series pistols use a unique "squeeze-cocker" mechanism, which renders each gun safe to carry and yet ready to fire instantly when needed. When the P7M10 is held loosely, the squeeze-cocking lever at the front of the grip relaxes and the striker remains cocked.

(DP) 180-grain subsonic jacketed hollowpoints. A follow-up five-shot, 25-foot group fired with Winchester's Black Talon 180-grain hollowpoints measured 1.9 inches. And our best five-shot group from 50 feet measured 2.3 inches, fired with Winchester's "Deep Penetrator" 180-grain subsonic jacketed hollowpoints. The best 50-feet, five-shot group using the Black Talon brand measured only

Because of their outstanding quality and design, the Heckler & Koch P7 series of pistols boast excellent accuracy. In testing, the Model P7M10 easily produced this 1.5-inch, five-shot offhand group from 25 feet.

slightly larger (2.4 inches across). The trigger pull is smooth and light, although the squeeze-cocker mechanism takes some getting used to, especially in a pistol with such a large grip.

The P7M10 proved one of the most accurate guns tested for this book. Its overall size might weigh against its use by small-handed individuals, and its high price will scare away still others. Fortunately for those who like the superb H&K quality and reliability—but who cannot or will not pay the steep price—H&K has since introduced the Model USP, discussed in a separate listing on page 229.

HECKLER & KOCH MODEL P7M10

Manufacturer	Years Produced	Caliber/Capacity	Dimensions
Heckler & Koch GmbH Oberndorf-am-Neckar, Germany Imported by: Heckler & Koch, Inc. Sterling, VA	1992–Present	.40 S&W/10 rounds	Barrel Length: 4.1" O.A. Length: 6.9" Height: 5.6" Width: 1.3" Weight: 43 oz. (unloaded); 51 oz. (loaded)

HECKLER & KOCH MODEL P7M13

Heckler & Koch introduced the original PSP pistol—later known as the P7—in 1975. The company's goal was to develop a new service handgun for the West German police, capable of carrying an 8-shot 9mm magazine with the gun loaded and ready to fire instantly but safely until the gun was fired. The P7 sold in large numbers to West German police forces during the late 1970s and was adopted in 1980 as the next West German service handgun. Several years later, the Greek Air Force took it, as have a number of other military and police forces around the world.

In the U.S., several police forces adopted the P7, leading Heckler & Koch to set its sights on the prestigious U.S Armed Forces XM9 pistol trials. With its 8-shot magazine, though, the pistol stood no chance of meeting the U.S. military's requirement of a 10-round or (preferably) larger magazine. To meet this requirement, H&K introduced in 1984 the P7M13 pistol, which was essentially a P7 upper half with an enlarged frame holding a 13-round magazine. The heel-mounted release of the original P7 is relocated to the trigger guard and is ambidextrous. A variation of the 8-shot P7—the P7M8—has the same type of magazine release. Although the U.S. Army eventually turned down the P7M13, several police forces bought it.

With the standards of workmanship at H&K exceedingly high, the fit and finish of the P7M13 are almost artistic in their excellence. The pistol is smoothly rounded off on all edges, but roughened where necessary for a good grip. Two finishes include a durable matte blue or a nickel finish that is especially striking in appearance.

Like the original PSP and P7, the mechanism of the P7M13 delays the opening of the breech by

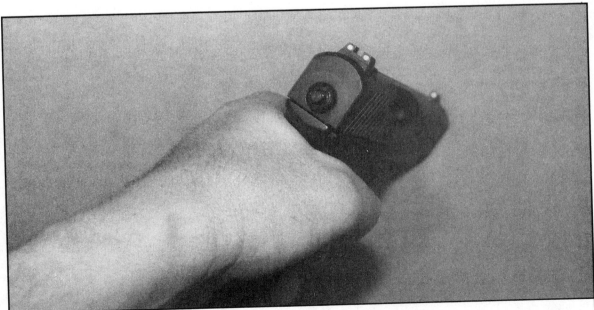

This view from the rear of a Heckler & Koch P7-series pistol shows the "striker cocked" indicator protruding from the rear of the slide. Note also the three-dot sight system, which Heckler & Koch helped popularize in the late 1970s.

allowing a portion of gas pressure to expand into a chamber beneath the barrel. This process holds the slide closed until pressures have dropped to a safe level. Unlike the P9S (*see* following listing), however, the gas system in the P7M13 actually reduces recoil by diverting some of the propellant gases into a lighter, more compact mechanism. It also allows H&K to fix the barrel to the frame for greater accuracy—as opposed to a tilting barrel of the Browning type. The only real drawback of this gas-delay system is that it requires extremely close tolerances and is expensive to manufacture—a problem experienced by Steyr with its similar Model GB (*see* separate listing).

For safe carrying of a loaded pistol, the P7 series features a squeeze-cocking mechanism located in the front gripstrap of the frame. When fully depressed, this "grip safety," if you will, cocks the striker. It then requires only a light pull on the trigger to fire the pistol. Depressing the squeeze cocker, which takes about 20 pounds of force, is really not that difficult, because now the shooter's entire hand (except for the trigger finger) is put to use. Once the squeeze cocker is depressed, it takes only a slight pressure to hold it there. When the shooter relaxes his hold, the squeeze cocker returns to its rest position and uncocks the striker. This squeeze-cocking system is easy for a novice to learn, although hand-gunners who've trained and practiced on more traditional systems sometimes have a rough time adapting to it. For left-handed shooters, any P7-series pistol is an excellent choice, because everything (except for the direction of cartridge ejection) is fully reversible.

In addition to the squeeze cocker, the P7M13 has in common with the P9S an extractor that does double duty as a loaded chamber indicator. When a round is in the firing chamber, the extractor warns the shooter that the gun is loaded. Another feature shared by the P7M13 with the P9S is polygonal rifling, an especially important feature in the P7 pistols with their short barrels and gas-operated actions. Polygonal rifling ensures adequate cartridge velocity by reducing the friction that occurs as the bullet spins down the barrel.

Because of its clever design and incredibly high manufacturing standards, the P7M13 produces stellar accuracy. The excellent sights and trigger pull on this pistol really help shooters get all they can get from this remarkable weapon. Our best five-shot offhand group fired from 25 feet measured a mere 1.5 inches across, using Geco's high-tech 86-grain "Action" cartridges; and our next best group from the same distance using Norinco 124-grain FMJs measured only 1.8 inches across. From 50 feet, a five-shot offhand group fired with the same Norinco ammunition measured 4.2 inches across. The P7M13 experienced no jams during this test-firing with a wide selection of U.S. and foreign-made ammunition, including hollowpoints and FMJ rounds.

Aside from the large grip necessary to accommodate the 13-shot magazine, the P7M13's only weakness is its relatively high cost. If the price is bearable, but the grip is too large, H&K also makes an excellent 8-shot version of the P7 (the P7M8).

HECKLER & KOCH MODEL P7M13

Manufacturer	Years Produced	Caliber/Capacity	Dimensions
Heckler & Koch GmbH Oberndorf-am-Neckar, Germany Imported by: Heckler & Koch, Inc. Sterling, VA	1984–Present	9mm/13 rounds	Barrel Length: 4.1" O.A. Length: 6.5" Height: 5.6" Width: 1.4" Weight: 31 oz. (unloaded); 37 oz. (loaded)

HECKLER & KOCH MODEL P9S

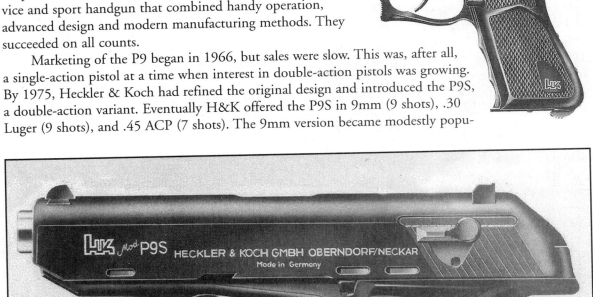

When Heckler & Koch started work on its Model P9 pistol in 1966, the goal was to develop a new service and sport handgun that combined handy operation, advanced design and modern manufacturing methods. They succeeded on all counts.

Marketing of the P9 began in 1966, but sales were slow. This was, after all, a single-action pistol at a time when interest in double-action pistols was growing. By 1975, Heckler & Koch had refined the original design and introduced the P9S, a double-action variant. Eventually H&K offered the P9S in 9mm (9 shots), .30 Luger (9 shots), and .45 ACP (7 shots). The 9mm version became modestly popu-

Introduced by Hecker & Koch in 1975, the P9S boasted excellent quality and accuracy and has armed several military and police forces worldwide.

lar in the U.S. despite its high price. The .30 Luger variant is now quite rare, at least in the U.S.; a 9mm variant is easily converted to this caliber, however, simply by changing the barrel and possibly substituting a lighter recoil spring.

The P9S quickly gained a reputation for extraordinary durability, accuracy and reliability. It went into service with a number of military and police forces, including the Saarland state police and the elite GSG-9 counterterrorist unit in West Germany. Foreign sales were made to the Sudanese military and the U.S. Navy SEALS. The P9S also participated in some of the early testing for a new U.S. armed forces pistol. The limited magazine capacity of the P9S knocked it out of the running after 1980 and it was not entered in the second XM9 pistol trials of 1984. The gun went out of production in the late 1980s and was replaced by the P7 pistol series.

Unique in its construction and workmanship, the P9S locking mechanism uses rollers that, upon recoil, delay the opening of the breech, then open up once pressures have dropped to a safe level. Technically, this is a delayed blowback system, similar in concept to that used on the Czech Vz52 service pistol and the notorious MG42 machine gun of World War II fame. The P9S also uses advanced manufacturing techniques designed to reduce machining to an absolute minimum. These techniques include stamping, pressing and spot welding of components, a barrel that has polygonal rifling, and extensive use of plastics. Unfortunately, the trigger guard is recurved for that style of shooting, one that involves a "first-finger-forward" hold by the support hand. The P9S became one of the first pistols to use this unattractive and snag-prone feature on an otherwise sleek design.

Among the unusual safety features of the P9S is a slide-mounted safety lever on the left side of the slide. When this lever is pushed down ("up" is the fire position), the hammer does not decock. Because the hammer is concealed within the slide, a cocking indicator, which protrudes from the rear of the slide, lets the shooter know when the gun is ready to fire a single-action shot. When a round is in the firing chamber, the extractor rises to function as a loaded chamber indicator. Typical of German design practice, the P9S does not use a magazine safety. A lever used to cock or uncock the hammer is located on the leading edge of the left grip, which forced H&K to place the magazine release in the heel (lower rear) of the frame, rather than behind the trigger guard.

Partly because its barrel recoils in a straight line, the P9S is capable of excellent accuracy. The sights—both fixed and adjustable—are also very good. The trigger pull is light and crisp, running about 9 pounds in double action and 3.5 in single action. The relatively light weight of the P9S translates into heavy recoil, but the gun's good grip shape helps reduce this. It also enhances the pistol's instinctive pointability.

Aside from its limited magazine capacity and rather large dimensions, the chief problem with the P9S during its commercial lifetime was excessive cost (it retailed for well over $1,000 in the late 1980s), forcing H&K to remove the pistol from its catalogs in 1990. Considering the relatively high prices set by Heckler & Koch for its guns, it's reasonable to assume that they continue to sell because their performance is superb.

HECKLER & KOCH MODEL P9S

Manufacturer	Years Produced	Caliber/Capacity	Dimensions
Heckler & Koch GmbH Oberndorf-am-Neckar, Germany	1975–Late 1980s	9mm/9 rounds .30 Luger/9 rounds .45 ACP/7 rounds	Barrel Length: 4.0" O.A. Length: 7.6" Height: 5.4" Width: 1.3" Weight: 28 oz. (unloaded); 32 oz. (loaded)

HECKLER & KOCH MODEL SP89

One of the most interesting pistols in the H&K pistol line is the SP89, which is essentially a semi-automatic version of the world-famous MP5K submachine gun. It has found worldwide use with elite police and military forces and others, including aviators who require maximum firepower in the smallest package possible.

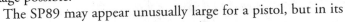

The SP89 may appear unusually large for a pistol, but in its

When compared to a compact automatic like the Walther PPK, the Heckler & Koch Model SP89 is a huge firearm. Basically a 9mm semiautomatic pistol on a submachine-gun frame, the SP89 is well-constructed, extremely accurate and has found worldwide use with elite police and military forces who require maximum firepower in the smallest package possible.

submachine-gun form it's one of the smallest fully automatic weapons that can boast any degree of control and accuracy. Large as it is, the pistol can be worn comfortably on the leg; in fact H&K makes a special holster for this purpose. The MP5K/SP89 can even be concealed in a shoulder holster. Its size provides additional capabilities in mounting extra equipment, such as suppressors or improved sighting gear, beyond what a traditional pistol can be expected to handle.

The front sight on the H&K SP89 features a rugged military pattern with a protective ring. The checkered control in front of it is the cocking handle.

The SP89 is sold with a 15- or 30-round magazine. Mechanically, it has the same roller-locked action as the G3 rifle and is similar to the P9S (*see* preceding listing). Indeed, H&K's entire rifle and submachine gun line, including the SP89, is remarkably similar in construction and operation. This, together with the uncompromising quality and attention to detail shown in the design and construction of these guns, help explain the world-wide popularity of the Heckler & Koch line.

The SP89, with its large size and stability, proves slightly more accurate than most conventional pistols. A five-shot offhand group from 25 feet measured 1.3 inches, using the Winchester Silvertip 115-grain hollowpoint. We also test-fired a five-shot 50-foot group with the Silvertips that measured 2.0 inches across. The SP89 offers total reliability using a variety of ammunition.

Like other H&K firearms, the SP89 is expensive. Moreover, legislation has forbidden the importation of such large

Unlike the MP5K submachine gun that inspired it, the safety level on the SP89 allows semiautomatic fire only.

HECKLER & KOCH

pistols, which means prices for these weapons will go up even further over time. For special service, this interesting gun offers the possibility of rapid and accurate firepower beyond what most pistols can

HECKLER & KOCH MODEL SP89

Manufacturer	Years Produced	Caliber/Capacity	Dimensions
Heckler & Koch GmbH Oberndorf-am-Neckar, Germany	1989–1993	9mm/15 or 30 rounds	Barrel Length: 4.5" O.A. Length: 12.8" Height: 7.9" Width: 2.4" Weight: 70 oz. (unloaded) 77–84 oz. (loaded)

HECKLER & KOCH MODEL USP

In 1993, following a grueling developmental phase that began several years earlier, Heckler & Koch introduced the Model USP. Its testing phases included adverse weather conditions, endurance, water and salt spray exposure, and safety. The testing was successful on all counts. In fact, much of the USP's manufacturing methods and testing procedures duplicated those of H&K's experimental SOCOM Pistol, which was submitted in 1992 for testing by the U.S. military. This pistol in .45-ACP caliber may, in fact, eventually become standard issue to all elite military forces.

H&K's goal in developing the USP was to create a new handgun suitable for military, police and civilian shooters alike. Its performance, moreover, must be equal to or better than H&K's legendary P7, but with features more suitable to American shooters, and with a much lower price. Fortunately, H&K has succeeded on all counts.

Like the P7 series, the USP is made in 9mm, .45 ACP and .40 S&W calibers, with the latter predominating. Its fit and finish are outstanding, with a polymer frame reinforced with steel for added strength, weight and balance. The forward portion of the receiver features grooves on either side to simplify the mounting of a laser sight; and the slide is made of rugged steel.

The Heckler & Koch Model USP, introduced in 1993, features the SIG-type modified Browning locking system supplemented by an innovative doubled-spring recoil buffer. The buffer is visible directly above the rear of the frame in this disassembled view.

Mechanically, the USP utilizes the same modified Browning short-recoil system of operation found in the Glock, SIG, Walther P88 and several other types of pistols. The USP, however, features a unique buffer at the rear of the recoil spring, an innovation that greatly reduces strain on the frame, while at the same time reducing felt recoil slightly.

H&K offers numerous variations on the USP design, such as ambidextrous or single-sided safety levers and double-action-only systems of operation. The pistol used in testing the USP had a one-sided manual safety lever to allow cock-and-locked carry. Like the Colt M1911, this lever pushed up to safe and down to fire; but it could also

Remarkably accurate, the Heckler & Koch Model USP produced this 1.9-inch five-shot offhand group from 25 feet.

be pushed onto its safe setting with the hammer uncocked. The USP has a firing-pin lock, too, which has become almost standard on modern automatic pistols.

The USP's sights, which are dovetailed into the slide for easy replacement or windage adjustment, are large enough to provide a clear, quick sight picture. The trigger pull is smooth and easy in both single-action and double-action shooting. As for accuracy, the test USP seemed to prefer 155-grain ammunition to the larger 180-grain bullets. Reliability was flawless with all ammunition tested, however. Our best five-shot offhand group fired from 25 feet measured 1.9 inches across, while at 50 feet a follow-up group measured 3.4 inches (of which two inches were taken up in the switch from double-action to single-action shooting); hence four shots fired in the single-action mode went into a remarkably tight 1.4-inch pattern. All in all a good performer.

HECKLER & KOCH MODEL USP

Manufacturer	Years Produced	Caliber/Capacity	Dimensions
Heckler & Koch GmbH Oberndorf-am-Neckar, Germany	1993–Present	9mm, .40 S&W, .45 ACP/10 rounds	Barrel Length: 4.1" O.A. Length: 7.6" Height: 5.4" Width: 1.3" Weight: 28 oz. (unloaded); 38 oz. (loaded)

HI-POINT MODEL JC

The origins of the Hi-Point Model JC (also known as the Stallard Arms Model JS-40 and the Iberia Arms JS-40) date back to the 9mm-caliber Maverick pistol introduced in 1987.

After four years, the .40 S&W-caliber JS-40/Model JC came on line in 1991. What makes this big pistol different from most other large-caliber pistols is that it has no locking mechanism to contain the powerful pressure of the .40 S&W cartridge. Instead, it relies upon an unusually heavy slide to prevent the breech from opening prematurely after firing. Although it's certainly safe with the unlocked breech, the Model JC handled the worst of all the Hi-Point pistols tested for this book. Its slide was especially stiff, making loading and cocking the gun a difficult proposition. And because the slide is long and heavy, it amplified the gun's recoil.

Despite the Model JC's acceptable sights and good trigger, the best five-shot offhand group fired from 25 feet measured a disappointing 2.25 inches, though it was well-centered. The truth is, the .40 S&W cartridge may be pushing the limits of blowback operation for this type of pistol—not from a safety standpoint, but from one of rapid and accurate handling.

This five-shot offhand group fired from 25 feet with a .40-caliber Hi-Point Model JC measures a disappointing 2.25 inches across. Note the heel-type magazine release mounted at the bottom of the frame below the disclaimer sticker

HI-POINT MODEL JC

Manufacturer	Years Produced	Caliber/Capacity	Dimensions
Beemiller, Inc. Mansfield, OH	1991–Present	.40 S&W/8 rounds	Barrel Length: 4.5" O.A. Length: 7.7" Height: 5.7" Width: 1.4" Weight: 44 oz. (unloaded); 53 oz. (loaded)

ISRAEL ARMS KAREEN

The Kareen Pistol was originally introduced in 1969 as an export arm and a domestic source for the FN Browning High Power, a very popular sidearm in Israel at the time. Both Israeli civilians and the military have used High Power pistols for many years to supplement Beretta's Model 951, which has seen official issue in Israel since the late 1950s.

In its original form, the Israeli-made Kareen was virtually identical in appearance to the pre-1982 commercial FN Browning High Power, with its polished blue finish, rounded hammer and single-sided manual safety. Subsequent versions included the same spur hammer that had been standard on Belgian-made High Power pistols since 1973, and a built-up fixed barrel bushing to protect the muzzle crown from damage. The finish on the newer Kareen is high-polish blue and its stocks are thin checkered hardwood. Overall, this is an attractive pistol, with fit and finish competitive with those of a 9mm FN High Power.

The Kareen's sights, however, which are too small, and its trigger pull, which is too heavy, are typical of the older FN High Power. The safety lever, unlike that found on many older Belgian High Power pistols, was easy to operate.

Although not quite up to the standard of a Belgian-made High Power or the Argentinian FM Hi-Power (*see* separate listing), the Kareen performs capably. A five-shot offhand group fired from 25 feet measured just 0.8 inch across, but that was unusual. The ammunition used on this group was Hornady's excellent XTP round with 115-grain jacketed hollowpoint bullets. A more typical five-shot 25-foot offhand group measured 2.1 inches. At 50 feet, our best five-shot offhand group measured 3.1 inches. All in all, the Kareen is an interesting pistol, sure to appeal to High Power pistol fans who are looking for something a little different.

Kareen Mark II. The Israelis have updated the original Kareen into a Mark II version, which has been developed over a five-year period in close cooperation with Israeli

Introduced in 1969, Israel's Kareen pistol is a high-quality copy of the legendary FN High Power. An accurate 9mm version, it test-fired a five-shot offhand group from 25 feet measuring a mere .8 inch using Hornady XTP ammunition.

The newer Kareen Mark II features a duo-tone finish, squared trigger guard, ambidextrous manual safety levers and enlarged improved sights.

military and police experts. It offers some of the same improvements to the High Power design made by FN itself, including ambidextrous manual safety levers, enlarged improved sights (mounted in dovetails) and a spur hammer. At the behest of Israeli authorities, some unique changes were made in the Kareen Mark II, too, including a squared trigger guard, an improved trigger mechanism and barrel, and an enlarged, extended grip tang to eliminate, once and for all, any chance of hammer bite. The Mark II stocks are made of either a plastic material, shaped like the standard High Power stock, or an entirely new pattern made from a neoprene-like material, with finger grooves molded into that portion covering the front gripstrap.

Having met or exceeded all requirements in Israel's extensive five-year development program, the Kareen Mark II is certain to make an excellent addition to the famed 9mm High Power family tree. The Kareen continues to offer features and performance on a par with the Belgian High Power's— and at considerably less cost.

ISRAEL ARMS KAREEN

Manufacturer	Years Produced	Caliber/Capacity	Dimensions
KSN Industries Ltd. Israel and Beretta U.S.A. Accokeek, MD Imported by: Israel Arms Int'l Houston, TX	1969–Present	9mm/10 or 13 rounds	Barrel Length: 4.66" O.A. Length: 7.8" Height: 5.0" Width: 1.3" Weight: 32 oz. (unloaded); 37 oz. (loaded)

ISRAEL MILITARY INDUSTRIES (IMI) BABY EAGLE

The Baby Eagle, which Israel Military Industries produces with help from Tanfoglio in Italy, is yet another copy of the world-standard 9mm Czech CZ 75 pistol (*see* page 117). Most Baby Eagles are built in Italy, but their barrels and other components come from Israel. After final assembly, the guns must pass stringent inspections by Israeli quality-control experts. Introduced in 1990 and first imported into the U.S. by KBI as the "Jericho 941," IMI's pistol, now known as the Baby Eagle, is imported by Magnum Research, which also brings in IMI's famous Desert Eagle pistol.

Mechanically, the Baby Eagle is a CZ 75 styled to look like a Desert Eagle. Its construction is all steel, and its workmanship is excellent. The grips are made of plastic with stippling and an IMI logo (a cogwheel, sword and olive branch). The gripstraps, both front and rear, are serrated for a firm hold. The trigger guard is large and squared off in "combat" style, and the front edge is serrated for those who insist on a finger-forward hold. With a 16-round magazine in, one more than the standard CZ 75, the Baby Eagle is easily loaded to its maximum capacity, with three witness holes for checking the ammunition supply.

The sights are large but well-shaped and radiused for concealed carry. Although earlier versions from KBI had a tritium-illuminated 3-dot setup, the current Baby Eagle distributed by Mag- num Research has unmarked sights. They provide an excellent sight picture, however, and are dovetailed into the slide for easy windage adjustment or replacement.

The safety mechanisms on the Baby Eagle differ considerably from those of a standard CZ 75. The ambidextrous manual safety lever— located on the slide, not on the frame—pushes up to fire and down to safe. When the Baby Eagle is pushed down to its safe setting, the mechanism retracts the firing pin, preventing the pistol from firing a chambered cartridge, and

IMI's Baby Eagle pistol may be a Desert Eagle on the outside, but inside it's a CZ 75. In this disassembled view the Baby Eagle's debt to the CZ 75 is obvious.

Like most modern military-style pistols, the Baby Eagle features an ambidextrous manual safety and squared serrated trigger guard. A precision handgun capable of excellent accuracy, it is also able to use a wide range of ammunition. The five-shot offhand group (above) fired from 25 feet with Federal 9BP JHPs measures 1.8 inches. With other 9mm ammo, the results were similar. In .40 S&W, the Baby Eagle was equally accurate, as shown by the five-shot offhand group below. Fired from 25 feet, it measures only 1.2 inches across.

The powerful appearance of the Desert Eagle shown above influenced the outward lines of the Baby Eagle.

then drops the hammer. The safety lever is easy to put on safe, but it's more difficult to move into the fire position.

The Baby Eagle shoots quite well and is extremely accurate for a combat pistol—that is, if you can get a decent sight picture. Although the sights are large, it's difficult to distinguish them against a dark background. Another problem arises with the double-action trigger pull, which is heavy, rough and gritty for a CZ-type pistol. Fortunately, the single-action trigger pull is a big improvement over the double-action first shot.

Unlike many other automatic pistols, this Baby—in any of its caliber offerings, i.e., 9mm, .40 S&W or .41 AE—is a very consistent shooter with almost any brand of ammunition. In the 9mm version, one offhand, 25-foot five-shot effort using Norinco 124-grain FMJs measured 1.7 inches. With Federal 9BP 115-grain jacketed hollowpoints, a 1.8-inch group was fired, and with Winchester Silvertip 115-grain hollowpoints a 2.2-inch group resulted under the same conditions. At 50 feet, the best five-shot group measured 3.5 inches, again using Norinco FMJs, followed very closely by a 3.6-inch group made with Silvertips. This kind of consistency says a lot for the quality and workmanship of the Baby Eagle design.

Likewise, the .40-caliber version we tested handled both 155-grain and 180-grain bullets consistently. For instance, it shot a 1.2-inch, five-round offhand group from 25 feet with very little spread between the double-action first shot and the single-action follow-up shots. Accuracy was good at extended distances, too.

As for reliability, the Baby Eagle proved flawless, with no experiences of ammunition-related failures occurring in our testing. If you like a CZ 75-type pistol, but don't insist on cocked-and-locked capability, the Baby Eagle is a good choice. And the gun's total lack of fussiness about what ammunition it's fed is especially impressive. The Baby Eagle's only weaknesses lie in the difficulty of picking up the sights against a dark background, plus the positioning and movement of the safety levers. Otherwise, this is truly an outstanding gun.

ISRAEL MILITARY INDUSTRIES (IMI) BABY EAGLE

Manufacturer	Years Produced	Caliber/Capacity	Dimensions
Israel Military Industries Ramat Hasharon, Israel Imported by: Magnum Research, Minneapolis, MN	1990–Present	9mm/16 rounds .40 S&W/10 rounds .41 AE/11 rounds	Barrel Length: 4.7" O.A. Length: 8.2" Height: 5.5" Width: 1.4" Weight: 35–38 oz. (unloaded) 45 oz. (loaded)

ISRAEL MILITARY INDUSTRIES (IMI) UZI PISTOL

The world-famous UZI is best known as a submachine gun, but in 1984 Israel Military Industries (IMI) began offering this design as a 9mm pistol. The standard magazine holds 20 rounds, but longer 25-round and even 32-round magazines used in the military-issue submachine gun will also fit and function in the UZI pistol. Later, IMI began to make an alternate version of the pistol in .45 ACP caliber, complete with a 16-shot magazine.

Based on the smallest submachine gun in the UZI line, the Micro UZI, the UZI pistol uses a heavy bolt that's blown back after each shot, making a breech lock unnecessary. In fact, the first thing one notices

The UZI pistol, based on the Micro UZI submachine gun, is a sturdy and reliable semiautomatic pistol. Originally chambered in 9mm with high-capacity magazines holding 20, 25 or 32 rounds, it is also available in .45 ACP with a 16-shot magazine. Note the submachine-gun type cocking handle atop the receiver, just behind the front sight.

about the UZI is its large size—almost 10 inches long and weighing nearly 4 pounds. Its large size also makes it extraordinarily rugged; and although not especially suitable for concealed carry, it's not out of the question to carry one inside a trench coat. Indeed, the current IMI catalog shows a man doing just that—carrying a Micro UZI submachine gun concealed in a shoulder holster under a trench coat. When President Reagan was shot in 1981, for example, U.S. Secret Service agents were observed carrying UZIs in that manner. In general, though, the UZI pistol would seem more useful for home defense or in a vehicle.

The fit and finish on the UZI are excellent even though the pistol is built mostly of sheet-metal stampings. Functionally, it's identical in operation to the UZI submachine guns, except that it lacks a selective-fire feature and is therefore capable of semiautomatic fire (i.e., one shot for each pull of the trigger) only. The safety lever, located on the top of the frame on the left side, pushes forward to fire and back to safe. The magazine release is located at the bottom of the grip on the left side only, while the ambidextrous cocking handle is found at the top of the receiver. When pulled straight back, this handle forces the bolt back, cocks the hammer, and allows the top round from the magazine to enter the firing chamber. Because the bolt does not remain open after the last shot has been fired, no slide lock or release is required. The sights, which are protected by large military-style ears, are highlighted with white dots for easier aiming—one on the front sight and two on the rear.

Despite its large size and vertical grip that make for rather awkward handling, the UZI pistol is still reasonably accurate. The grip safety is stiff and some shooters may find it difficult to depress. In the UZI pistol's favor, though, are its incredible sturdiness and utter reliability. Shooters also like the way the magazine reloads, pistol-style, into the grip rather than in front of the trigger guard.

Tactically, the UZI pistol is similar to the American Arms Spectre, the Heckler & Koch SP89, the Intratec TEC-9 and the Steyr SSP—and it's as good as any one of them. If size and portability are not a consideration, the UZI pistol is worth considering as a defensive handgun, especially in a truck or boat.

ISRAEL MILITARY INDUSTRIES (IMI) UZI PISTOL

Manufacturer	Years Produced	Caliber/Capacity	Dimensions
Israel Military Industries Ramat Hasharon, Israel Former Importer: Action Arms Philadelphia, PA	1984–Present	9mm/20, 25 or 32 rounds .45 ACP/16 rounds	Barrel Length: 4.5" O.A. Length: 9.5" Height: 7.2" Width: 1.5" Weight: 58 oz. (unloaded); 68 oz. (loaded)

NORINCO MODEL OF THE 1911

Norinco's .45-caliber Model M1911 represents
one of the best efforts yet toward making a copy of
the original U.S. military-style Colt M1911A1 pistol used in World
War II and beyond. Best of all, it's reasonably priced. Early versions built
in the late 1980s were, except for their markings, virtually identical to government-
issue M1911A1 pistols of the World War II period, but Norinco .45s currently
issued have slightly bigger sights and a 3-dot sighting system. Grips are mostly brown
checkered plastic, although checkered wooden grips are also available. In addition,
many of the custom grips made for Colt and other 1911-type pistols will fit this gun as
well. In fact, there's at least some partial interchangeability of parts between this Norinco pistol and
other M1911 variants made by various manufacturers.

Norinco's Model of the 1911 (top) is not as elegant as Colt's stainless steel Enhanced Government Model (bottom), but it offers competitive performance at much less cost. Inset: Shown back to back, the similarities between Norinco's Model of the 1911 (left) and Colt's Enhanced Government Model are obvious.

The Norinco M1911 shoots well and is exceptionally accurate. Don't be fooled, though, by its looks—this won't shoot sloppily like a well-worn military-issue pistol. The Chinese lavishly hand-fit this and other Norinco handguns, like the Type 59 (Makarov) and TU-90 (Tokarev), to make them even more accurate, hence more competitive in a tough, crowded market. Our best five-shot offhand effort measured 1.6 inches at 25 feet, using ChinaSports 230-grain FMJ ammunition (which Norinco also makes). At 50 feet another five-shot offhand group, fired with Remington's hot 185-grain +P jacketed hollowpoints, patterned within 3.5 inches. In fact, this same gun performed with near flawless reliability throughout the testing, even though one of the loads used was the 200-grain CCI/Speer jacketed hollowpoint. This bullet, nicknamed the "Flying Ashtray," has a huge open hollowpoint cavity and is notorious for jamming unmodified military-type M1911 pistols—but not the Norinco.

Indeed, the only shortcoming experienced with the Norinco "Model of the M1911" was its trigger, which is heavy and quite stiff. Since the trigger design lends itself well to modification, however, this condition can be easily corrected. But even with the trigger pull left as is, this is still a great-shooting gun, preferred by many over the competing Auto-Ordnance or Colt M1991A1 models. Best of all, it's reasonably priced.

Norinco's Model of the 1911 is surprisingly accurate. This well-centered five-shot offhand group fired from 25 feet measures 1.6 inches. From 50 feet an offhand group measured 3.5 inches across and would have been tighter if the pistol had better sights.

NORINCO MODEL OF THE 1911

Manufacturer	Years Produced	Caliber/Capacity	Dimensions
Norinco* Beijing, China Imported by: ChinaSports Inc. Ontario, CA	1980s–Present (Importation halted 1995)	.45 ACP/7 rounds	Barrel Length: 5.0" O.A. Length: 8.5" Height: 5.4" Width: 1.3" Weight: 39 oz. (unloaded); 46 oz. (loaded)

* China North Industries Corporation

NORINCO MODEL TU-90

Although Norinco's TT-33 "Tokarev" pistol has always been a rugged and reliable weapon, until recently it was not widely available in a configuration that suited it well for modern handgunning techniques as practiced in the U.S. But with the advent of its Model TU-90 (imported by Navy Arms), the old Soviet Tokarev design has finally come of age. This latest clone, chambered in 9mm Parabellum, interchanges with the original 7.62 X 25mm caliber (and, with a little extra work, to .38 Super as well). These alternate calibers are achieved by switching barrels, recoil springs and magazines.

What makes the TU-90 unique and more useful among the Tokarev variations are its manual safety, which pushes forward to fire and back to safe, and its grip. Indeed, the TU-90 is the first Tokarev-type pistol with such a convenient safety procedure. Most Tokarev copies found in the West either have no manual safety at all, or they have an awkward manual safety that moves backward to the fire position, similar to cocking the hammer. (For more details on the Tokarev, *see* page 148).

The grips have a well-shaped, ribbed pattern similar to those of a Walther P.38 from World War II days. This combination of a good manual safety and an ergonomic grip makes the TU-90 a viable combat pistol. Ironically, this "new" pistol is almost identical to the Tokagypt pistol first made in Hungary in 1958 and offered to Egypt's armed forces in a bid for the contract won by the Beretta Model 951. About 15,000 Tokagypts, many of which were marked "Firebird," made it into Europe and a few wound up in North America; but the great improvements in their design went unnoticed and uncopied until the U.S. importer, Navy Arms, convinced Norinco that it should offer a Tokarev-type gun with the improved grips

Two improvements in the TT-33 pistols, revealed in this disassembled TU-90 (shown), are the packaged hammer mechanism and locking ribs machined all the way around the barrel.

The grip on the TU-90 has been enlarged in the manner of the Hungarian Tokagypt pistol, extending well beyond the frame (bottom rear) to improve pointability over other Tokarev pistols. Inset: The TU-90's grips can be easily removed and standard Tokarev grips installed for improved concealability, if desired, although pointability and handling will suffer.

and safety mentioned above.

Along with these improvements, the TU-90 retains all the features that made the original Tokarev a great pistol. Those include the simplified M1911 construction and the rugged reliability of the original Soviet service pistol. The trigger is single-action-only, construction is completely from forged and machined steel, and a matte blued finish is standard. Fit and finish are reasonably good, although the enlarged grips fit the frame with some gapping. The TU-90's box magazine holds eight rounds and is easy to load. The sights are typical Tokarev-style, sturdy but slightly undersized.

The safety mechanisms include a half-cock notch on the hammer, an inertial firing pin, and a manual safety lever located on the left side of the frame. In its safe setting, the manual safety locks the sear lever, trigger, hammer and slide. Interesting to note, the manual safety can be placed on safe whether the hammer is cocked or uncocked. The TU-90's rounded grips help instinctive pointing, while recoil is light, making the gun comfortable to shoot.

In test-firing the standard Tokarev pistols, our groups, though tight, tended to be high, due mostly to the unergonomic grips and sights. On the other hand, it was much easier to shoot to point-of-aim with the TU-90. Our best five-shot 25-foot group measured only 0.9 inch across, using 115-grain

The TU-90 is extremely accurate, as demonstrated by this five-shot offhand group fired from 25 feet and measuring just 1 inch across.

Winchester Silvertip hollowpoints. With other types of ammunition, a five-shot group from 25 feet measured about 2.5 inches. From 50 feet away, using Silvertips again, we were able to shoot a group that measured 2.3 inches across. Other groups fired from 50 feet measured 3.3 to 4.1 inches across. The trigger pull was much smoother and lighter than we experienced with previous Chinese-made Tokarev copies. Following only a slight creep, the trigger released crisply.

Overall, the TU-90 handles and shoots well. If necessary, it would be easy to fit the standard Tokarev grips to the TU-90 for added concealability. The only weaknesses are its slightly undersized sights and no ambidexterity in its operating controls, particularly the safety lever. Aside from that, the TU-90 offers real value in a 9mm pistol and is by far the best combat pistol among the Tokarevs.

NORINCO MODEL TU-90

Manufacturer	Years Produced	Caliber/Capacity	Dimensions
Norinco* Beijing, China Imported by: Navy Arms Co. Ridgefield, NJ	1990–1995	9mm/ 8 rounds	Barrel Length: 4.5" O.A. Length: 8.0" Height: 5.0" Width: 1.2" Weight: 31 oz. (unloaded); 35 oz. (loaded)

* China North Industries Corp.

PARA-ORDNANCE P14·45

The Para-Ordnance company first entered the gun business in 1985 with a training pistol that used dye-filled projectiles. Once this product was safely on the market, the company directed its efforts toward developing a pistol that combined the legendary power, accuracy and reliability of Colt's classic M1911/Government Model with a high-capacity magazine.

This ambitious project (some said it couldn't be done) began in 1989 as a conversion kit intended for use with a Colt Government Model Series '80. Para-Ordnance supplied an enlarged frame, a 13-round magazine and its release, a trigger (and associated components), a recoil spring and buffer, a metal filler for use with pre-Series '80 Colts, and new grips and screws. Buyers of this kit could then disassemble their own Colt Government models and use the parts to assemble a new 13-shot .45-caliber pistol with what amounted to a Colt upper half and a Para-Ordnance bottom half. Series '70 Colt Government models, along with Auto-Ordnance M1911A1 versions of the Colt design, have also been successfully converted to Para-Ordnance configuration but only with insertion of the metal filler (or plug) mentioned above. Other Colt M1911 copies would probably require various degrees of fitting to accept a Para-Ordnance high-capacity magazine and frame, or might not work with the Para-Ordnance kit at all. Before adding this conversion kit to any .45-caliber pistol, though, check with a gunsmith who has some experience in working with this product.

In 1990, Para-Ordnance got more ambitious and began building its own complete pistols, among them the Model P14·45. This full-sized, 5-inch barrel pistol is available in an alloy-framed model, which weighs almost exactly the same as Colt's steel-framed Government Model, and in all-steel or stainless steel models weighing 10 ounces more. The finish is available in all black (steel or alloy frame), duotone or stainless (stainless frame only). The box magazine on the P14·45 has an advertised capacity of 13 rounds

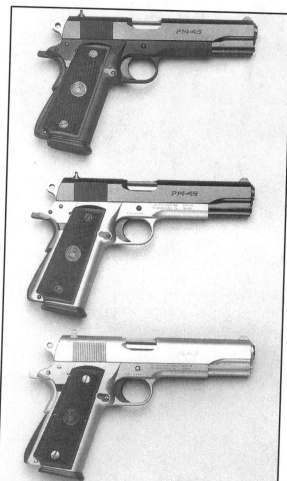

The P14 in .45 ACP is a well-made Colt 1911A1 look-alike and is available with an alloy, all steel or stainless steel frame/receiver with matte black (top), duotone (center) or stainless finish (bottom).

for law-enforcement purposes (10 rounds for recreational use). The "P14" part of the designation, incidentally, comes from the idea that a person can carry this pistol cocked and locked, with an additional round in the chamber, for a total of 14 rounds. The P14 is now also available in .40 S&W caliber with a 3.5-inch barrel.

Other full-size offerings in this series include the P13 in .45 ACP with 4.25-inch barrel; P15 in .40 S&W with 4.25-inch barrel; and the P16 in .40 S&W with 5-inch barrel. A smaller Officer's ACP-sized pistol with 3.5-inch barrel called the P12·45 also went into production, as did a still smaller P10 in .45 ACP or .40 S&W with 3-inch barrel.

These Para-Ordnance guns use a firing-pin lock, a grip safety, and a thumb safety that's pushed down to fire and up to safe. The ejection port is slightly relieved (beveled) to enhance reliability and to spare the shooter's brass for reloading purposes. The workmanship throughout is excellent. The pistol tested had a businesslike matte black finish that looked much like the Parkerizing on a Colt M1991A1. The sights are high-profile and use a 3-dot sighting system— much like the improved sights used on Colt Government models, rather than the skimpy sights of old military M1911A1 models.

Incredibly, the grips on the Para-Ordnance P14·45 are hardly larger than those found on the standard Government Model, even though the pistol holds five or six more shots (depending on whether it's compared to an older Government Model with a seven-shot magazine or a newer one with an eight-shot magazine). Moreover, the Para-Ordnance grip is more circular than the Colt's and more comfortable to shoot compared to the Government Model's longer, elliptically shaped grip, which tends to twist in one's hands upon recoil.

Although the magazine is difficult to load all the way to its full capacity because of its stiff spring, the handling and shooting qualities of the Para-Ordnance P14·45 are generally good. The pistol, which is large and substantial, feels good in the hand, even over a long period of time. As for accuracy, our best efforts firing five-shot offhand groups measured 2.6 inches at 25 feet and 6.5 inches at 50 feet. Recoil is noticeable but travels straight up and back, without the twisting problem some shooters have experienced with the standard Government Model.

Reliability was flawless. The P14·45 handled every brand of ammunition tested successfully, including Federal Hydra-Shok 230-grain hollowpoints, Remington 185-grain +P hollowpoints, Hansen 230-grain FMJs, and Norinco/China Sports 230-grain FMJs. The test pistol was most accurate, however, with the Hansen FMJs and least accurate with the Winchester Silvertips. This disparity was almost certainly a characteristic of that particular pistol; indeed, any given pair of nearly identical guns, originating within a few serial numbers of each other in the same production range, may shoot quite differently from one another. That's another reason to test any new gun with as many brands of ammunition as possible before making a commitment.

PARA-ORDNANCE P14·45

Manufacturer	Years Produced	Caliber/Capacity	Dimensions
Para-Ordance Mfg. Scarborough, Ontario, Canada	1990–Present	.45 ACP/10 or 13 rounds	Barrel Length: 5.0" O.A. Length: 8.5" Height: 5.4" Width: 1.4" Weight: Alloy—30 oz. (unloaded); 41 oz. (loaded) Steel—40 oz. (unloaded); 51 oz. (loaded)

RUGER MODEL P85/P89

Rumors that Sturm, Ruger would have an American-made high-capacity 9mm double-action automatic pistol ready for the U.S. Armed Forces XM9 pistol trials in 1984 proved false. Despite tantalizing glimpses of pre-production models hastily described by gun magazines anxious to be the first to report on the new Ruger pistol, it was not until 1987 that the long-awaited "P85" finally appeared in series production.

The Ruger P85 series has gone on to a highly successful career with law-enforcement and private individuals, along with a few military units abroad. Modified P85s even competed against Beretta's M9 and Smith & Wesson's Model 459M in the second XM9 pistol trials of 1988–1989. Although the Beretta won for the second time, the Ruger pistols reportedly performed well.

Since the appearance of the original 9mm P85, Ruger has not rested on its laurels. Beginning in 1990, numerous derivative models have been introduced, including several stainless steel versions. Other new pistols appeared in decocking-only and double-action-only versions in .45 ACP and .40

Introduced by Ruger in 1993, the 9mm P89 is available with blued or stainless slide and in manual-safety, decock-only (DC) or double-action-only (DAO) configurations.

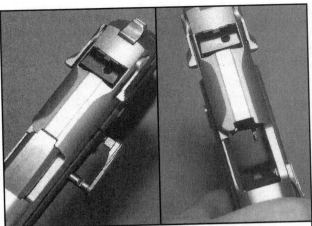

Ruger's Model P85, like other 9mm handguns designed for the U.S. M9 and M10 service trials, is well set up for ambidextrous operation. When disassembling the P85, the slide stop lever (left) cannot be removed completely from the frame (to prevent its loss). To complete disassembly, the ejector must be pushed down (right), but only after the slide has been locked open.

S&W as well as in 9mm. Even as late as 1993, compact versions with shortened barrels and slides made their debut. Nevertheless, all Ruger P85-series automatic pistols have in common durable construction, reliable operation, and highly competitive pricing.

Noteworthy is the fact that Ruger's P85 uses a breech-locking mechanism, in which the swinging barrel link of the veteran M1911 model combines with the rear end of the barrel, which is locked into the top of the ejection port. The absence of lugs normally milled into the top of the barrel saves money by eliminating a machining operation. Indeed, it's the same system used on the Browning BDM, the SIG P220-series pistols and the Walther P88, among other advanced designs.

All Ruger P85-series pistols now in use feature investment-cast steel slides and strong but lightweight aluminum-alloy frames. Recent experiments at Ruger with titanium frames could presage a huge step forward in gunmaking. While titanium weighs only about half as much as steel, it is even stronger. In addition, Ruger's extensive use of investment casting (the company helped pioneer this technique in the firearms industry) allows the company to hold down costs. Although Ruger P85-series automatic pistols have wide slides, their frames are thinner than those of most competing 15-shot pistols, with the exception of the Browning BDM, the Glock models and Colt's Model 2000.

All P85-series pistols test-fired for this book proved accurate and reliable. Using an original P85, our three best five-shot offhand efforts measured 1.2, 1.7, and 1.8 inches, respectively, from 25 feet using (in the same order) 124-grain Norinco FMJs,

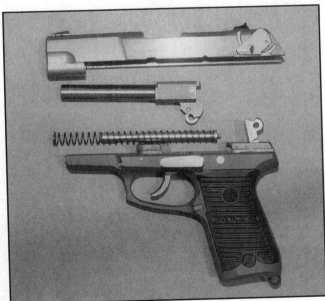

The P85, shown disassembled, features the famous Browning short-recoil system of breech locking. Note that the Petter-type squared barrel top is allied with an M1911-type link located beneath the barrel. The slide is made of stainless steel, while the frame is a lightweight but strong aluminum alloy.

115-grain Winchester Silvertips, and 124-grain Winchester FMJs. With a P89 made in 1993, a five-shot offhand group went into 1.4 inches with 115-grain Winchester Silvertips and 2.5 inches with Norinco FMJs. The best five-shot 50-foot offhand groups measured 2.4 inches using Winchester 115-grain Silvertip hollowpoints and 4.7 inches with Norinco FMJs.

Among its odd handling traits, the P85's magazine release, which is conveniently ambidextrous, pushes forward to release the magazine. The single-action trigger has an extremely long pull with a lot of slack to take up before the pistol fires. On most models, the slide has no cocking serrations; this forces the shooter to grasp the rear of the slide by the ambidextrous safety levers. Also, when disassembling this pistol, once the magazine has been removed and the slide is locked, the shooter must reach into the open ejection port area in order to push the ejector down by hand. Only then can the slide be removed from the frame. And lastly, this Ruger pistol, with its wide slide and narrow grip, has a heavy recoil. Once you get used to these minor oddities, though, a Ruger P85-type pistol shoots quite well.

RUGER MODEL P85/P89

Manufacturer	Years Produced	Caliber/Capacity	Dimensions
Sturm, Ruger & Co. Southport, CT	1987–1993 (P85) 1993–Present (P89)	9mm/10 or 15 rounds	Barrel Length: 4.5" O.A. Length: 7.8" Height: 5.4" Width: 1.5" Weight: 32 oz. (unloaded); 39.5 oz. (loaded)

RUGER MODEL P90

When Sturm, Ruger and Company joined the .45-caliber pistol lineup in 1991, it did so with not one but two guns: the P90 and P90D. Both models are nearly identical in size, appearance and construction to Ruger's 9mm Model P85 (*see previous listing*), except they carry seven-shot magazines (in .45 ACP) and have more substantial slides. The standard P90 features a conventional hammer-dropping safety lever (the P90D has a spring-loaded decocking lever), is strongly built and extremely reliable.

When Ruger first announced this pistol, it was hoped by many that its large P85-type frame, which holds 15 shots in 9mm, would accommodate a large number of .45-caliber rounds. But when the seven-round pistol actually arrived, many shooters expressed disappointment at

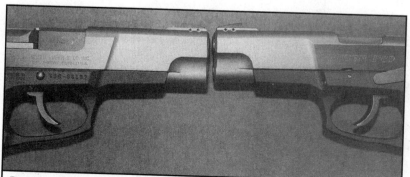

Because of the greater size of its .45 ACP cartridge, the P90 (left) has a slightly thicker and taller slide than the 9mm P89 (right). In addition, the P90 holds only seven rounds.

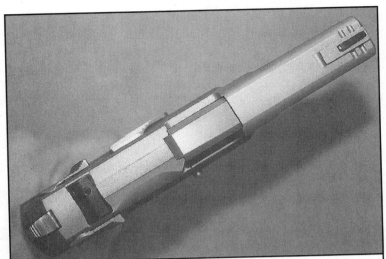

This top view of the P90 shows its SIG-type locking system, with the rear end of the barrel mating with the squared rear section of the ejection port. Note also the ambidextrous safety levers.

the magazine capacity. Moreover, the magazine release, unlike Ruger's 9mm pistols, was not ambidextrous (although no problem exists for a left-handed shooter in operating the magazine release with the trigger finger).

Fortunately, all such disappointments disappeared at the shooting range, for the P90 is both accurate and reliable. A five-shot offhand group fired from 25 feet measured only 1.1 inches (all bullet holes touching), using Federal 230-grain FMJs. From 50 feet, another five-shot offhand group measured 3.9 inches, with the same ammunition. Recoil is

A modern, accurate pistol, Ruger's P90 fired this five-shot offhand group from 25 feet; it measures just 1.1 inches.

greater than that of the tried-and-true M1911, but is by no means unmanageable. This added recoil can be attributed to the P90's lightweight alloy frame and its higher bore axis. Typical of a Ruger double-action automatic pistol, the P90 has a long, heavy double-action trigger followed by a much lighter single-action trigger stroke with considerable slack, all of which makes this pistol's trigger pull something to get used to. Still, the Ruger P90 is an excellent (and inexpensive) choice for military, police or civilian use. While it's not as smooth as the SIG P220 (*see* separate listing), the P90 is every bit as effective.

RUGER MODEL P90

Manufacturer	Years Produced	Caliber/Capacity	Dimensions
Sturm, Ruger & Co. Southport, CT	1991–Present	.45 ACP/7 rounds	Barrel Length: 4.5" O.A. Length: 7.9" Height: 5.5" Width: 1.5" Weight: 33.5 oz. (unloaded); 40.5 oz. (loaded)

RUGER MODEL P91

Ruger added a .40 Auto caliber P85-type pistol to its line in 1991, the same year the company introduced the .45-caliber Model P90. The P85's platform, which is a bit thick for a 9mm cartridge, is a natural for the .40 Auto cartridge. Like the P85 and P90, Ruger makes the P91 in several operating modes. The P91DC is a conventional double-action pistol that switches to single action for follow-up shots and has ambidextrous decocking levers to lower the hammer after loading. A double-action-only version — the P91DAO — is also offered. The KP91DAC features a push-forward firing-pin safety system, ambidextrous decocking levers and a short-throw 45° decocker lever arc. All Model 91s feature stainless steel slides and alloy frames. Unlike the Model P90 in .45 ACP, the P91 has an ambidextrous magazine release.

The Model P91DC

The Ruger .40-caliber Model P91 shot this 3.5-inch five-shot offhand group from 50 feet, with four of the five shots going into a 2.3-inch pattern.

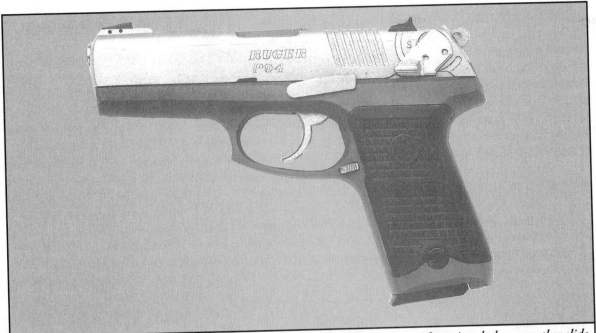

Inspired by the compact P93, Ruger introduced the P94 in 9mm and .40 Auto featuring sleeker, smoother slide contours than the P85 series, plus an improved grip design and "Terhune Anticorro" stainless steel for maximum corrosion resistance. Note the design differences at the muzzle compared to the P91.

tested for this book proved to be an excellent shooter. The two best five-shot offhand groups measured 2.5 inches at 25 feet, one using Winchester Super-X and the other Federal's Hi-Shok, both with 180-grain bullets. Our five-shot 50-foot offhand group measured a near-perfect 3.5 inches with the Federal ammunition.

Despite its spongy double-action and creepy single-action triggers, the P91DC is an easy pistol to shoot effectively in rapid fire situations. Recoil is mild—much gentler than with the .45 caliber P90—and the sights are excellent. The grip feels good in the hand and the trigger reach, while a trifle long, proved manageable in medium-sized hands.

The newer P-Series Model P94, also with 4.5-inch barrel, is available in both .40 Auto and 9mm with 10-round magazine capacity—in manual safety, double-action-only or decock-only configurations. Inspired by the compact P93, the P94 features sleeker, smoother slide contours than the P85 series, plus an improved grip design and "Terhune Anticorro" stainless steel for maximum corrosion resistance.

RUGER MODEL P91

Manufacturer	Years Produced	Caliber/Capacity	Dimensions
Sturm, Ruger & Co. Southport, CT	1991–1995	.40 Auto/11 rounds	Barrel Length: 4.5" O.A. Length: 7.9" Height: 5.4" Width: 1.5" Weight: 33 oz. (unloaded); 41 oz. (loaded)

SIG P220 SERIES

The P220 first appeared as a 9mm pistol in 1974–1975 to compete in West German and other European military and police service pistol trials. Walther's former dominance of West Germany's military and police handgun market was finally being replaced by a sharing of markets with other manufacturers. The handgun specifications that had spawned Walther's P4 in 1975 and P5 in 1979 also spurred SIG-Sauer—a Swiss-West German partnership—into creating its own competing designs: the 9mm P220 and P225 pistols, introduced in 1975 and 1978, respectively.

Because of Switzerland's neutrality laws, the Swiss-based SIG (the abbreviation for "Schweizerische Industrie Gesellschaft" or in English "Swiss Industrial Company") firm was forced to sign a contract with Germany's J.P. Sauer & Sohn before it could actually build the P220. Thus, these pistols are sometimes known as "SIG-Sauers," and their left slide flats are so stamped. By the mid-1980s, SIG bought out J.P. Sauer & Sohn, which became a subsidiary of the Swiss firm, not an equal partner; hence, the pistols are now usually referred to as just "SIGS."

As a result of the West German pistol trials, the German police officials did not buy the original P220, but it made a very favorable impression in Germany, Switzerland and Japan. The German police indicated that a smaller version—7 inches long and 5 inches high—would be better received. In 1978, SIG matched Walther's development of the P5 by submitting its improved P225 design. A smaller version of the P220, this 3.9-inch barrel pistol lost only one round of magazine capacity (totaling eight rounds in 9mm), its magazine release having been relocated to the rear of the trigger guard, American-style, rather than in the heel of the newly improved grip. Known in West Germany as the P6, the P225 received widespread acceptance there among state police forces.

The P225 above, introduced in 1978, was a smaller version of the P220 pictured above right. With its shorter 3.9-inch barrel, the P225 better met the needs of the West German police forces and was known there as the P6.

Late in the 1970s, the Browning Arms Company, noting the P220's global success, arranged to import the P220 into the U.S., calling it the Browning BDA (for "Browning Double Action"). Anticipating the lack of interest among American shooters in 9mm pistols—this was years before the U.S. armed forces adopted Beretta's Model 92—Browning talked the SIG-Sauer consortium into

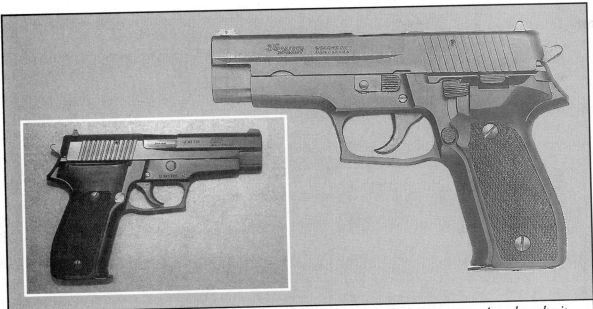

The P226 competed fiercely in 1984 against the Beretta 92F for U.S. military acceptance. An enlarged grip frame with 15 rounds of 9mm ammunition made it very attractive for service use. Note, however, in the inset that there is no decocking lever on the right side, making this model unfit for ambidextrous operation.

adding the "All American" .38 Super and .45 ACP cartridges to the P220's caliber offering. For some reason, despite its many excellent features, the BDA version of the P220 failed to excite American pistol buyers. Perhaps it was still too early in the game for a double-action pistol. Eventually, of course, the U.S. military accepted Beretta's Model 92 and the floodgates were opened, not only for the concept of a 9mm pistol, but for double-action pistols as well.

By 1985, SIGARMS had taken over importation and the pistol was officially known in the U.S. as the P220, just as it was almost everywhere else. A year later SIG announced it had already sold over 100,000 P220s. For a time SIGARMS limited its P220 sales in the U.S. to .45 ACP only, but later added .38 Super and 9mm calibers. In Europe and other places where 9mm Parabellum guns are illegal for civilians to buy, SIG offers instead a 7.65mm Parabellum [.30 Luger] version. SIGARMS now imports two versions of the P220: a "European" style (with the magazine release located in the heel of the frame) and an "American" style (with a pushbutton magazine release located aft of the trigger guard). The latter version, made in .45 ACP and .38 Super, is, not surprisingly, the best-selling P220 variant in the U.S.

A modified Browning short-recoil locking system, combined with an inexpensive stamped sheet steel slide and an aluminum-alloy frame, make the P220-series pistols considerably easier to manufacture than SIG's classic but expensive P210, widely regarded as the Rolls-Royce of 9mm service pistols.

The influence of Sauer & Sohn in the design of this pistol has been greatly overshadowed by SIG's contributions. However, the decocking lever (on the upper forward portion of the left grip) is vaguely reminiscent of Sauer's famous wartime Model 38H pistol. The P220's decocking-lever design, though, is less complicated (and less flexible) in its operation. When the shooter lowers the P220 decocking lever, the hammer drops safely and automatically. Then, once the shooter releases his hold, the decocking lever springs back up to its fire position. For added safety, the loaded, decocked pistol relies on an automatic internal firing-pin block that is released only when the trigger has been pulled all the way to the rear at the moment of firing the pistol. SIG claims this system combines all the advantages of a revolver and automatic pistol, but without any of the disadvantages.

The P220 Series. From the P220 and the P225 has grown a line of modern SIG handguns. The most famous of the series, the P226, competed fiercely in 1984 with the Beretta Model 92F (please *see* page 167) for the U.S. M9 military pistol contract. Created in 1983, the P226 is essentially a P225 with a longer barrel (4.4 inches) and an enlarged grip frame to accommodate a 9mm 15-round magazine, thus making it competitive in U.S. service trials. Also chambered in .357 SIG caliber, it is available to civilians with a 10-round magazine.

The P228, which is smaller than the P226, has the same upper half of a P225, but its frame has been widened to accept a 13-round magazine. SIG's P228 later won the U.S. M11 military pistol contract calling for a slightly smaller pistol than the full-sized Beretta M9.

The P229 with 3.8-inch barrel is the only model in the series offered in .40 S&W caliber and with blackened stainless steel finish; it is also available in 9mm and .357 SIG with 10-round magazine. For a more detailed discussion of the smaller models, consult COMPLETE GUIDE TO COMPACT HANDGUNS, the companion volume.

Offered in blued finish, K-Kote or two-tone (except the P229), all the guns in the series have gained great popularity in the U.S. With their smooth triggers and excellent sights (all the models have optional "Siglite" night sights), the P220 series shoots well and accurately. Recoil is more pronounced than one may encounter with a Colt Government Model or EAA Witness, doubtless because of the P220's lighter weight and higher bore axis. Still, the SIG guns handle well, are comfortable to hold and carry, and boast excellent reliability. Overall, they are top double-action pistols and, assuming price is not a problem, remain excellent choices as defensive firearms.

SIG P220 SERIES
Made by J.P. Sauer & Sohn, Eckenförde, Germany, for SIG, Switzerland
Imported by SIGARMS, Exeter, NH. Years Produced: 1974–Present

Model	Caliber/ Capacity (in rounds)	Barrel Length	O.A. Length	Weight (in oz., empty)	Height	Width
P220* American	.45 ACP/7 .38 Super/9	4.4"	7.8"	28 35 (loaded)	5.6"	1.4"
P225	9mm/8	3.9"	7.1"	26 30 (loaded)	5.2"	1.25"
P226	9mm/10,15 .357 SIG/10	4.4"	7.8"	26.5 30.1	5.5"	1.4"
P228	9mm/10,13	3.9"	7.1"	26	5.4"	1.5"
P229	.40 S&W/10+	3.8"	7.0"	27.5	5.4"	1.5"

* Originally made in 9mm with 9-round capacity. + Other calibers available.

SMITH & WESSON MODEL 411

Smith & Wesson developed the Model 411 in 1993 to appeal to policemen and civilians who liked the .40 S&W cartridge but could not afford a top-of-the-line price for a pistol. The idea was to cut out the extras found on, say, the Model 4006, its nearest equivalent in the Smith & Wesson line. These changes included simplified sights, elimination of the milled step on the frame (near the muzzle), a matte finish (instead of polished blue or stainless), simplified vertical grooving on the front of both the trigger guard and gripstrap, and elimination of the ambidextrous safety in favor of a safety lever mounted on the left side of the slide only. These changes cut the price of the pistol significantly compared to the price of a Model 4006.

The frame of the Model 411 is made of aluminum alloy, making the gun weigh in at only 29 ounces unloaded. The size is virtually identical to that of the Model 915; in fact, it's difficult to tell the two apart (*see* next listing). However, the caliber marking on the barrel helps distinguish between them, as does the model marking on the left side of the frame just above the trigger guard. Although the 11-shot .40 S&W- caliber magazine of the Model 411 is nearly identical in its external dimensions to the 15-shot 9mm magazine of the Model 915, neither magazine will insert fully into the grip of the other pistol.

Likewise, the sights on the Model 411 are identical to those found on the Model 915. Basically, the rear sight is the same as the earlier (1983–1988) Model 469, with a front sight highlighted by a single large white dot dove-

Despite its unprepossessing appearance and relatively low price, the Smith & Wesson Model 411 (now replaced by the nearly identical Model 410) shoots well. This five-shot, 25-foot offhand group measures just 1.2 inches across.

tailed into the slide. Rather than use a 3-dot Novak sight setup, the configuration found in the Models 915 and 411 not only saves money, it actually provides superior sight markings. The single dot on the front sight of the Model 411 effectively draws the shooter's eye to it; in other words, there are no markings on the rear sight to distract the shooter from concentrating on the front sight.

Aside from its single-sided safety lever, the safety systems on the Model 411 are those of any modern Smith & Wesson pistol, with the safety lever moving up to fire and down to safe. In its safe setting, it lowers (decocks) the hammer mechanically. A firing-pin lock prevents firing—even with the manual safety on its fire setting—until the trigger is pulled all the way to the rear. The Model 411 also has a magazine disconnect safety, a feature found on almost every Smith & Wesson pistol.

Recoil on the Model 411 is primarily a matter of a pronounced muzzle rise rather than a backwards push. Still, the gun is easily controllable. The double-action trigger mode is heavy but smooth, while in single action there is considerable slack before the trigger releases. Both modes have been well designed to help reduce the chances of accidental discharge.

Accuracy is excellent. Our best five-shot effort at 25 feet measured a mere 1.2 inches, using Federal's exotic Black Talon 180-grain jacketed hollowpoints. At 50 feet, the best five-shot group measured 2.4 inches, using Winchester's "Deep Penetrator" (DP) 180-grain subsonic jacketed hollowpoints. No malfunctions occurred with three ammunition brands tested. All in all, the Model 411 is a fine handgun offering high performance at an attractive price.

The newer .40 S&W-caliber Model 410, introduced in 1996 to replace the Model 411 at still lower cost, features the same aluminum-alloy frame, blued carbon steel slide and non-reflective matte finish, although the sights are now the 3-dot type and magazine capacity has been reduced to 10 rounds.

SMITH & WESSON MODEL 411

Manufacturer	Years Produced	Caliber/Capacity	Dimensions
Smith & Wesson Springfield, MA	1993–1996	.40 S&W/11 rounds	Barrel Length: 4.0" O.A. Length: 7.9" Height: 5.5" Width: 1.25" Weight: 29 oz. (unloaded); 37 oz. (loaded)

SMITH & WESSON MODEL 915

The introduction of its Model 915 in early 1992 was a brilliant move on Smith & Wesson's part, for this 9mm pistol had all the quality and features of the company's top-of-the-line 9mm pistols without any unnecessary extras. This approach created a gun with tremendous appeal for policemen and civilians alike who sought an absolutely reliable pistol, and one that didn't cost a small fortune.

Smith & Wesson developed this fine pistol from the Model 5904, itself a descendant of the classic Model 59, the world's first commercially successful high-capacity, double-action 9mm automatic pistol. The cost-cutting measures it took to make the Model 915 were all strictly cosmetic without impairing the basic functions of the solid

Like the Model 411, Smith & Wesson's Model 915 dispenses with the ambidextrous safety levers usually found on more expensive S&W pistols. With the Model 915, this 2.1-inch pattern was fired in a five-shot group from a distance of 25 feet.

Model 5904 system. Alterations included simplified sights; a slightly heavier frame to eliminate machining near the muzzle; a matte finish; vertical grooving on the front of the trigger guard and front gripstrap instead of the checkering found on more expensive Smith & Wesson pistols; and a single-sided safety lever instead of an ambidextrous safety.

Despite its lightweight aluminum-alloy frame, the Model 915 has substantial frame contours that add about 1.5 ounces to the weight of the gun. Still, it remains a handy size and is well balanced for a holster pistol. Moreover, the trigger guard is rounded, not squared—a feature other pistol manufacturers should consider.

Not only are the sights on this pistol less expensive, they're actually an improvement over the 3-dot system now in fashion. The rear sight is radiused on its corners for a snag-free draw and is unmarked to save costs. It also allows the shooter to concentrate fully on the front sight, further highlighted by a single large white dot, rather than be distracted by the rear sight.

The single-sided safety lever on the Model 915 moves up to fire and down to safe. In its safe setting it decocks the hammer, then stays in the down (safe) position until the shooter resets it. Some shooters prefer a decocking lever, which resets itself automatically after the hammer is lowered, leaving the pistol ready to fire. Smith & Wesson has offered decocking levers on a few of its pistols, but most employ this manual safety arrangement. One advantage of the single-sided safety setup is that it narrows the width of the pistol slightly compared to an ambidextrous safety. Those who feel the need for an ambidextrous safety lever—left-handers, for example—can buy the parts necessary to add this feature direct from Smith & Wesson. In addition to its safety lever, the Model 915 includes a firing-pin lock and magazine disconnect safety.

Overall, the Model 915 handles and shoots with accuracy, comfort and ease. Its double-action trigger pull is noticeably heavier than the single-action trigger, thus opening up groups slightly, but the effect is not pronounced and can be mastered in time. In test-firing, our best five-shot effort from 25 feet measured 2.1 inches with Winchester Silvertip 115-grain hollowpoint ammunition. From 50 feet, a five-shot group measured 3.4 inches with Federal's Hydra-Shok 124-grain jacketed hollowpoint rounds. No malfunctions occurred with any of the ammunition brands used.

Despite Smith & Wesson's extensive cost-cutting measures, the Model 915 is still an effective 9mm defensive pistol. Adding to its appeal and versatility is the availability of parts should the owner want to upgrade it. After discontinuing the Model 915 in 1995, S&W replaced it with two very similar pistols, the Models 908 and 910. The 908 uses an eight-shot magazine, while the 910 offers a 10-shot magazine for private sale or a 15-shot version for police use. Both have a Sigma-type rear sight, but they are otherwise very similar to the 915 that inspired them.

SMITH & WESSON MODEL 915

Manufacturer	Years Produced	Caliber/Capacity	Dimensions
Smith & Wesson Springfield, MA	1992–1995	9mm/15 rounds	Barrel Length: 4.0" O.A. Length: 7.5" Height: 5.4" Width: 1.25" Weight: 28.5 oz. (unloaded); 36 oz. (loaded)

SMITH & WESSON MODEL 1000 SERIES

The history of Smith & Wesson's 1000-series automatic pistols dates back to 1989. The appearance that year of the Model 1006 — the first Smith & Wesson pistol made to fire the 10mm cartridge — gave that flagging round a huge boost. The Model 1006, which is similar to, and developed from, the Model 4506 (*see* next listing), sports a 5-inch barrel and overall length of 8.5 inches (*see* photo above). There soon followed S&W Models 1066, 1076 and 1086, all of which had 4.25-inch barrels.

Like the original Model 1006, the 1066 uses a traditional double-action mechanism that switches to single action after the first shot. These two guns also share an ambidextrous hammer-dropping manual safety lever of the type commonly found on Smith & Wesson pistols. By contrast, the Model 1076 has its decocking lever mounted on the left side of the frame, while the Model 1086 features a double-action-only lockwork.

All of the pistols in the 1000 Series are made of stainless steel and share the Third Generation's features, including a trigger linkage that is an improvement over earlier Smith & Wesson automatics. Options include a curved one-piece backstrap and adjustable sights. Interestingly, the Model 1076 was accepted temporarily by the FBI in the late 1980s for use with the attenuated "10mm Lite" round (although it functions as well with full-powered 10mm Auto ammunition). The 1076 pistols issued to FBI agents do not include the magazine disconnect safety, among the few Smith & Wesson pistols ever to omit this device.

The Model 1066 tested for this book produced outstanding accuracy, with one five-shot offhand group measuring 1.3 inches from 25 feet away, and another spanning just 2.4 inches from 50 feet.

Smith & Wesson's Model 1066 is an easy gun to shoot and handles the powerful 10mm cartridge with good results. This five-shot offhand group fired from 25 feet measures only 1.3 inches. Unfortunately, paltry sales did not support the continuance of the 10mm pistol series.

Reliability was flawless with all brands of ammunition tested, ranging from 10mm Lite loads all the way up to the stout 10mm Auto rounds made by Norma. Surprisingly, the gun's recoil, even with the Norma ammunition, was not at all uncomfortable. Trigger pull was typical for a modern Smith & Wesson pistol, and the Novak sights worked well. This is an outstanding gun, especially for experienced pistol shooters who are willing to master a demanding but powerful handgun.

Although Smith & Wesson discontinued its 10mm line, the round itself refuses to die, as pistol makers continue to produce guns for it. The current champion of the 10mm cartridge is Glock, with its Model 20 (*see* separate listing).

SMITH & WESSON MODEL 1000 SERIES

Manufacturer	Years Produced	Caliber/Capacity	Dimensions
Smith & Wesson Springfield, MA	1989–1993	10mm Auto/9 rounds	Barrel Length: 4.2" O.A. Length: 7.8" Height: 5.8" Width: 1.4" Weight: 38.5 oz. (unloaded); 46 oz. (loaded)

SMITH & WESSON MODEL 4506

Smith & Wesson has been making double-action .45-caliber automatic pistols since it introduced the Model 645 in 1986. A few years later, as part of its upgrading of the Third Generation pistol line, S&W brought out an improved Model 645, the Model 4506. At the same time, a compact version, the Model 4516, made its debut with a shorter 3.75-inch barrel (overall length of about 7 inches and weight of 34 ounces) and a shortened frame that held seven rounds instead of eight. The gunmaker also briefly offered a compact lightweight Model 4536 featuring an alloy frame that reduced the weight of the Model 4516 by 10 ounces. This model, unfortunately, was dropped in a major purge of Smith & Wesson's product line that took place in 1992.

The company still makes several intermediate-sized double-action .45-caliber pistols (with 4.25-inch barrels and eight-round magazines). These include:
- Model 4566, with traditional double action and safety lever;
- Model 4586, a double-action-only version;

Now discontinued are the:
- Model 4546, similar in size to the Model 4506 with the double-action-only trigger mechanism of the slightly smaller Model 4586; and
- Model 4576, with traditional double action and a decocking lever.

The breech-locking mechanism of the Model 4506 employs the modified Browning short-recoil system, which Smith & Wesson has used since it first began making the Model 39 in the early 1950s. Naturally, the working parts in a .45-caliber pistol are suitably enlarged to handle the heavier recoil of a big cartridge compared to a 9mm. This increase in size and strength becomes apparent when one handles this pistol's powerful recoil spring. The safety mechanisms on the Model 4506 include an automatic internal firing-pin block, a magazine safety, and an ambidextrous manual safety lever, which pushes down to safe and up to fire.

All Smith & Wesson automatic pistols in .45 ACP caliber are now made completely of stainless steel, with wraparound one-piece grips of black checkered Xenoy, the same rugged synthetic material used on the Ruger P85 and Colt Double Eagle pistols.

Wisely Smith & Wesson has finally abandoned the unsightly squared-off (or recurved) trigger guards that have burdened so many automatic pistol shooters over the past decade or so. The trigger guards on most Smith & Wesson automatic pistol models, including the Model 6906, now feature a more rounded shape. To satisfy those who still insist on the finger-forward hold, Smith & Wesson continues to checker and serrate the leading edge of the trigger guard. Even that can cause snags, but it is certainly preferable to having the whole front edge shaped like some grotesque hook.

Despite the popularity of the Novak Lo-Mount sights S&W introduced with the Third Generation guns, adjustable sights are still optional on some of its automatic pistols. The rear sight, with its large protective ears,

A disassembled S&W Model 4506 reveals a long and heavily tensioned recoil spring that is needed to contain the recoil force generated by the powerful .45 ACP round.

is adjustable for both windage and elevation, using an ordinary screwdriver. The popular 3-dot configuration, moreover, provides an ample, clear sight picture.

All of these refinements make the hefty .45-caliber Model 4506 a solid, reliable and consistent performer. It is reasonably slim, however, due in part to its single-column eight-shot magazine, and is fairly easy to carry comfortably, or even to conceal. Although slightly muzzle heavy, it handles well, has a relatively light recoil, and comes back on target quickly. The trigger clearly shows its heritage as a service gun. The double-action trigger offers a short, crisp release. There's also a consider-

Although the Model 4506 is quite accurate, its double-action trigger pull is different in feel from the single-action trigger. As a result, the first shot is thrown wide as shown.

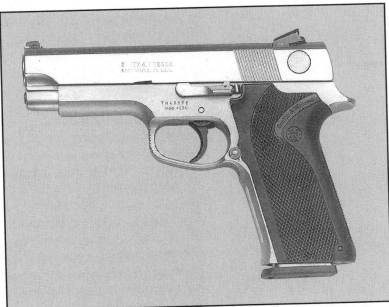

The Smith & Wesson Model 4506 has spawned a whole series of variants, including the double-action-only Model 4586 with fixed sight (above).

able amount of slack, however, which the shooter must take up before he gets to the release point. The reason for this type of trigger, by the way, is to let a police officer know, while holding a suspect at gunpoint or in some other stressful situation, that his handgun is ready to fire.

The Model 4506 tested for this book produced a pattern of 2.1 inches from 25 feet, while from 50 feet a five-shot offhand group measured 2.5 inches. Reliability was flawless. Gone are the days when Smith & Wesson automatic pistols—primarily first-series Model 39s and some early Model 59s—had trouble feeding hollowpoint ammunition. Most of the Smith & Wesson pistols now experience little trouble with whatever ammunition is used, so long as it's the right caliber. The only real drawback with the powerful Model 4506 is its considerable size. Many shooters prefer the smaller Model 4516 in this caliber; or better yet, the now-discontinued lightweight Model 4536, or the seven-shot aluminum-framed Model 457 currently in production.

SMITH & WESSON MODEL 4506

Manufacturer	Years Produced	Caliber/Capacity	Dimensions
Smith & Wesson Springfield, MA	1989–Present	.45 ACP/8 rounds	Barrel Length: 5.0" O.A. Length: 8.5" Height: 5.9" Width: 1.3" Weight: 37 oz. (unloaded); 45 oz. (loaded)

SMITH & WESSON SIGMA (SW40F)

Smith & Wesson's original Sigma pistol made its first appearance in May 1994 at the annual meeting of the National Rifle Association. A year later, S&W announced the addition of 9mm full size and .380-caliber compact versions to the Sigma line.

The Sigma's origins, however, begin in the late 1980s, when the Glock pistols—particularly the 9mm Models 17 and 19 and the .40-caliber Models 22 and 23—were making huge inroads into the police handgun market once dominated by Smith & Wesson. S&W's answer was the Sigma. Similar to the Glock pistols in a number of ways, the Sigma has a polymer frame with satin black finish, and its breech-locking mechanism and disassembly procedure are also clearly modeled on the Glock design. The Sigma's trigger design and ergonomics (low barrel centerline), however, are quite different. These changes, plus improved 3-dot sights (Tritium night sights are available), magazine and grip, have made the Sigma a

The Sigma disassembles into the following components (top to bottom): slide, barrel, recoil spring assembly, frame and magazine.

The Sigma is impressively accurate, as demonstrated by this five-shot offhand group fired from 25 feet and measuring 1.6 inches across.

more comfortable and more functional gun than the Glock.

In tests conducted with various .40 S&W-caliber pistols in rapid fire at close range, the Sigma ranked among the best in accuracy and reliability. A typical five-shot offhand group fired with the Sigma pistol from 25 feet measured just 1.6 inches across; and from 50 feet, it spanned a mere 2 inches. That's no mean feat for any mass-production automatic pistol, particularly one with a double-action trigger pull for every shot. The Sigma handles the recoil of the .40 S&W cartridge impressively for such a relatively light pistol. There's no denying that Smith & Wesson has created an excellent handgun. While it's eminently suitable for police holsters, the Sigma is also small enough for concealed carry. Its future is bright indeed.

SMITH & WESSON SIGMA (SW40F)

Manufacturer	Years Produced	Caliber/Capacity	Dimensions
Smith & Wesson Springfield, MA	1994–Present	.40 S&W/10 or 15 rounds	Barrel Length: 4.5" O.A. Length: 7.4" Height: 5.5" Width: 1.2" Weight: 26.5 oz. (unloaded); 36 oz. (loaded)

SPRINGFIELD ARMORY M1911-A1

If imitation is the ultimate form of flattery, then John Browning's design that became the famous .45-caliber Colt Model 1911A1 heads the list in the gun industry. Here by Springfield Armory, now owned by Springfield, Inc., of Geneseo, Illinois, is an entire line of "modern" 1911-A1s with new features to satisfy a wide array of preferences and uses.

Springfield Armory's 1911-A1 is made with a forged ingot of aluminum alloy, with stainless or chrome-moly steel for the frame. Recent improvements include a beveled magazine well, skeletonized hammer, long trigger, throated barrel, and lowered/flared ejection, among others. Models that closely resemble the original include the Trophy, Match, Champion, Mil-Spec, Factory Comp, V10 and a series in stainless steel.

Springfield Armory, now Springfield, Inc., produces a large series of .45 ACP-caliber pistols based on the superb Colt M1911A1. Shown here is the Defender model with improved sights and other minor refinements (left). Other variations are the Trophy Match Bi-Tone (center), and the High-Capacity Factory Comp (right), the latter available with 13- or 17-round magazines for law-enforcement and military use.

SPRINGFIELD ARMORY M1911-A1 (STANDARD)

Manufacturer	Years Produced	Caliber/Capacity	Dimensions
Springfield, Inc. (Formerly Springfield Armory) Geneseo, IL	1987–Present	.45 ACP/7 rounds .38 Super/9 rounds	Barrel Length: 5" O.A. Length: 8 5/8" Weight: 38.5 oz. (unloaded)

SPRINGFIELD ARMORY OMEGA

When the Bren Ten pistol project collapsed in the mid-1980s (*see* page 176), it appeared that the highly promising and powerful 10mm automatic pistol cartridge might die also. Then, in 1987, Colt introduced the Delta Elite, an M1911-type pistol chambered for the 10mm round, giving the cartridge a new lease on life. A year later, Springfield Armory, then an aggressive and innovative company competing against Colt for a share of the .45 ACP M1911 market, introduced the Omega.

Like the Delta Elite, the Omega started with an M1911A1 frame, but soon incorporated a radically different slide, barrel and locking system. The Peters Stahl Company of Germany made the Omega's top half, consisting of a ported 5- or 6-inch barrel and a cam-type locking system that replaced the swinging link of the M1911 and Delta Elite. All of this was topped by a stronger, larger slide with adjustable sights.

Similar in handling and operational features to the M1911, the Omega is capable of firing in single-action only and can be carried cocked and locked. Best known as a 10mm handgun, it can be modified to accept also .38 Super and .45 ACP. Magazine capacity is seven cartridges (plus one in the chamber) for 10mm and .45 ACP, and nine cartridges (plus one in the chamber) for .38 Super.

Disassembled, the Omega is nothing more than an M1911A1-type frame (lower half) with a redesigned upper half (slide and barrel). Inset: The barrel of the Omega (right) has a linkless locking system not unlike that of modern SIG and Glock pistols. Contrast that to the traditional M1911 system found on the Colt Government Model barrel (left).

Because it's a big gun, the Omega is not likely to be used for concealed carry, but it does offer some possibilities as a defensive handgun for home or business. With a ported barrel and Pachmayr signature grips to aid in recoil control, plus an excellent fully adjustable rear sight, the Omega handles and shoots well. Thanks to its excellent grips, ported barrel, muzzle-heavy balance and weight, recoil is

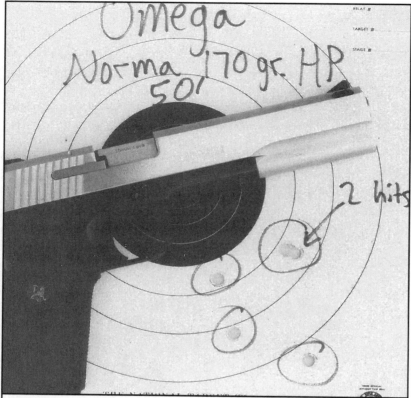

With its improved locking system, the Omega is strong enough to handle even the most powerful 10mm loads — the kind used to make this offhand group measuring 2.6 inches.

mild. The sights, which are large and provide a good aiming picture, unfortunately do not show up well against dark backgrounds.

Handling is comparable to a .45-caliber M1911-type pistol, but the Omega's longer slide and greater weight make it a little slower coming out of the holster. As for accuracy, our best five-shot offhand group from 25 feet measured 1.7 inches, using Remington 170-grain hollowpoint ammunition, and 2.6 inches from 50 feet. The latter group used the high-powered Norma 170-grain hollowpoint, which is about the stiffest factory-made ammunition available in this caliber.

In addition to being an accurate target gun and hunting pistol, the Omega offers possibilities as a self-defense arm for home or business. The 10mm round in particular is an excellent choice for this pistol, but those who prefer .45 ACP or .38 Super might better opt for the smaller and more manageable Colt Gold Cup or any of the Springfield 1911-A1 compacts. Still, the Omega's versatility—its ability to use the same pistol for three calibers—has considerable appeal. That and its precision workmanship make this a fine pistol, with handling proficiency close to that of the ever-popular M1911. Add to this the Omega's improved extraction and faster barrel locking and unlocking design and it clearly outshines much of the competition. Its only serious drawback is availability since Springfield, Inc., has stopped production.

SPRINGFIELD ARMORY OMEGA

Manufacturer	Years Produced	Caliber/Capacity	Dimensions
Peters Stahl (PSW GmbH) Aachen, Germany Former Importer: Springfield Armory Geneseo, IL	1988–1991	10mm/7 rounds .45 ACP/7 rounds .38 Super/9 rounds	Barrel Length: 5" or 6" O.A. Length: 8.53" to 9.53" Height: 5.8" Width: 1.45" Weight: 43–45 oz. (unloaded) 51 oz. (loaded/5" bbl.)

SPRINGFIELD ARMORY MODEL P9

Springfield Armory's Model P9 was originally a
CZ 75 copy made from parts built in Italy by
Tanfoglio and then assembled in the U.S., with compact, subcompact and longer-barreled compensated models added. When
Springfield Armory went out of business in early 1993, the P9 series was
taken over by Springfield, Inc., which promptly sold off the remaining stock of P9
pistols and concentrated instead on the M1911-style pistols that had been the foundation of Springfield Armory's earlier success. We've included the P9 in this book,
however, because so many used copies remain on the market.

Almost identical to the Czech-built CZ 75, the standard Model P9 includes the same
frame-mounted safety and rounded trigger guard—and no firing-pin lock. The chief difference
between the two models was in their finish, with the P9 featuring attractive checkered wooden grips
and highly polished blued slides.

Using a Springfield Armory Model P9 pistol, this five-shot offhand group fired from 25 feet measures 1.6 inches.

Typical of the CZ 75 series, the P9, while quite accurate, had a pronounced tendency to throw the double-action first shot—with its longer, heavier trigger pull—away from the lighter, single-action follow-up shots. Firing from 25 feet with Federal's excellent 9BP 115-grain JHP load, we managed to place four shots within a .75-inch pattern, but the initial double-action first shot went almost two full inches off course. Our best five-shot offhand group from 25 feet measured 1.6 inches while another five-shot 50-foot offhand group measured 3.0 inches. Top results were gained with Norinco 124-grain FMJs, but several brands of hollowpoints and Winchester USA 115-grain FMJ ammo functioned flawlessly as well.

Although it is no longer in production, Springfield Armory's P9 is still an excellent pistol. And because it's so similar to Tanfoglio's Model TZ 75 or the Witness, spare parts should be available. Like all CZs, it's a good-sized gun with large grips to match, it shoots well, and is well made.

SPRINGFIELD ARMORY MODEL P9

Manufacturer	Years Produced	Caliber/Capacity	Dimensions
Fratelli Tanfoglio Gardone, V.T., Italy Former Importer: Springfield Armory Geneseo, IL	1989–1993	9mm/15 rounds	Barrel Length: 4.7" O.A. Length: 8.1" Height: 5.4" Width: 1.35" Weight: 32 oz. (unloaded); 40 oz. (loaded)

Star Megastar

Like Star's earlier and highly popular Model 30 variants, not to mention the phenomenal Firestar series in 9mm, .40 and .45 calibers, the Megastar was significantly influenced by the CZ 75. For example, its slide sits inside the frame rather than surrounding it. While this design in the CZ serves to reduce its slide dimensions and slim down the pistol as a whole, it does no such thing for the Megastar. Looking like a hugely overgrown Firestar, the Megastar, which made its first appearance in 1993, is a monstrous pistol, weighing almost four pounds fully loaded. It is noticeably larger even than other double-action .45 ACP automatic pistols, such as the EAA Witness, Ruger P90 and SIG P220. (For a complete discussion of the Star Firestar series, please consult COMPLETE GUIDE TO COMPACT HANDGUNS, the companion volume.)

Being big does have its advantages, however. The Megastar's construction is extraordinarily rugged, including an all-steel frame whose weight serves to hold down recoil. The pistol's gargantuan size also enables it to hold a 12-round magazine, which is the most of any high-capacity .45-auto pistol except for the full-sized Para-Ordnance pistol and Glock's Model 21. Its box magazine easily loads the 12 rounds; in fact, it's easier to load than the magazines of most Star pistols.

The Megastar's excellent sights use the popular 3-dot configuration. The rear sight is a large square notch, shaped somewhat like a Novak Lo-Mount found on modern Smith & Wesson pistols. The front sight is set in a dovetail, hence it's adjustable for windage. Despite their size, the sights have smooth contours to minimize snagging or catching. Indeed, the whole gun boasts smooth contours, as though Star designed the shape of the gun to help compensate for its

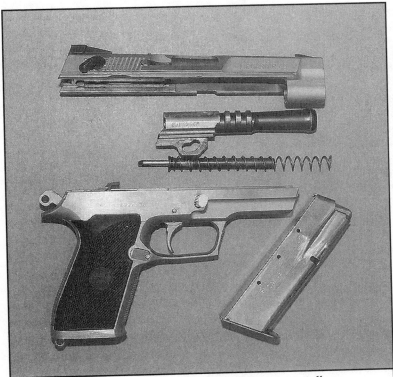

This disassembly of Star's Megastar shows that it's essentially an enlarged Firestar.

bulk. For instance, most of the slide release mechanism is concealed within the frame, leaving exposed only a small rectangular button with smooth, radiused edges.

The Megastar's safety mechanisms include an automatic internal firing-pin block, which is released only when the trigger has been pulled all the way back at the moment of firing. The manual safety lever is ambidextrous and offers a choice among several operating features. For example, after it has been pushed down to the safe position, exposing a white dot, the safety lever locks the firing pin and retracts it into the slide. Thus, even if the hammer should fall, causing the pistol to break safety, the hammer still cannot reach the firing pin. This safety mechanism combines the best operating features developed on famous European automatic pistols over a period of many years. Moreover, placing the safety on safe does not automatically lower the hammer. After pushing the safety lever down to safe, the hammer can then be lowered in one of two ways: by pulling the trigger, or by pushing the

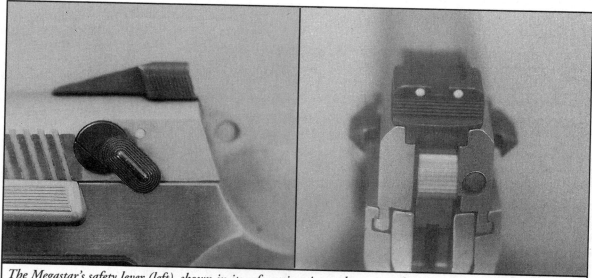

The Megastar's safety lever (left), shown in its safe setting, is poorly conceived and unergonomic in its operation. Note, however, the slide release and the low profile of the rear sight. This low, no-snag profile (right) combined with the 3-dot sight configuration (only 2 dots show here) provides a large, clear sight picture.

safety lever down a little further. This system, which is similar in concept to the latest Taurus automatic pistols, allows greater flexibility and a variety of carrying modes than one usually finds in an automatic pistol.

The Megastar also includes a magazine disconnect safety that can immobilize the pistol. When the magazine is withdrawn from the pistol grip, the trigger is disconnected from the firing linkage. The magazine safety does not interfere with the magazine release, however. Once depressed, the magazine release button pops the empty magazine out of the grip—a major improvement over Star's smaller Firestar, which releases its magazine only a hard-to-grasp fraction of an inch.

The Megastar is available in a blued finish as well as Star's proprietary "Starvel" hard chrome finish. The grips are an attractive and functional checkered black plastic. Checkering on the front and rear gripstraps, as well as on the front of the trigger guard (for shooters who put the index finger of their support hand forward), helps the shooter get a handle on this large gun. Fit and finish are excellent throughout, as one has learned to expect of Star.

The Megastar shoots well partly because of its large, recoil-reducing size. The trigger has plenty of slack in both double-action and single-action modes, but the trigger pull is surprisingly light. These and other factors contribute to good accuracy. As an example, our best five-shot group fired offhand from 25 feet measured 2.0 inches, using Remington's powerful 185-grain +P jacketed hollowpoint round. From 50 feet using the same ammunition, a five-shot pattern went into 4.0 inches. All ammunition brands tested with the Megastar produced flawless reliability (incidentally, a 10mm version of the Megastar with 14-round magazine was also offered).

Overall, despite its size and the way its manual safety controls are arranged, there's no denying that the Megastar is a well-made pistol with an impressive performance record and above-average appearance.

STAR MEGASTAR

Manufacturer	Years Produced	Caliber/Capacity	Dimensions
Star Bonifacio Echeverria Eibar, Spain Imported by: Interarms Alexandria, VA	1993–1995	.45 ACP/12 rounds 10mm/14 rounds	Barrel Length: 4.56" O.A. Length: 8.34" Height: 5.8" Width: 1.4" Weight: 48 oz. (unloaded); 60 oz. (loaded)

STAR MODEL 31P/31PK

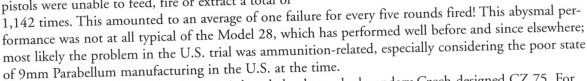

In the late 1970s Star's Model 28—along with Astra's A-80 and Gabilondo y Cia's Llama Omni—entered a competition to determine Spain's next service pistol. Star won this competition handily, and its Model 28 went on to win several Spanish military and police orders, among others. Later, in 1979, the Model 28 competed in a U.S. service pistol trial but failed dismally. Incredibly, out of 5,526 rounds fired in endurance testing, the Star pistols were unable to feed, fire or extract a total of 1,142 times. This amounted to an average of one failure for every five rounds fired! This abysmal performance was not at all typical of the Model 28, which has performed well before and since elsewhere; most likely the problem in the U.S. trial was ammunition-related, especially considering the poor state of 9mm Parabellum manufacturing in the U.S. at the time.

The design of the Model 28 series is based closely on the legendary Czech-designed CZ 75. For example, the Star pistols have the same slide-to-frame relationship and double-action trigger linkage. Likewise, the Star's trigger pull owes its smoothness to the CZ 75's design and construction. Star also uses a modular hammer lockwork based on the efficient Tokarev and SIG P210 units, so the CZ 75 is not Star's only design influence.

In 1984, Star, through its longtime North American agent, Interarms, introduced the Model 28 to the American market, and it established itself in this country as a solid, reliable performer among civilians and police forces alike. The improved Model 30 came out in the late 1980s (replacing the Model 28) followed in 1990 by the slightly downsized Model 31 (replacing the Model 30).

The latest version of Star's Model 28 — the Model 31P, used by the Spanish armed forces — can produce fearsome short-range accuracy.

The standard Model 31, sometimes called the Model 31M, features all-steel construction and weighs in at 40 ounces unloaded; its companion, the alloy-framed Model 31PK, weighs 10 ounces lighter. Finish choices for the Model 31 are either matte blue or Starvel (chrome). The grips of checkered rubber are a bit wide but offer a comfortable handle on the pistol.

Safety arrangements on the Model 31 are somewhat different from those found on the compact single-action Firestar (*see* the companion volume, COMPLETE GUIDE TO COMPACT HANDGUNS). After the slide-mounted ambidextrous safety has been pushed down to its safe setting, with the hammer cocked, it does not automatically drop the hammer. Instead, the hammer is blocked on its way to the firing pin by the safety, which pushes the firing pin forward into its well, where the hammer can't reach it. Thus the pistol can be carried cocked and locked when a single-action first shot is desired, or the hammer can be lowered (once the safety lever has been placed on its safe setting) by pulling the trigger. By pushing the safety up and forward, the block is removed and the gun is ready for firing. One disadvantage to this system is that the direction in which the safety lever moves is not optimal. Since a person under stress will tend to grip the pistol tightly, it would be better to have the safety go down to fire. Under those circumstances, it's unnatural to raise the thumb in order to flick the safety lever up and off. This same complaint can be lodged against Smith & Wesson and Walther pistols, including their many copies and clones, all of which use this kind of safety arrangement. The manual safety found on the Colt Government Model, Browning High Power and CZ 75 pistols is a better way to go.

In test-firing the all-steel Model 31 and the lighter alloy 31PK, both proved to be good shooters. The heavier 31 had less recoil, of course, although the 31PK offers no problem in that respect. The Model 31 also has a better trigger pull, especially in double action, and is more accurate. A five-shot offhand effort with it measured 1.5 inches 25 feet and a sensational 1.8 inches at 50 feet. Both groups were fired with IMI "Samson" brand 115-grain FMJ ammunition.

With the 31PK, our best five-shot 25-foot offhand group was exactly 2 inches across, while the 50-foot group measured 4.3 inches, both with Winchester Silvertip 115-grain hollowpoints. No jams occurred in either gun with a variety of hollowpoint and FMJ ammunition, although accuracy varied according to what brand was fired. The Model 31 provided poor accuracy with the Winchester Silvertips, with one group measuring 5.1 inches at 25 feet. Any handgun owner is wise to experiment with different brands and types of ammunition before deciding what works best in a particular pistol.

Like the CZ 75 from which they inherited their major design influences, the Star Model 28-series pistols are rugged, reliable and efficient guns that will serve their owners well under the most difficult conditions.

STAR MODEL 31P/31PK

Manufacturer	Years Produced	Caliber/Capacity	Dimensions
Star Bonifacio Echeverria Eibar, Spain Imported by: Interarms Alexandria, VA	1990—1994	9mm/15 rounds	Barrel Length: 3.9" O.A. Length: 7.6" Height: 5.5" Width: 1.4" Weight: 40 oz. (unloaded); 47 oz. (loaded) (10 oz. less w/alloy frame)

STEYR GB

In 1969 Steyr began working on a new service pistol for use by the Austrian armed forces. The developmental phase took nearly ten years before importation of the new 18-shot pistol could begin in the U.S. The resulting pistol, called the Rogak P-18 (named after the then importer of Steyr products here), proved a dismal failure. Production ceased after a year or two with only about 2,300 pistols having been built.

Steyr then eliminated the P-18's problems and in 1980 introduced an improved version as the Model GB-80, or simply GB (for *Gas Bremse*, which means "Gas Brake" in German). This model became one of the most advanced 9mm pistols of the early 1980s, and should have been successful. Unfortunately, it came on the market a little too soon; the American public, in particular, was not quite ready then for a large, high-capacity 9mm pistol like the GB. Nevertheless, Steyr's pistol participated in at least two major 9mm pistol test series, one in Austria in 1983 and another in the U.S. (the XM9 pistol trials of 1984). In the Austrian tests, the GB lost out to Glock's Model 17 and in the U.S. trial the GB finished second to Beretta's Model 92F (*see* page 167). In 1986, when sales to civilians and a few small police forces proved insufficient, Steyr decided to halt manufacture of the pistol. Total production came to a disappointing 15,000–20,000, but the guns have retained a small but loyal following.

The GB departs from the typical 9mm pistol in many ways, but its most important difference is its operating principle. While most 9mm pistols use a locked breech— most often some form of Browning's short-recoil mechanism for containing the high pressures of that cartridge — the GB utilizes pressures generated by the expanding powder gases to help hold the breech closed. From this method of operation comes the pistol's name, "Gas Brake." Milliseconds after firing the GB, expanding powder gases are vented through two holes drilled into the midpoint of the barrel and thence into a chamber inside the slide. With no way to escape, the gases exert high pressure against the muzzle bushing until the bullet has left the barrel. Once that happens, the gases are free to follow the bullet out the barrel and into the atmosphere. With the gas pressure now released, the slide is free to recoil rearward in normal automatic pistol fashion. This system of operation may not be new, but it is rarely encountered. Even though it was developed in Nazi Germany as early as the end of World War II, the only modern pistols that use a similar concept are Heckler & Koch's P7 series (*please see* page 220) and a 9mm pistol made in China.

Other unusual features of Steyr's GB pistol include a magazine that holds up to 18 rounds, making it one of the highest-capacity pistols ever developed, and a chrome-lined barrel to facilitate cleaning. The barrel bore is also rifled in polygonal fashion for extra velocity and easier cleaning. Steyr's manufacturing methods for the GB included a stamped steel frame, consisting of two halves welded together, and an investment-cast slide. Typical of Steyr products, the GB was extraordinarily well-made. Its all-steel construction and the braking effect of its gas-delay method of operation made this pistol sturdier than its alloy-framed, recoil-operated competitors, such as Beretta's Model 92 and SIG's Model P226 (*see* page 253).

Like the Beretta pistol, the GB makes good use of its relatively large size. As a result, it's not too awkward to handle and operate even by shooters with small or medium-sized hands. The GB has a double-action trigger and a decocking lever mounted on the left side of the slide (although on the 40 pistols submitted to the U.S. Army in 1984 the decocking lever was ambidextrous). With the hammer decocked, a firing-pin lock prevents firing until the trigger is pulled to the rear. The trigger pull, by the way, is heavy enough to make an accidental discharge extremely unlikely. That helps make this pistol as easy to operate as a double-action revolver or a SIG automatic pistol.

Although the double-action first shot with the GB is fairly heavy, it doesn't take long to make an adjustment. The gun handles well and, thanks in part to the gas brake system, is very controllable. Recoil is greatly reduced, especially when compared to that found in the typical locked-breech 9mm automatic pistol; also, muzzle flip is minimal.

The GB features good sights, too. In fact, it was one of the first guns to be equipped with the now-fashionable 3-dot sighting system. The sights not only offer a large, clear sight picture, they are also nicely radiused to minimize snagging when the pistol is drawn in a hurry. Indeed, this entire gun is well-contoured to remove any rough edges and, despite its considerable size, is a viable concealed-carry pistol.

As for accuracy, our best five-shot offhand group from 25 feet made a 1.1-inch pattern using Federal's 9BP with 115-grain jacketed hollowpoint (JHP) bullets. Another group from 25 feet using Winchester Silvertips (with the same 115-grain bullet size) covered 1.2 inches. From 50 feet, our best five-shot offhand group fired with 115-grain Silvertips—with the first shot in double-action mode—measured only 2.2 inches.

No malfunctions occurred with the GB pistol after firing more than 300 rounds of ammunition of assorted types. It also handled a wide variety of ammunition, including Remington and Cor-Bon +P rounds, without trouble. The U.S. Army did withdraw the GB from XM9 testing, however, because of its "inadequate reliability"; but with the M1911A1 pistol used as the Army's standard of measurement, a gun could be highly reliable yet fail to make the grade. While Steyr apparently did manage to work out any bugs in the gas system, shooters are advised to test-fire a GB before purchasing one for use in self-defense.

The GB's main shortcomings are its size, which may deter those with small hands from buying it, and its limited production, which could make spare parts scarce. Many GB owners doubtless are holding onto these guns for their collector status rather than actually using them. That's unfortunate, because the GB is really a

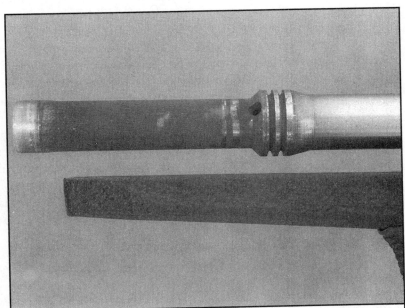

This closeup view of a Steyr GB barrel shows one of two venting holes used in the pistol's gas-delay mechanism. With this design, fouling powder accumulated forward of the holes, rather than plugging them up, thus allowing longer intervals between cleanings.

superior shooting piece. In fact, it's a far better pistol than its limited production warrants and deserves better success than it has. In many ways, Steyr's GB is superior to the Glock, Beretta and SIG pistols, the very ones that bested it in military testing. So those who can find a GB in good condition are fortunate indeed, because they'll own one of the best handguns ever made.

STEYR GB

Manufacturer	Years Produced	Caliber/Capacity	Dimensions
Stey-Daimler-Puch Steyr, Austria Former Importer: Gun South, Inc. Trussville, AL	1980–1986	9mm/18 rounds	Barrel Length: 5.3" O.A. Length: 8.5" Height: 5.5" Width: 1.4" Weight: 30 oz. (unloaded); 39 oz. (loaded)

STEYR SPP

Steyr's fully-automatic TMP (Tactical Machine Pistol) represents an interesting attempt to create what's called in military circles a "Personal Defense Weapon." Considered to be among the best small submachine guns in the world, it has a cyclic rate of fire of 900 rounds per minute, placing it in the same class of weapon as the H&K MP5K and the Micro-Uzi.

In 1993 Steyr introduced a pistol version—the SPP (Special Purpose Pistol)—of its TMP submachine gun. By contrast, the semiautomatic-only SPP belongs in the same class as the H&K SP89 and UZI pistol. Aside from its capability as a semiautomatic-fire-only pistol, the SPP is different in several other ways from the selective-fire TMP. It's slightly longer, comes equipped with a barrel shroud, and lacks a forward grip. The SPP features a standard 15-shot magazine that fits flush with the bottom of the grip making it easier to reload under stress. Because its magazine is locked in front of the trigger guard, rather than into the grip, there is no forward handgrip.

With its rotary-barrel locking system—the same used in the Steyr-Hahn Model 1912 pistol—the SPP's barrel does not tip; rather, it recoils straight back for more and better accuracy. Although the SPP makes extensive use of plastics, it is still large and heavy by pistol standards. Overall, the SPP is a well-made, accurate and reliable pistol, one that's designed for minimal maintenance. And, like most pistols derived from submachine gun designs, it's extremely sturdy. It's also quite expensive, though, and probably too large for most people's tastes. Steyr may well have made a mistake in producing this gun, which strays a bit too far off the beaten path, instead of focusing on a revival of its Model GB.

STEYR SPP

Manufacturer	Years Produced	Caliber/Capacity	Dimensions
Steyr-Daimler-Puch Steyr, Austria Former Importer: Gun South, Inc. Trussville, AL	1993–Present (Importation halted 1995)	9mm/15 or 30 rounds	Barrel Length: 5.9" O.A. Length: 12.75" Height: 6.1" Width: 1.5" Weight: 42 oz. (unloaded); 49 oz. (loaded)

TAURUS MODEL PT-92 SERIES

When Beretta won a contract from Brazil in 1977 for 40,000 Model 92 pistols, one of the stipulations was that the 9mm guns be produced in Brazil. To satisfy that requirement, Beretta expanded its already existing plant in Sao Paulo. Brazil's military Model 92 took a few years to complete, but once it was finished Beretta was faced with the problem of what to do with the machinery it had used to make the pistols. The cost of shipping it all back to Italy would be exorbitant; moreover, it wasn't really needed there—Beretta already had Model 92 production facilities at its home factory. In a decision which Beretta planners have surely regretted ever since, Beretta sold the machinery, drawings and jigs for Model 92 production outright to Brazil. The company exacted no licensing or royalty arrangements from Brazil, and the sale price (which is still undisclosed but was certainly very large) gave Brazil the right to unlimited production of the Model 92. Apparently Beretta simply underestimated how much Brazil could do in competing with them. But serious competition it became, for Brazil's Taurus PT-92 is not only fully competitive in features and performance with Beretta's best products, but it also sells for a lower price.

The Taurus PT-92, like the Beretta original, is a 9mm double-action automatic pistol with a 10- or 15-shot magazine. It uses the same underbarrel locking block and open slide as Beretta's Model 92, plus an aluminum-alloy frame to reduce weight. As with most guns that have been in production for a long time, the PT-92 has had several changes made since its introduction in 1980. Early examples had a rounded trigger guard, while more recent models show a prominent recurved one. The magazine release on early PT-92s was located at the bottom of the left side of the grip, in common with Beretta's Model 92 and Model 951.

The Taurus PT-92 series pistols retain the popular M1911-style frame-mounted safety. A third decocking position is also added, making it even more competitive with the Beretta Model 92FS (top).

In 1982, Taurus introduced a variation of the PT-92, the PT-99, with adjustable sights. In 1985 another improved version, the Model 92AF, appeared, complete with ambidextrous safety levers and magazine release repositioned to the left rear of the trigger guard. This redesigned pistol also

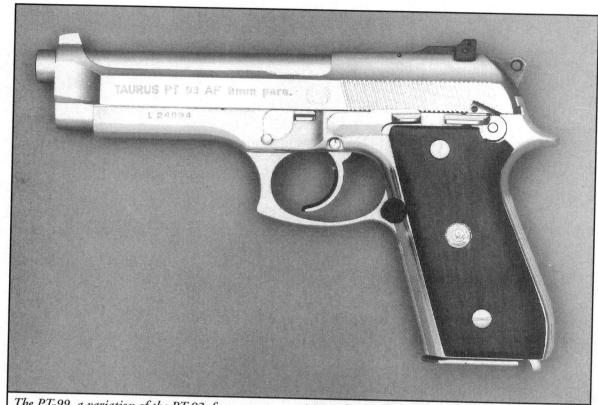

The PT-99, a variation of the PT-92, features a two-position safety lever and blued, stainless steel or nickel finish (shown above). Note also the adjustable sight.

had a firing-pin lock that could be deactivated only by pulling the trigger, and an improved feeding ramp for chambering hollowpoint bullets more effectively. A stainless-steel PT-92AFS appeared in 1990, although its frame remained aluminum alloy anodized to match the top half of the pistol in color.

Taurus further modified the PT-92 series in 1992 by adding a third position to the safety levers, allowing mechanical decocking of the hammer. This was in response to U.S. police demands for a pistol that didn't force them to deactivate the safety while at the same time restraining the hammer (with the thumb) and pulling the trigger. This improved version, along with the PT-100/101 series in .40 S&W, also underwent the change to AFD configuration.

Even though Brazil's updates of the PT-92 series roughly parallel those which Beretta made on its own Model 92, the Taurus pistol has evolved somewhat differently and currently has very little, if any, interchangeability of parts with the Italian-made Model 92. Otherwise, the two guns are very similar in size, performance and operating features.

In whatever generation of the PT-92 being discussed, the manual safety goes down to fire and up to safe. In the latest variation, the PT-92AFS, a third safety position below the fire setting decocks the hammer, while the upper portion of the grip is relieved so the safety lever can go down to the decock setting. All PT-92s — except the PT-92D (for police only) — have a half-cock notch on the hammer.

Because of its versatile safety system, the Taurus PT-92 offers outstanding tactical flexibility. The shooter can carry it with the hammer decocked and the safety off, ready for an immediate double-action first shot (top). The pistol can also be carried with the hammer cocked and the safety up in its "on" position — in the well-known "cocked and locked" position (center); or it can be carried with the hammer decocked and the manual safety applied (bottom).

The PT-92 is a well-made pistol, although some will argue that it doesn't quite meet Beretta's high standards of fit and finish. This may be true, but the Taurus PT-92 comes mighty close. Of its three finishes—blued, satin nickel or stainless steel—the blued finish is most common, consisting of highly polished slide flats and matte blue on the rest of the slide. The satin nickel gun is the most attractive, while the stainless-steel version is too bright and poorly matched in color between the slide and its anodized aluminum frame. The grips of early models are usually made of smooth, thick hardwood, although many pistols made since 1994 have checkered wooden ones. Checkered plastic grips are available on special order. Because of basic differences in their magazine releases and safety arrangements, the grips of the three generations of PT-92s do not interchange. The thick, smooth wooden grips, by the way, are awkward for small-handed shooters to use, a shortcoming partially compensated by the superior safety arrangement.

Unlike recent Berettas, which require an

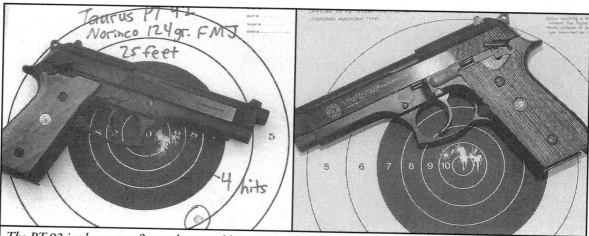

The PT-92 is pleasant to fire and reasonably accurate, although its heavy double-action first shot tends to spoil otherwise tight groups. The five-shot offhand group shown at left was fired from 25 feet. With the DA shot included, the group measures 3.3 inches; without it, the measurement is an outstanding .8 inch. Another five-shot group (right) with a newer model spanned a mere .9 inch and is perfectly centered on the target.

awkward upward motion on the manual safety to fire, the manual safety on the Taurus wipes down quickly into the fire position. However, the gun must be taken off safe for loading and unloading. Its sights are quite good, too, although not as prominent as those found on the newer Berettas.

All pistols of the PT-92 type are flawlessly reliable when used with both FMJ and jacketed hollowpoint ammunition. Although these pistols tend to throw a double-action first shot wide of the single-action follow-up shots (because of the heavier double-action trigger pull) accuracy is quite good. Our best five-shot offhand groups from 25 feet ran 0.8 inch (using Federal 9BP 115-gr JHP) for the 1992 version a PT-99AFD with adjustable sights. From 50 feet, two five-shot offhand groups measured 2.0 inches (using Winchester 124-gr FMJ) for the PT-92AF and 2.7 inches (using Winchester Silvertip 115-gr JHP) for the PT-99AFD. A stainless-steel Model 92AFS was also tested and proved less accurate than its blued brethren. Its best group was a 2.5-inch five-shot pattern from 25 feet out, using Federal 9BP 115-grain JHPs.

Overall, the PT-92 is slightly less refined than the Beretta Model 92, with a somewhat inferior trigger pull and—at lease in the stainless versions—less exacting in fit and finish. However, the Taurus pistol has a significantly lower price tag than the Beretta pistol, which makes it a good value. Many people will also favor its safety arrangements, particularly the three-position manual safety lever currently in use.

TAURUS MODEL PT-92 SERIES

Manufacturer	Years Produced	Caliber/Capacity	Dimensions
Forjas Taurus Sao Paulo, Brazil Imported by: Taurus Int'l Miami, FL	1980–Present	9mm/10 or 15 rounds	Barrel Length: 4.9" O.A. Length: 8.5" Height: 5.39" Width: 1.45" Weight: 34 oz. (unloaded); 41 oz. (loaded)

WALTHER P4

By the mid-1970s, Walther's 7.65mm (.32 ACP caliber) Police Pistol (Model PP) had served the German police well for more than 40 years, and its 9mm Model P.38 had armed German troops for nearly as long. And yet, even while it enjoyed an almost undisputed monopoly of West Germany's military and police handgun production during the first 30 years of the postwar era, company officials were starting to think seriously about replacing the PP with a more powerful, more modern design. Increasing terrorist activity, notably the Palestinian terrorist attack on Israeli athletes at the 1972 Munich Olympics, caused the West German police to feel seriously outgunned. The appearance of the much-heralded Heckler & Koch Model P9S was yet another sign that Walther's comfortable lead in German handgun design and manufacture was fast eroding.

At first, Walther tried to solidify its deteriorating position by the logical and relatively inexpensive method of refining existing designs. In 1974 the company tried to interest the German police in a

Walther's P4 (bottom) represented a slight improvement over the standard P.38/P1 (top), but it was not nearly as successful; fewer than 7,000 were manufactured in the mid-1970s. Although externally they appear very similar, internally, the P4 featured a new decocking lever installed on the back of the slide and a hexagonal reinforcing pin made of steel set into the frame to strengthen it against recoil.

modified and upgraded PP, the PP Super, which was chambered in 9mm Ultra (also called 9mm police). This round was created originally in a prewar attempt by Germany to develop the most powerful round usable in a blowback pistol; as such, it offered substantial improvements in accuracy and power over the .32 ACP round of the PP. Even though the PP Super was a good pistol, the police sensibly decided against adopting a new round and chose instead a 9mm Parabellum handgun. This round was, after all, already NATO standard and would simplify the supply situation. It would also offer ammunition interchangeability with military stockpiles during an emergency. Thus did the PP Super fail rather quickly after only limited use by West German police services. A civilian version of the pistol, sometimes offered in .380 ACP caliber, also made little headway, forcing Walther to drop the PP Super after only a few years.

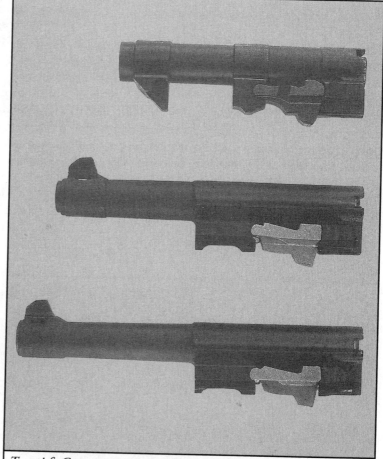

To satisfy German government requirements, the barrel of the P4 (center) was shortened by a half inch compared to the P.38 (bottom). The P5 (top), which followed the P4, featured yet a shorter barrel and was one of the reasons it was issued in the hundreds of thousands.

Once the decision was made to change the time-honored German police handgun caliber from .32 ACP to the more powerful 9mm, a committee of police experts developed a set of stringent specifications for a new pistol. The specifications included a magazine capacity of eight rounds in 9mm, a compact size of no more than 7 inches long and 5 inches high, reliability testing (including a 5,000-round endurance test without malfunction), and in the interest of speed, the elimination of a manual safety. The end result was a safe-to-carry handgun with an immediate double-action, first-shot capability—one that could be safely carried with a loaded chamber and still be drawn and fired immediately.

These specifications definitely pushed the pistol-making state-of-the-art at that time, but soon several German companies began working on weapons that could meet these requirements and thus win lucrative military and police contracts. They knew that large civilian sales frequently followed official orders, so there was plenty of incentive for Germany's best firearms designers to enter the competition.

The first entry, which appeared in 1974, was a pistol (although revolvers could also be chambered in 9mm, none were forthcoming), which came, not surprisingly, from Walther. Since the German police and military were already using the designations "P2" and "P3" for other pistols, Walther optimistically named its new gun the P4.

Built on the same anodized aluminum-alloy frame as the post-WWII P.38/P1, the new P4 featured an eight-shot magazine, with the barrel and slide altered to fit government requirements, making the barrel of the P4 shorter by almost half an inch than the P.38/P1 barrel. Its slide was heavier and stronger than the P.38's, with a removable cover over its firing pin and signal pin to make the slide a one-piece affair. As a result, no loaded chamber signal pin had to be installed, as in the earlier P.38. The P4 also had thicker sights and a shorter, straighter spur hammer than the P.38, while width and height were identical.

The greatest differences between the P4 and the famous P.38, however, were internal, not external. Its safety arrangements were greatly altered, for example, and a new decocking device, similar to the P.38's manual safety, was installed on the back of the slide. By pushing this lever down with the thumb, the hammer dropped safely onto a loaded chamber without the possibility of accidental discharge. While the manual safety on the P.38 worked in much the same way, there was an important difference: on the P.38, the manual safety could be kept in the down, or safe, position until the gun was fired; but on the P4, once the thumb lever was pushed down, releasing and lowering the hammer, it automatically returned to the up, or fire, position. That's why it was called a decocking lever and not a safety.

Another safety device on the P4 is its pin, which moves vertically. Also, thanks to its slightly altered internal arrangements and heftier slide, the P4 weighs slightly more than the P.38. Other P4 improvements that have been incorporated into P.38s from 1975 on are improved sights and a hexagonal reinforcing pin made of steel set into the frame to strengthen it against recoil.

Walther wanted the P4 to be carried with its hammer down and a round in the chamber, ready to fire instantly the way a modern

Walther offered an even shorter-barreled variant of the P4, the P.38K. Its barrel was so short —2.75 inches — that the front sight had to be fitted to the slide rather than the barrel.

double-action revolver does. Whereas a loaded chamber indicator and manual safety are not necessary in this design, safe gun handling becomes even more critical. The P4 was ready for a quick first double-action shot when a round was loaded into the chamber, and thus it met that part of the German pistol specification. Its design assumed (and required) an even higher degree of professionalism, maturity and responsibility on the part of its owner than was usual.

When Walther sent samples of the P4 to the German government for testing, the police handgun commission deemed the pistol unsatisfactory. It did not pass the endurance trials and failed to offer sufficient advantages over the PP or P1 to justify its purchase. Thus, the P4 never did receive the official police or military approval that Walther felt it deserved. Its similarity to the standard military P1, however, resulted in limited police and military use amounting to some 6,500 pieces (it was also available for civilian use as the P.38 IV).

At the same time, Walther offered smaller numbers of an even shorter-barreled variant, called the P.38K. Its barrel was so short (2.75 inches) that the front sight had to be fitted to the slide rather than the barrel. Both Walther and Manurhin—a French company that has built Walther pistols under license since 1952—made P4s, but the P.38K was made only by Walther. This pistol saw even less official use than the P4; in all, production of the entire P4/P.38K series amounted to less than 10,000 pieces.

Although the P4 is no longer in production, Interarms has, since the mid-1980s, imported many of them into the U.S., where they can often be found in gun stores or at gun shows. In view of their intended role originally as police/military pistols, the P4s sport a matte black Parkerized finish on the slide and barrel, with the aluminum frame anodized a glossy black.

Since most serious European and American handgunners are familiar with the P.38, the operating procedures of the P4 offer few surprises. To load, you merely insert a loaded magazine, draw back the slide, then release it to run forward and chamber the top round (remember, though, that the P4 has no loaded chamber indicator). Next, release the hammer, depressing and then releasing the decocking lever, which then lowers the hammer before springing back up into firing position. There's no way to lock the decocking lever in the "safe" position with the P4; hence, no carelessness in gun handling can be tolerated with this firearm (or with any other type of gun, for that matter). Once loaded, the pistol is ready for a double-action first shot. For a lighter single-action trigger pull on the first round, the hammer can also be thumb-cocked. Upon recoil, the slide cocks the hammer, so that all shots after the first one are single action.

Once the last shot is fired, the slide locks open, as in the P.38. The magazine is removed by pressing back the release latch at the bottom rear (heel) of the frame and then inserting either a fresh or empty magazine. Next, the slide is moved forward, either by depressing the hold-open lever with the right thumb or by pulling the slide back slightly before letting it go. Incidentally, neither the P4 nor the P.38 contain a magazine safety. Remember, once the magazine has been removed, with a round still in the chamber, this pistol will fire when the trigger is pulled back.

Despite its shorter barrel and reduced sight radius, the P4 does not seem to give up much if any accuracy to the P.38; in fact, the P4 is as accurate as most military-style handguns. Our best rapid-fire five-shot offhand group from 25 feet (with a double-action first shot) measured 1.1 inches, using Hansen 123-grain FMJ ammunition. Later, several 50-foot groups opened up considerably wider, sometimes to 5 inches or more, mostly because the double-action first shot landed two or three inches from the follow-up single-action shots. If all five shots were fired single-action at 50 feet, a P4 could easily shoot a 3-inch group.

With the new so-called "Wondernines" being produced by Beretta, SIG and Walther, how and where does the "failed" P4 fit in? Historically, it represents an important link in the evolution from the P.38—the first successful double-action military 9mm pistol—to our most modern pistols. The P4, which retains the basic configuration, rugged construction and classic design of the P.38, also pioneered in doing away with the manual safety (the classic Polish Radom pistol had a decocking lever as early as 1935, but it was a single-action gun that lay fallow for many years). For those interested in Walther pistols and the 9mm's designs, or who simply want to own a relatively inexpensive and compact automatic pistol, the P4 is worth a close look.

WALTHER P4

Manufacturer	Years Produced	Caliber/Capacity	Dimensions
Carl Walther Waffenfabrik Ulm, Germany Former Importer: Interarms Alexandria, VA	1974–1982	9mm/8 rounds	Barrel Length: 4.5" O.A. Length: 8.0" Height: 5.4" Width: 1.5" Weight: 29 oz. (unloaded); 33 oz. (loaded)

WALTHER P5

When the P4 (*see* previous listing) failed to attract a major West German official contract, Walther began to develop a new 9mm pistol design that would satisfy the authorities. Using the P.38 as a point of departure once again, the company eventually came up with a radically new, improved design: the P5.

Introduced in 1979, this pistol has a completely new design. While it utilizes the basic double-action mechanism and eight-shot magazine of the P.38, it shares none of the P.38's major components. Even its magazine, which holds the same number of rounds, is shorter than, and non-interchangeable with, the P.38. Other influences of the P4 on the P5 design are seen in its firing-pin safety, which moves vertically, and its use of a

This view of the Walther P5 clearly shows the highlighted sights, the left-hand ejection and the large decocking lever.

Although the P5 bears little external resemblance to the P.38, it owes much to the older pistol for its inspiration. With the P5 disassembled, the similarity is evident in the configuration of the barrel and magazine.

decocking lever instead of a manual safety. The decocking lever on the P5, however, is repositioned to the frame for more convenient use. The P5 also has the same hexagonal steel reinforcing pin running through its aluminum-alloy frame. This steel pin, which the P4 pioneered, appears to have eliminated the frame-cracking that occasionally occurred in weary postwar P.38s, most of which also had alloy frames.

Having passed stringent West German tests, including the firing of 10,000 rounds without malfunction, the P5 has proved a well-designed pistol whose widespread use has been hindered only by it high cost. Nevertheless, the P5 remains in use by the Dutch national police (whose original purchase was for 25,000 pistols and who have since ordered 10,000 more) and several West German and Scandinavian police forces as well.

The P5 is an accurate and reliable pistol, with a good grip and excellent sights. Its double-action trigger pull, typical of most Walthers, is a little too heavy and unresponsive for some, and it is much too thick. In fact, it was the result of numerous complaints about its size that Walther went on to develop the P5 Compact (discussed in the companion volume, THE COMPLETE GUIDE TO COMPACT HANDGUNS).

WALTHER P5

Manufacturer	Years Produced	Caliber/Capacity	Dimensions
Carl Walther Waffenfabrik Ulm, Germany Former Importer: Interarms Alexandria, VA	1979–1996	9mm/8 rounds	Barrel Length: 3.5" O.A. Length: 7.1" Height: 5.1" Width: 1.45" Weight: 28 oz. (unloaded); 32 oz. (loaded)

WALTHER P88

Walther's Model P88 was originally created to compete in the U.S. military's XM9 pistol trials of 1984. As the official testing agency representing all our armed forces, the U.S. Army found the Walther pistol unsatisfactory in several areas, notably for its poor resistance to corrosion. Walther subsequently refined the design and introduced it to the civilian market in the late 1980s. It has since been modestly successful among civilians, despite its high price.

In many ways, the P88 is a radical departure from traditional Walther designs. The company's other big-bore service pistols all use a variation of the underbarrel locking block that was pioneered in the P.38. While this makes for a sturdy and reliable mechanism and promotes good accuracy, it also requires a wide slide to accommodate the locking block. For the P88, Walther turned to an older design: the short-recoil system and tilting barrel designed by John Browning. In this system, the upper rear portion of the P.38 barrel locks into engagement with the forward edge of the ejection port on the slide. A cam under the rear

Compared to the left-side view above, this right-side view shows that virtually all of the P88's controls, including its magazine release and operating lever, are ambidextrous; only the slide release is set up exclusively for right-handed use.

end of the barrel then drops the barrel out of engagement with the slide. Interestingly, the P88 not only is the first production pistol made by Walther to use a variation of Browning's short-recoil system, it is also the company's first gun to use a double-column, high-capacity magazine. It originally came with a 15-round magazine, reduced later to 10 for civilians.

Operating controls on the P88 are similar to those found on the P5. An operating lever, located on both sides of the P88 frame, (the P5's operating lever appears only on the left side of the frame) decocks the hammer after the gun has been loaded; or it allows the slide to move forward after it has locked back on an empty magazine. A firing-pin lock prevents firing until the shooter presses the trigger all the way to the rear. Virtually all of the P88's controls, including its magazine release, are

Built with exacting care, the P88 is probably the most accurate production military-style pistol in the world, despite its heavy double-action trigger pull which tends to throw the first shot wide. In this test it did not, however, shooting a five-shot offhand group from 25 feet that measures only 1 inch.

ambidextrous; only the slide release is set up exclusively for right-handed use.

In developing the P88, Walther was anxious not to relinquish the inherent accuracy of the P.38-style underbarrel locking block found on the P.38, P4 and P5 pistols. Having built the P88 with exacting care, therefore, Walther created what is probably the most accurate production military-style pistol in the world. Despite its heavy double-action trigger pull, the P88 is a superbly accurate handgun. Like the P5C, the P88 pistol tested for this book performed best with Winchester USA brand ammunition, which uses 115-grain FMJ bullets. Our best five-shot 25-foot offhand group with this ammunition measured 1.1 inches across, while a 50-foot offhand group measured 3.7 inches (with most of the spread taken up by the double-action first shot). Reliability was flawless throughout using a wide variety of ammunition brands and types.

Among the P88's weak points are its overly thick grips, which make it tough for a small-handed shooter to hold. Also, its disassembly catch—located on the left side of the frame just above the trigger guard—can be lowered accidentally during shooting, thereby bringing the slide out of battery and rendering the pistol inoperable. The P88's takedown catch also lacks a detent like the one used by Beretta on its Model 92 (it locks the takedown catch in place until the shooter is ready to fieldstrip the pistol).

For all its exceptional qualities, the future of the P88 is by no means assured. In fact,

The P88 is the first Walther production pistol to use a variation of Browning's short-recoil system, the influence of which is obvious in this disassembled view. It is also the first Walther pistol to feature a double-column magazine.

the company did come out with a compact version, which seems to have replaced the larger model. The P88 Compact is lighter, with a shorter barrel and lower price tag, and boasts the same target-grade accuracy. So if you're a serious collector of Walther firearms, time may be running out. For all that, the P88 is truly an impressive gun. And, while expensive, it still ranks among the best-shooting 9mm pistols available at any price.

WALTHER P88

Manufacturer	Years Produced	Caliber/Capacity	Dimensions
Carl Walther Waffenfabrik Ulm, Germany Former Importer: Interarms Alexandria, VA	1983–1994	9mm/10 or 15 rounds	Barrel Length: 4.0" O.A. Length: 7.4" Height: 5.0" Width: 1.4" Weight: 31.5 oz. (unloaded); 39 oz. (loaded)

6. EMERGING TECHNOLOGIES AND FUTURE TRENDS

Many will argue that, barring some major technological advance, handgun development has reached a plateau. Nevertheless, some interesting developments are noteworthy. Not all of them will reach fruition, but it is worth looking at some of the present trends and possible future directions of handgun development.

Gun Metal. The traditional material used to make handguns and most other firearms is steel. This metal has many desirable qualities well-suit-

The increasing use of polymers instead of steel represents a trend in handgun production that is likely to continue. Shown here are a Glock pistol (top) and a Grendel, both of which feature strong, lightweight polymer frames.

ed for the manufacture of guns. However, steel also has its disadvantages. It is relatively heavy for its strength and, unless scrupulously maintained, is subject to corrosion. To produce handguns that are lighter, firearms engineers have for decades used aluminum alloys to make the frame, receiver and other parts. But while substituting aluminum for steel does indeed lighten a gun, it also weakens it, because aluminum does not possess the

same strength as steel. Guns made of plastic (polymer) frames and other components are gaining in popularity, thanks to gunmakers such as Heckler & Koch and Glock. These industry pioneers have been joined by several others, including Colt (Model 2000 All-American), Star (Ultra Star) and Smith & Wesson (Sigma Series).

For those who prefer all-metal construction, consider a material that is every bit as strong as steel yet weighs only about half as much: titanium. Not only is it strong and light, it is now used for making hammers, triggers and other parts. It has also been used in barrels, and Ruger has experimented with pistol frames made from titanium. And at least one handgun—a revolver—has been made almost entirely of titanium with good results. It will probably be only a matter of time before handguns made wholly or at least partly of titanium reach production status.

Sighting Devices. In the past, many of the sights found on handguns were terribly undersized. Fortunately, handgun sighting equipment has improved tremendously. To prove a point, simply compare the sights on an early-production pistol with a recent example of the same gun, such as a Walther PPK, FN High Power or Colt Government Model. Beyond merely increasing the size of handgun sights, there exists a considerable amount of interest in creating "night sights," which can operate in low light or even lightless situations. Actually, sights equipped with luminous highlights have existed for decades. Walther, for one, offered optional radium-illumined night sights for its PP and PPK pistols as far back as the 1930s. Modern versions of these sights generally consist of three tritium-filled capsules, with a single dot on the front sight and two dots on the rear sight. In a further development of this idea, some pistols are now set up to receive laser sighting devices, which project a beam of bright light onto a target. Modern laser units are small, light

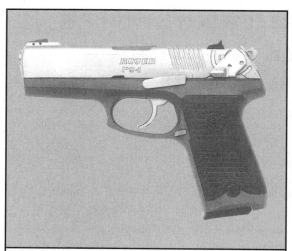

Sighting devices are witnessing improvements that are sure to continue. Ruger's Model P94, for example, comes from the factory with compact, lightweight integral laser sighting equipment already built into its frame.

and far less expensive than they once were. Some can project a beam bright enough to enable a gun/laser sight combination to work out to several hundred yards.

One major complaint with luminous and laser sights is that they don't identify clearly what the shooter is seeing. Is that looming black mass ahead a legitimate target? Before a shooter presses the trigger and fires a round, he or she had better be sure of the target. Small but powerful flashlights that attach to a pistol may prove superior. In any event, fancy sights are no substitute for good shooting skills.

Ammunition. Handgun ammunition has changed very little since the turn of the century. Although the propellants (powders) have improved, cartridge construction is much the same as it has always been. Since the 1960s, however, a promising development called caseless

A recent version of Smith & Wesson's Model 5904 (top) carries the fixed Novak sights first used on the "Third Generation" line. The Model 5904 is also offered with adjustable sights (bottom), which are protected by "ears" found on many military weapons.

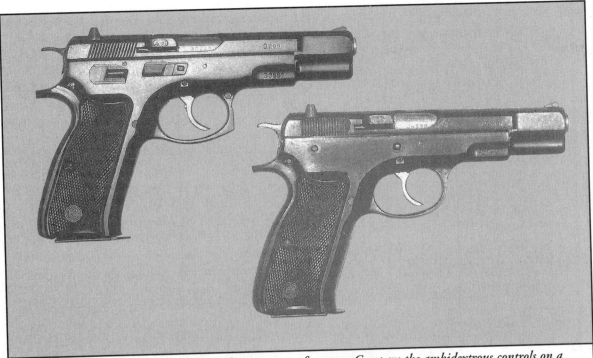

Ambidexterity is a growing trend among firearms manufacturers. Compare the ambidextrous controls on a recent CZ 85 (top) with the exclusively right-handed controls of an otherwise similar, early CZ 75.

ammunition has slowly reached production status. Here, a propellant material is molded into a solid shape without requiring a metal cartridge case to contain it. The primer fits into the rear of this solid propellant. Hence, the entire round is consumed in the act of firing it, thereby eliminating the extraction and ejection cycle that so often causes difficulties in all types of automatic and semiautomatic guns, including pistols. Caseless ammunition was originally conceived for use in rifles by Heckler & Koch, which explored its use in an innovative new rifle, the G11. After an extended 20-year development period, the West German government was about to approve this product for its armed forces when the reunification of East and West Germany became a reality. Faced with the enormous expense of rehabilitating East Germany, the new Germany put its plans for the G11 on hold. Voere in Austria also introduced a sporter rifle using a .223-caliber caseless round in 1993. It's only a matter of time

The Beretta Model 84 was probably the first production gun backed by a major manufacturer that catered to the needs of left-handed shooters. In addition to the ambidextrous safety shown, the magazine release can easily be turned to the right side of the frame.

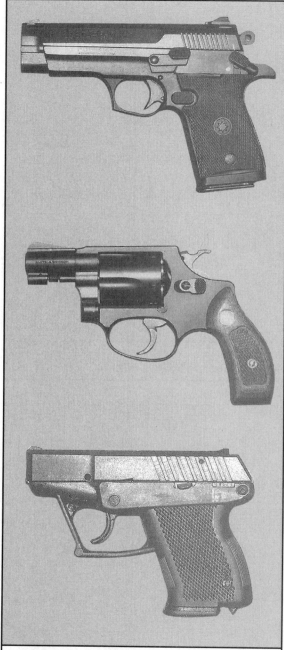

Modern technology allows smaller handguns to do more than they once did. The S&W Chiefs Special (center) with its late 1940s technology, offers five shots of .38 Special. Star's Firestar (top), which is similar in size, offers six rounds of the more powerful 9mm or .40 S&W, while the Grendel P-12 (bottom) can fire a full 11 rounds of .380 ACP ammo.

before some innovative company develops and markets a pistol using caseless ammunition. Its advantages would be considerable, chiefly in the area of greater reliability and rate of fire.

Meanwhile, improvements in the field of conventional cartridge ammunition have evolved. Thanks to improved propellants and bullet design, handgun rounds that were once considered marginal for self-defense—such as the .380 ACP, .38 Special and 9mm—have greatly improved. There may even be room for new conventional handgun cartridges. Until 1990 it was thought by some that the 9mm Parabellum, despite grave reservations about it, was virtually unassailable. Then along came the .40 S&W cartridge, causing the 9mm's commanding lead to erode virtually overnight. Another interesting cartridge backed by Smith & Wesson is the .356 TSW. Firing a 147-grain bullet at over 1200 feet per second, this powerful round surpasses the .40 S&W in energy and closely approaches the .357 Magnum round. Eventually, this new caliber could make a serious impact on American handgun design in the next millenium, just as the .40 S&W round has done. But don't look for the 9mm Parabellum, .45 ACP, .38 Special and .380 ACP to become obsolete—numerous guns already use these calibers.

Other Trends. As improved holster designs help shooters conceal larger handguns more effectively, look for gun manufacturers to make even smaller guns in effective handgun calibers. A truly compact 9mm Parabellum pistol, for instance, is not yet a reality, but such a development is certainly in progress. Also, as the needs of left-handed people become more generally known, more and more handguns are being modified—or made from scratch—with ambidextrous operating controls. Beretta's Model 84 pistol, introduced in 1975, was perhaps the first production handgun from a major manufacturer to be set up for ambidextrous operation. Actually, it makes sense to design any handgun for use by either hand.

7. DISASSEMBLING WALTHER PP-TYPE PISTOLS

A Walther PP-type pistol requires periodic disassembly for cleaning after maintenance, for inspection after storage, and for replacement of worn or broken parts. In general, this pistol and others like it should be disassembled and cleaned as soon as possible after firing, or about once a month when in storage (but on a daily basis while the gun is carried in a holster and immediately after it has been dropped into water, mud or sand). The Walther PP-type design has been copied throughout the world and remains the most common construction method for all medium-frame automatic pistols. Designed for field-stripping without tools, the Walther PP-type pistol does require a screwdriver for removing the grips. The model used to illustrate the following instructions is a Chinese Type 59, a copy of the Soviet-designed Model PM or Makarov pistol. With slight variations, these directions serve for virtually all Walther PP-type pistols.

Before beginning with the disassembly itself, let's look at the key parts of the pistol:

• **Slide:** the rectangular sleeve surrounding the top and sides of the barrel, holding it, the spring and all parts of the firing mechanism in position. During firing, the slide moves back and forth to operate the loading mechanism. To facilitate loading and cocking, the rear end of the slide has a serrated surface.

• **Barrel:** the cylindrical tube through which

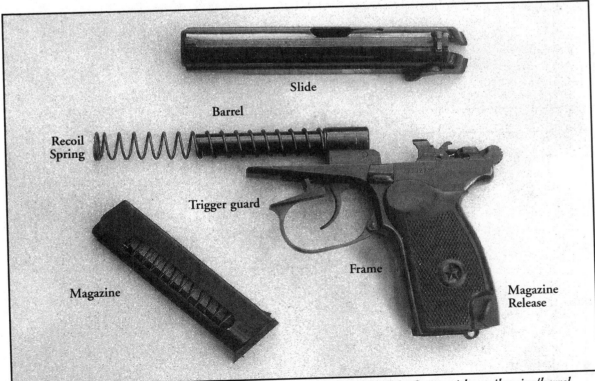

The Walther PP-type pistol can be disassembled into three basic parts: slide, frame with recoil spring/barrel, and magazine.

cartridges pass as they are fired.

- **Recoil spring:** the strong coil spring that allows the slide and barrel to move forward following recoil after each shot. In PP-type pistols, the spring is coiled around the out side of the barrel, which also serves as a guide rod to prevent the spring from kinking.

- **Frame:** also called the receiver, it is the large part of the pistol that the shooter holds or grips. It houses the magazine and other internal parts of the pistol, while providing the base to which the trigger guard is attached on the outside.

- **Magazine:** the rectangular metal container that holds the cartridges.

- **Magazine release:** lever or button at the bottom of the frame which, when pressed, releases the magazine from the frame.

1. The first step in disassembling any firearm is to remove all ammunition from the magazine and the firing chamber. With the Walther PP, press the magazine release, then draw the magazine completely out from the bottom of the handle portion of the frame.

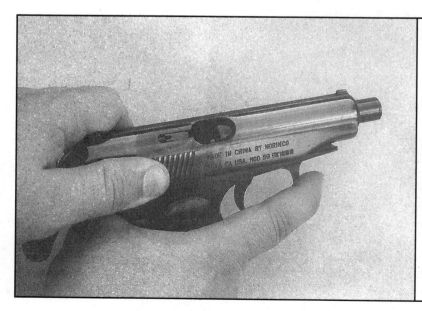

2. Next, draw the slide back as far as it will go, thereby ejecting any rounds left in the firing chamber. Warning: Removal of the magazine alone will not make the gun safe. If a round remains in the firing chamber, one shot can still be fired from the pistol, whether intentionally or by accident. Therefore, the chamber must be carefully cleared of any round. Also remember to unload in the order outlined above—removing the magazine, then drawing back the slide. Reversing the order will reload the pistol with one round, creating a dangerous situation.

3. With the gun now completely unloaded, pull down the trigger guard from the front with the left hand and push it all the way to the left until it stays in the open position. In some models, it may be necessary to hold the trigger guard in the open position.

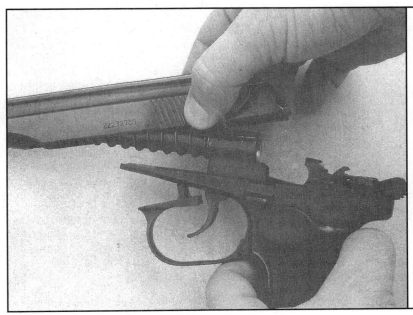

4. With the trigger guard hinged down, draw back the slide and lift up the rear end, detaching it from the frame. Then push the trigger guard forward off the barrel, separating it from the frame. The pistol has now been disassembled into three basic parts—slide, frame and magazine—which is usually sufficient for normal cleaning.

If necessary, the recoil spring can be removed from the barrel by pulling it off from the front of the pistol. The grip screw(s) can also be removed if desired. Once the slide has been removed from the frame, DO NOT press the trigger. Doing so can cause the hammer to fly forward in an uncontrolled, hyper-extended fashion, thus damaging it.

Reassembly is a straight forward reversal of steps 1-4. If the recoil spring has been removed, reassemble it by sliding the narrow end closer to the breech (rear) end of the barrel and its wide end closer to the muzzle (front) end of the barrel.

8. HANDGUN SAFETY

Every time you pick up a gun, you're risking your life and that of anyone who falls within range. Remember, some handgun bullets can travel a mile or more. It stands to reason that we all need to take reasonable precautions to avoid accidents. One of these precautions is avoidance. "An ounce of prevention is worth a pound of cure" may be old advice, but it's still valid. By avoiding situations that foster illegal use of handguns, you'll have gone a long way toward achieving gun safety. Take precautions that include handling guns yourself in a safe and sane manner, and seeing to it that members of your family do likewise.

JEFF COOPER'S FOUR RULES FOR SAFE GUN HANDLING

Jeff Cooper, whose teachings and writings on handgunning have contributed more to the development of combat pistolcraft than any other expert in the field, has developed four easy-to-learn safety rules. If faithfully followed, they can make accidental shootings virtually impossible. Cooper's rules are:

1. Always assume that all guns are loaded, and that there's no such thing as an unloaded gun. Observing this simple rule can provide the proper sense of awe and respect for the potential dangers that gun ownership engenders. Always remember that any type of gun—no matter how small, old or worthless it may be—can cause death and tragedy.

2. Never point a gun at anyone or anything you don't intend to shoot. Remember, not only is every gun presumed to be loaded, it's always pointing somewhere. Unless you've determined that your life depends on shooting your handgun, keep the muzzle pointed away from all innocent persons and valuable property.

3. Keep your finger off the trigger until you're ready to shoot. The fact is, your trigger finger is most comfortable when it's resting on the trigger. Guns are designed that way. To avoid

a needless tragedy, teach yourself never to put your finger on the trigger until the moment you're ready to fire a shot. Until then, your finger must stay off the trigger, usually alongside the frame next to the trigger, or resting with its tip on the leading edge of the trigger guard. In fact, the trigger guard is a safety device designed to prevent foreign objects from catching against the trigger and causing the gun to fire. Following this one rule alone can greatly reduce the number of accidental shootings.

4. Before you shoot, identify your target. Once a bullet begins its deadly flight, you cannot recall it. No amount of hand-wringing can restore a lost life. Make certain you know who or what lies in the path of a bullet before you fire.

Some corollaries to these four basic rules are also worth mentioning:

Become Thoroughly Familiar with Your Firearm. Know how it works and what it can—and cannot—do. Know all the features it possesses, then practice firing it under safe conditions. When target shooting, check the backstop before firing. Is it adequate to stop the kind of cartridges you're using? In general, it's better to shoot at an approved shooting range rather than out in the woods, because you'll have the added protection of established safety regulations and procedures, plus an approved backstop. Practice different "styles" of shooting in addition to target shooting.

Keep Your Gun Clean. Keep your handgun scrupulously clean, and make sure the barrel is clear of obstructions before you begin shooting. Always make sure the gun is completely unloaded before cleaning it. Removing the magazine of an automatic pistol, remember, does not fully clear the weapon. There could still be a round left in the firing chamber. To be sure, always remove the magazine fully from the pistol, then draw back the slide to its fullest extent. This will eject any round that's left in the chamber.

Use Safety Features to the Fullest. If there's a decocking lever or hammer-dropping safety, use it—not the trigger—to lower the hammer onto a loaded firing chamber. And when using the decocking control, remember Cooper's rule about pointing the muzzle in a safe direction. With a round in the firing chamber, do not carry an automatic pistol on the half-cock hammer setting. Even with revolvers that are mechanically safe, with a loaded cylinder and the hammer down (uncocked) over a loaded round, never cock a loaded revolver for a single-action shot unless you're absolutely certain you will fire. With the hammer of a revolver cocked, there's no way to unload the gun safely.

Don't assume that all firearms of similar make or type have the same safety features. Again, become familiar with your firearm so you know how it works. Sometimes all the designed safety features may not be fully operational.

Wear Safety Glasses and Hearing Protection When Shooting. Guns have been known to blow up and eject metal parts at high speeds back into the shooter's face, so the glasses must be sturdy and impact-resistant. Earplugs or ear-muff-type hearing protectors are fine for the ears; and using both at the same time is better still.

Use the Proper Ammunition. Some guns will operate effectively with different cartridges, but it's always a good idea to use the type of ammunition marked on the gun. Carefully inspect each round of ammunition as it's placed in the gun. Cartridges that are dented, scratched or otherwise deformed should not be fired.

Buying Previously Owned Firearms. When buying a gun secondhand, insist that all papers that came with the gun be given to you as a condition of the sale. Having all that original packaging and paperwork increases the value of the gun and helps ensure your safety—provided you stop long enough to read the owner's manual! If the seller of a secondhand gun does not have an owner's manual, then contact the manufacturer. Most reputable gun companies will send you an owner's manual free of charge. It's a good idea to read up on handguns in general before buying one. Look through some of the trade magazines and gun annuals to find out what the experts recommend. Some of the better magazines devoted to handgun-related matters include Combat Handguns, Guns, Guns & Ammo, Gun World, Petersen's Handguns, and American Handgunner.

Be Cautious about Gunsmithing. In general, it's unwise to have a gun worked on unless something is obviously wrong with it, or you've handled and fired it enough to know exactly what's needed. Most guns work reasonably well as they come from the factory, and the "break-in" period is probably as useful for shooters to accustom themselves to the gun as it is for the gun to "wear in" properly. A great deal of money can be spent on custom work in some cases, far more than the gun itself costs. Frequently extensive gunsmithing can invalidate a factory warranty on a new gun. Aside from changing a grip or a stock for a more comfortable fit, and perhaps replacing the sights or marking the front sight with bright paint, not much more should be needed.

On the other hand, some people want "action jobs" to smooth the trigger pull or "carry bevel" work to break sharp corners or edges. These improvements are fine, within reason, but they can also cost serious money. If you absolutely must have your gun customized, be sensible about it. Be certain the gun is a "keeper," because if you decide later on to sell it, you may not be able to recover whatever you've put into it. Whatever custom work you do decide to have done, be certain that the person who works on your gun knows what he or she is doing. Make sure your gunsmith is capable of doing quality work on your handgun. Just because he's an expert on M1911-type pistols doesn't make him one with a High Power.

Learn More about Safe Gun Handling. To learn more about safe gun handling, contact a local gun store, many of which conduct classes or know about someone in the area who provides qualified instruction. The National Rifle Association encourages safe gun handling and can provide the names of certified instructors in your area. You may also want to purchase a videotape on safe gun handling and review it periodically.

SAFE GUN HANDLING IN THE HOME

The precautions cited above should be taught to, and learned by, all those who own guns or are exposed to them. That leaves us with the problem: how to keep guns safe in the home. We've already discussed how important it is to keep your finger off the trigger. That way, you're much less likely to shoot an innocent person unintentionally. The movies have done a great disservice in this regard, because so many of them show unsafe gun handling practices.

Small children are curious about everything, guns included. At some point early in their lives, you need to teach your children about firearms. When they're old enough to understand, allow your children to see and touch the guns in your home and explain to them how dangerous guns are when handled improperly. As they get a little older, allow your children to fire the guns, but only under close supervision, and only if they want to. Teach them to respect guns and the power that is inherent in them. Removing the "forbidden fruit" aspect of guns usually goes a long way toward reducing the chances of your children being hurt by them. But never assume that by merely telling children not to touch guns that that will automatically keep them safe. And don't assume that a gun can't harm your children by storing it with an empty firing chamber. No safety devices are absolutely foolproof. Children are, after all, very clever at finding hidden objects and are likely to play with anything new that arouses their curiosity.

The NRA's "Eddie Eagle" Program has excellent gun safety advice for children. For a child who discovers a gun in the home or elsewhere, he/she should do three things:

1. don't touch,
2. leave the area, and
3. tell an adult.

As your children get older, stress the importance of being careful in other people's homes. You don't want your children exposed to hazards from someone who hasn't been taught properly about safe gun handling.

Always store guns locked up and unloaded. And always keep ammunition separate from the gun. It's also a good idea to invest in gun safety devices that physically disable a gun so it can't be fired. Should you find it necessary to carry a gun on the street, don't ever flash it or mention its presence merely to impress (or threaten) people. The fewer persons who know that you own or carry a gun, the better. Learn handgun retention methods in case of attack, and always stay alert or you're likely to have your own handgun taken away and used against you. Check with state and local ordinances about the legality of carrying a concealed weapon. Let your elected representatives know how you feel about the rights of law-abiding citizens to defend themselves.

Finally, some guns are safer than others, but virtually all revolvers of modern design are well-designed mechanically against accidental discharge. However, transfer bars, rebounding hammers, trigger guards, heavy double-action trigger pulls and other mechanical devices may well enhance the safety features of a given revolver, but they can never substitute for respect and common sense. Remember, you are a gun's most important safety feature. Use your head and stay safe. Your family, neighbors and all law-abiding gun owners are relying on you.

Action Arms, 191, 238
Adams double-action revolver, 15
Albion Motors, Ltd., 25-26
American Arms, Inc.
 Regulator revolver, 50, 51-52
 Spectre pistol, 161-162, 238
Ammunition, general, 21-22, 158-160, 292-294
AMT Backup, 188
Argentine FM Hi-Power pistol. *See* FM Hi-Power
Argentine Model 1927, 109
Astra Unceta y Cia pistols, 128, 196-197
 A-75, 159
 A-80, 159, 163, 271
 A-90, 163
 A-100, 159, 163-165
 Model 400, 99-101, 145-146
 Model 600, 100-101
 Model 900 series, 137, 140
 Model 1921, 99
Auto-Ordnance 1911A1 Government pistols, 166, 240

Bacon, Roger, 12
Bauska Arms, 208
Beemiller, Inc., 231
Belgian/Russian Nagant revolver, 18
Beretta, Pietro, S.p.A., 19, 117, 150, 161, 213, 284
Pistols
 Jetfire (.25 Model 950), 102-103
 Minx (.22 Model 950), 102-103
 Model 84, 293, 294
 Model 92, 104-108, 144, 152, 173-174, 206, 277
 Model 92D/92DS, 170-172
 Model 92F/92FS/M9, 40, 108, 112, 158, 167-172, 181, 191, 246, 252, 253, 254, 274, 276, 277, 280
 Model 92FSS, 169
 Model 92G, 172-173
 Model 92S/92SB/92SB-F, 106-108, 112, 158, 167-168
 Model 93R, 108
 Model 950/950B/950BS, 102-103
 Model 951/Helwan, 104-107, 241, 277
 Model 96, 173-175
 Model 96 Centurion, 159, 174
 Model 1934, 19, 104-106
 Model 1938, 104
 Model 1948, 104
Beretta U.S.A., 103, 170, 172, 173, 175, 233
Bessemer, Sir Henry, 18
Borchardt pistol, 134
Bren Ten pistols (Dornaus & Dixon), 159, 176, 265
British service revolvers, 24-26
Browning Arms Company, 120, 127, 124, 135, 138-139, 148, 177, 211, 214, 216. *See also* **Fabrique Nationale**
 Model BDA pistol, 252
 Model BDM pistol, 177-180, 190, 247
Browning, John, 21, 109-110, 120, 124, 127, 133, 138, 145, 153, 185. *See also* **Colt Model 1911/1911A1**
Browning short-recoil locking system (modified), 21, 133, 178-179, 193, 198, 229, 230, 253, 260, 287-289

Calibers, Pistols listed by. *See also* individual listings under specific manufacturers
7.62x25mm
 CZ Model 52, 115-116
 Tokarev TT-30/33, 115, 148-149
 Norinco Model TU-90, 241-243
7.63mm
 Mauser C.96 "Broomhandle", 134-137
7.65mm Longue
 French Model 1935A, 123-126
7.65mm Parabellum (.30 Luger)
 Beretta Model 92 variant, 108
 FN High Power, 121
 Heckler & Koch Model P9S, 225-226
 Luger, 129-133

Calibers, Pistols listed by (cont.)
 7.65mm Parabellum (.30 Luger)(cont.)
 Navy Model 1904, 130
 SIG P220 European, 253
 Walther PP, 281
9mm Largo
 Astra Model 400, 99-100
 Star Model A, 145-146
9mm Parabellum
 American Arms Spectre, 161-162
 Astra A-100, 163-165
 Model 600, 100-101
 Auto-Ordnance 1911A1 Government, 166
 Beretta M9/Model 92F/92FS/SB-F, 106-108, 167-174
 Model 92D/92DS, 170-172
 Model 92G, 172-173
 Model 951, 104-105
 Model 1938, 104
 Browning BDM, 177-180
 Colt Double Eagle, 181-184
 Model 2000 All-American, 188-190
 CZ Model 52, 115-116
 Model 75, 117-119
 Model 85/85 Combat, 191-192
 Daewoo DP51, 193-195
 EAA FAB-92, 196-197
 Witness, 197-200
 FEG FP9/PJK-9HP, 201-204
 MBK-9HP, 205-207
 P9R, 205-207
 F.I.E. Model TZ 75, 208-209
 FM Hi-Power, 210
 FN Browning
 High Power (Model 1935), 120-122
 High Power Mark II, 212-214
 High Power Mark III, 214-216
 Glock Models 17 and 19, 262
 Heckler & Koch P7 series, 220
 Model P7M13, 223-224
 Model P9S, 225-226
 Model SP89, 227-229
 USP, 229-230
 Israel Arms Kareen, 232-233
 Israel Military Industries (IMI)
 Baby Eagle, 234-236
 UZI pistol, 237-238
 Llama Model XI "Especial," 127-128
 Luger 1902, 129, 140
 New Model 1906, 130
 Parabellum, 129-133
 Maverick, 231
 Norinco Model TU-90, 241-243
 Radom Vis-35, 138-139
 Ruger Model P85/P89, 246-248
 P94, 251
 SIG Model P210, 140
 P220, 252-254
 P225 (P6), 252-254
 P226, 253-254
 P228, 254
 Smith & Wesson
 Model 39, 141-142
 Model 59, 142-144
 Model 908/910, 258
 Model 915, 255-258
 Model 5904, 143, 256
 Sigma, 262
 Springfield Armory P9, 267-268
 Star Model B Series, 147
 Model 31P/31PK, 271-273
 Steyr GB, 274-276
 SPP, 276
 Taurus PT-92 Series, 277-280
 Tokarev, 148-149
 Walther P.38, 150-153
 P4, 281-285
 P5, 285-286
 P88, 287-289
9mm Ultra (9mm Police)
 Walther PP Super, 282

Calibers, Pistols listed by (cont.)
 10mm
 Auto-Ordnance 1911A1 Government, 166
 Bren Ten (Dornaus & Dixon), 159, 176
 Colt Double Eagle Mark II, 181-184
 Delta Elite, 113, 159
 Delta Gold Cup, 113
 Glock Model 20, 217, 259
 Smith & Wesson 1000 Series, 258-259
 Springfield Armory Omega, 265-266
 Star Megastar, 269-271
.22 Long Rifle
 Colt Ace/Service Ace, 111
 Ruger Standard Automatic, 68
 Walther PP/PPK, 154-156
.22 Short
 Beretta Model 950 (Minx), 102-103
.25 ACP
 Beretta Model 950 (Jetfire), 102-103
 Walther PPK, 154
.30 Luger (*see* 7.65mm)
.32 ACP
 Colt Pocket Model, 109
 Sauer & Sohn, J.P., Model 38H, 58
 Walther P.38, 153
 PP/PPK, 154-156
.357 SIG
 P226, 253-254
.38
 Colt Military Model of 1902, 109
 Model 1900, 109
 Pocket Model of 1903, 109
 Police Special, 29
 Sporting Model of 1902, 109
.38 Super
 Auto Ordnance 1911A1 Government, 166
 Colt Double Eagle, 181-184
 Gold Cup, 112
 M1911A1, 44, 111
 EAA Witness, 197-200
 Norinco Model TU-90, 241-243
 SIG P220, 252-254
 Springfield Armory M1911-A1, 264
 Omega, 265-266
.380 ACP
 Beretta Model 1934, 104
 Colt Pocket Model, 109
 Walther P.38, 153
 PP/PPK, 154-156
 PP Super, 282
.40 Auto
 Ruger P91 (DC/DAO/KP91DAC), 250-251
 P94, 251
.40 S&W
 American Arms Spectre, 161-162
 Astra A-75, 159
 A-80, 159
 A-100, 159, 163-165
 Beretta Model 96, 173-175
 Model 96 Centurion, 159, 17
 Colt Double Eagle, 181-184
 Government Model, 159
 EAA FAB-92, 196-197
 Witness, 159, 197-200
 FEG GKK-45, 205-207
 FN High Power, 121, 159, 211
 Glock Model 22, 159-160, 218-219
 Model 23, 159-160, 218
 Models 24 and 27, 159
 Heckler & Koch P7M10, 159, 220-222
 USP, 159, 229-230
 Hi-Point Model JC, 231
 IMI Baby Eagle, 159, 234-236
 Llama Large Frame, 159
 Model 82, 160
 Para-Ordnance P10, P14, P15, P16, 245
 Ruger P91, 160, 250-251
 SIG P229, 160, 254
 Stallard Arms Model JS-40, 231
 S&W Model 410, 255-256
 Model 411, 160, 255-256

Calibers, Pistols listed by (cont.)
.40 S&W (cont.)
Smith & Wesson (cont.)
Model 1006, 159
Model 4006, 160, 255
Model 4013/4014, 160
Model 4026, 160
Model 4053, 160
Sigma, 262-263
Sphinx AT-2000, 160
Star Firestar, 160
Taurus PT-100/101, 160, 278
.41 Action Express
IMI Baby Eagle, 234-236
.45 ACP
Astra A-100, 163-165
Auto-Ordnance 1911A1 Government, 166
Bren Ten (Dornaus & Dixon), 176
Colt Double Eagle, 181-184
Enhanced Government Model, 185-187
Government series, 110-114
Model 1905, 109-110
Model 1911/1911A1, 109-114
Model 1991A1, 114
EAA FAB-92, 196-197
Witness, 197-200
FÉG GKK-45, 205-207
Glock Model 21, 218-219
Heckler & Koch P7M45, 220
Model P9S, 225-226
SOCOM Pistol, 229
USP, 229-230
IMI UZI, 237-238
Norinco Model of the 1911, 239-240
Para-Ordnance P10, P12, P13, 245
P14, 244-245
Ruger Model P90/P90D, 248-250
SIG P220, 252-254
Smith & Wesson Model 4506, 259-262
Model 4536, 259, 262
Models 4546, 4566, 4576, 4586, 260
Springfield Armory M1911-A1, 264
Omega, 265-266
Star Megastar, 269-271

Calibers, Revolvers listed by. *See also* individual
listings under specific manufacturers
7.62x38mm
Nagant Model 1895, 35-36
.22 Long Rifle
EAA Windicator, 61-62
Ruger Bisley, 72-74
New Bearcat, 72
New Model Single-Six, 72-74
.22 LR/.22 WMR
Ruger New Model Super Single-Six, 72
.22 Magnum (WMR)
EAA Windicator, 61-62
Ruger New Bearcat, 72
New Model Single-Six, 72-74
.30 Carbine
Ruger New Model Blackhawk, 73
.32 Colt
Colt Police Positive Special, 29-30
.32 H&R Magnum
Ruger Bisley, 72-74
New Model Super Single-Six, 72
.32 S&W Long
EAA Windicator, 61-62
.32-40 Winchester
Colt Police Positive Special, 29-30
.357 Magnum
American Arms Regulator, 51-52
Cimarron Arms Peacekeeper, 53-54
Colt King Cobra, 56-57
Python, 30-31
Single Action Army, 32-34
EAA Big Bore Bounty Hunter, 58-60
Windicator, 60-62
Rossi Model 971, 66-67

Calibers, Revolvers listed by (cont.)
.357 Magnum (cont.)
Ruger Bisley, 72-74
GP100, 68-70
New Model Blackhawk, 73-74
Police Service-Six, 38
Security-Six, 37-38
Speed Six, 38
Smith & Wesson Model 13, 43
Model 19 Combat Magnum, 42-44, 81
Model 27, 44-47
Model 65, 43-44
Model 66, 42-44, 81
Model 686, 81-83
Taurus Model 65, 85
Model 66, 86
Model 607, 90
Model 669, 91-92
Wesson Model 14-2/714-2, 95-96
.38 Special
Cimarron Arms Peacekeeper, 53-54
Colt Detective Special, 155
King Cobra, 56-57
Police Positive Special, 29-30
EAA Big Bore Bounty Hunter, 58-60
Windicator, 60-62
Rossi Model 851, 64-65
Model 971, 66-67
Ruger GP100, 68-70
Smith & Wesson
Military/Police Model 10, 39-42
Model 15, 75-76
Taurus Model 65, 85
Model 66, 86
Models 82 & 83, 87-88
.38 Special +P
Smith & Wesson Model 13, 43
Taurus Model 65, 85
Model 66, 86
.38 S&W
Colt Police Positive, 29-30
Police Positive Special, 29-30
Enfield No.2, 24-26
Webley Mark IV, 24-26
.38-40
Colt Single Action Army, 32-34
.38-44
S&W .38-44 Heavy Duty/Model 20, 45
.38-44 Outdoorsman, 45
.38/200
Enfield No. 2, 24-26
Smith & Wesson M&P models, 26
Webley Mark IV, 24-26
.41 Magnum
EAA Big Bore Bounty Hunter, 58-60
Ruger Bisley, 72-74
New Model Blackhawk, 73
Smith & Wesson
Models 57 & 58, 77-78
Model 657, 77-78
.44 Magnum
Colt Anaconda, 55-56
EAA Big Bore Bounty Hunter, 58-60
Ruger Bisley, 74
New Model Super Blackhawk, 73
Redhawk, 70-72
Vaquero, 74
Smith & Wesson Model 29, 48, 80-81
Model 629/629 Classic, 48, 80-81
Taurus Model 44, 84-85
Texas Longhorn Arms Grover's Improved No.5,
93-94
.44 Russian
Colt Anaconda, 55
.44 Special
Colt Anaconda, 55
New Service, 27-28
Single Action Army, 32-34
Rossi Model 720, 63-64
Taurus Model 431, 88-89

Calibers, Revolvers listed by (cont.)
.44-40
American Arms Regulator, 51-52
Colt Single Action Army, 32-34
Ruger Vaquero, 74
.45 ACP
American Arms Regulator, 51-52
Colt Model 1917, 28
New Service, 27-28
Smith & Wesson Model 25, 78
Model 625, 78-80
Model 1917, 78
.45 Colt
American Arms Regulator, 51-52
Colt New Service, 27-28
Single Action Army, 32-34, 158
Ruger New Model Blackhawk, 73
.45 Long Colt
Colt New Service, 27-28
Single Action Army, 32-34
EAA Big Bore Bounty Hunter, 58-60
Ruger Bisley, 72-74
Vaquero, 74
.45 Russian
Colt Anaconda, 55
.455
Webley Mark VI, 24-26
Campo-Giro service pistol, 99
Centerfire cartridges/revolvers, 16-18
Century International Arms, 116, 201-207, 210
Ceska Zbrojovka Strakonice (CZ). *See* CZ
Charter Arms Bulldog, 64, 88
China North Industries Corporation. *See* Norinco
ChinaSports, Inc., 240
Chinese pistols. *See* **Norinco**
Cimarron Arms Peacekeeper Revolver, 50, 53-54
Colt Industries, 67, 68, 84, 91, 95-96, 140, 193
Pistols
Double Eagle series, 173, 181-184, 185-186,
190, 260
Model 1911, 19, 21, 28, 78, 109-114, 120, 127,
138-139, 141, 145, 148, 158, 173, 182-183,
185, 202, 230, 242, 247, 250, 265, 267, 277
Model 1911A1, 19, 44, 75, 106-108, 109-114,
116, 119, 122, 147, 166, 185-186, 194, 239,
244-245
Delta Elite, 113, 159, 265
Delta Gold Cup, 113
Gold Cup, 112, 266
Government series (Commercial M1911A1),
111-114, 159, 181-184, 245, 254, 265, 273,
291
Ace/Service Ace, 111
Combat Commander, 110, 112-113
Commander, 112
Enhanced Government Model, 185-187, 239
Lightweight Officer's Model, 185
National Match, 111
Officer's ACP, 112-113, 185
Model 1900, 109
Model 1902 Military/Sporting, 109
Model 1905, 109-110
Model 1991A1, 240, 245
Model 2000 All-American, 171, 188-190, 247,
291
Stainless Steel Pistol (SSP), 181
Revolvers
Anaconda, 55-56, 57, 64
Bisley, 93
Detective Special, 155
King Cobra, 55-57, 79, 81
Lightning, 16
Master Shooter, 27
Model 1851 Navy, 14, 15
Model 1860 Army, 14, 15
Model 1917, 28
New Army & Navy, 27
New Service, 27-28
Paterson, 14
Police Positive/Police Positive Special, 29-30

Colt Revolvers (cont.)
Python, 30-31, 42, 55-57, 64, 201
Single Action Army, 17, 18, 27, 32-34, 36, 42, 50, 51-54, 58, 60, 72, 93-94, 158
Artillery, Buntline, Sheriff's Model, 33
Colt, Samuel, 14-19
Cooper, Jeff, 179, 298
Croft, Harold, 93
CZ (Ceska Zbrojovka Strakonice) pistols, 150
CZ 52 (Czech vz.52 service), 115-116, 226
CZ 75, 68, 76, 92, 107, 117-119, 140, 144, 152, 170, 176, 191-192, 196-199, 208-209, 216, 234, 236, 267-268, 269, 271, 273, 293
CZ 75 Compact, 118-119
CZ 83, 116
CZ 85, 119, 191-192, 293
CZ 85 Combat, 119, 191-192
Model 38, 115
VZ. 22, 138
ZKP 524, 115

Daewoo DP 51 pistols, 193-195
Desert Eagle pistol. *See* Israel Military Industries
Deutsche Waffen und Munitionsfabriken (DWM), 129-133
Disassembling Walther PP-type pistols, 295-297
Dornaus & Dixon, 176

Egyptian Helwan pistol, 104-105
Enfield No. 2, Mark 1 revolver, 24-26
Erfurt Arsenal, 131-133
European American Armory (EAA), 118, 163, 208-209
Pistols
FAB-92, 196-197
Witness, 159, 196-200, 208-209, 254, 268, 269
Witness Compact, 118, 200
Revolvers
Arminius, 60
Big Bore Bounty Hunter, 50, 58-60
Windicator, 60-62

Fabrique Nationale (FN) pistols, 150
High Power (Model 1935 Grande Puissance), 19, 21, 26, 75-76, 106, 107, 112, 116, 118-119, 120-122, 128, 135, 138, 139, 140, 141, 142, 158-159, 168, 170, 177, 179, 193-194, 201-207, 210, 211, 232, 273, 291
High Power (.40 S&W), 211, 212
High Power Mark II, 212-215
High Power Mark III, 122, 213-216
Model 1900, 18
Model 1903, 127, 135, 148-149
Model 1910, 99, 127
Model 1922, 124
Federle brothers, 134
FÉG pistols, 215
FP9, 201-204
GKK-45, 205-207
MBK-9 (R9)/MBK-9HP, 205
PJK-9HP, 201-204
P9R, 205-207
F.I.E. (Firearms Import/Export Corp.), 60
Model TZ 75 pistol, 208-209, 268
Firearms International, 103
Flintlock pistols, 12-14
FM Hi-Power pistol (Argentina), 210, 232
FM Rosario, 210
French Model 1892 revolver, 18
French Model 1935A/S pistols, 123-126, 140

Gabilondo y Cia, 150. *See also* Llama
Gas-brake or gas-lock system. *See* Heckler & Koch P7 series, Steyr GB
Gas-seal revolver, 35-36
Glock pistols, 171, 177-178, 180, 188-189, 190, 230, 247, 265, 291
Model 17, 21, 217-218, 274, 276

Glock Pistols (cont.)
Model 19, 178, 218
Model 20, 159, 217
Model 21, 218-219, 269
Model 22, 159-160, 218-219, 262
Model 23, 159, 160, 179, 218, 262
Models 24 and 27, 159
Grendel P-12, 294
Gun Control Act of 1968, 103
Gun South, Inc., 276

Handgun, Evolution of the, 11-22
Handgun safety, 298-300
Heckler & Koch pistols, 21, 291
P7 Series, 220-224, 229, 274
P7MP/PSP, 223
P7M8, 220, 224
P7M10, 159, 220-222
P7M12, 158
P7M13, 220, 223-224
P7M45, 220
P9S, 158, 224, 225-226, 228, 281
SOCOM, 229
SP89, 162, 227-229, 238, 276
USP, 159, 222, 229-230
VP-70, 135, 158
Helwan pistol. *See* Egyptian Helwan pistol
Hi-Point Model JC pistol, 231
Hogg, Ian, 128
Holster design, 294
Hungarian Tokagypt pistol, 241, 242. *See also* FÉG
Huntsman, Benjamin, 13

Iberia Arms Model JS-40 pistol, 231
IMI. *See* Israel Military Industries
Inglis, John, 121
Inglis High Power pistol, 12
Interarms, 64-65, 105, 156, 205, 271, 272, 273, 285, 286, 289
Intratec TEC-9/TEC-9M pistols, 162, 238
Iraqi Model 951, 105
Israel Arms International, 233
Israel Arms Kareen pistols, 232-233
Israel Military Industries (IMI) pistols
Baby Eagle, 68, 159, 197, 208, 209, 234-236
Desert Eagle, 234, 236
Jericho 941, 208, 234
UZI, 237-238, 276
Ithaca Gun Co., 111
ITM AT-84 & AT-88 pistols, 208

Jericho pistol. *See* Israel Military Industries
Johnson, Iver, Enforcer pistol, 162

Kareen Pistol. *See* Israel Arms
Kassnar, 205
K.B.I., 201-207, 234
Keith, Elmer, 48, 93
Kimber of America, 195
Knight, Reed, 188
Knight's Armament Company, 188
Kollner, Gaspard, 16
Kotter, August, 16
Krieghoff, 132, 133
KSN Industries, 233

Llama Gabilondo y Cia S.A. pistols, 145
Large Frame, 159
Model 82, 160
Model IX, 128
Model XI "Especial", 127-128, 145
Omni, 271
Ruby series, 127
Luger pistols, 112, 134, 140, 148, 150
American Eagle, 132
Artillery Model, 131

Luger Pistols (cont.)
Model 1900 (.30 Luger, Old Pattern), 125, 129-131
Model 1902, 129
Model 1904 Navy Model, 130
Model 1906 New Model, 130-131
Model 1906/29, 132
Model 1908, 131
Model 1923, 131
Parabellum P08, 19, 131, 136

Maadi Company, 105
Magnum Research, 119, 191, 197, 234-236
Magnum Research revolver, 35-36, 138, 148, 149
Makarov pistol, 124, 295. *See also* Norinco
Chinese Type 59
Manurhin, 156
Mauser, Paul, 134
Mauser-Werke pistols, 129, 132, 133, 137, 150-151
C.96 Bolo, 135-136
C.96 "Broomhandle", 18-19, 109, 131, 134-137, 150
Model 1916, 136
Model 712/Schnellfeuerpistole, 136-137
Maverick pistol, 231

Nagant, Léon, et Companie gas-seal revolvers, 35-36
Model 1895 revolver, 35-36, 138, 148, 149
National Rifle Association, 262, 300
Navy Arms Co., 241-243
Norinco pistols
Chinese Type 59, 240, 295-297
Chinese Type 80, 137
Model 213, 136
Model of the 1911, 239-240
TT-33 "Tokarev," 241
TU-90, 240, 241-243
North American Arms Company, 110

Para-Ordnance P14 pistols, 244-245, 269
P10, P12, P13, P15, P16 pistols, 245
Peregrine Falcon pistol, 176
Petter, Charles, 140
Pinfire revolvers, 14
Pistols, automatic, 18-21, 97-156, 157-289
Pistols by caliber. *See* Calibers, pistols listed by
Pistols, Classic Service, 97-156
Pistols, Service—9mm, .40 & .45 Caliber, 157-289
Polish Radom pistols. *See* Radom

Radom Vis-35 pistols, 115, 138-139, 140, 158, 285
Remington Arms, 48
Remington-Rand M1911A1 pistols, 19, 110-111
Revolvers by caliber. *See* Calibers, revolvers listed by
Revolvers, Classic Service, 23-48
Revolvers, Service, 49-96
Revolvers, the First, 14-18
Rifling, 16
Rogak P-18 pistol, 274
Rossi, Amadeo S.A., revolvers, 91
Model 720, 63-64, 88-89
Model 851, 64-66
Model 951, 64
Model 971, 66-67
Royal Small Arms Factory, 24-26
Ruger, 67, 84, 91, 117, 291
Pistols
P85-series (P85/P89), 183, 246-248, 260
P90/P90D, 248-250, 269
P91, 160, 250-251
P94 (& P93), 251, 292
Standard Automatic, 68
Revolvers
Bearcat/New Bearcat, 72
Bisley, 72-74
Blackhawk, 58, 72, 74
GP-100, 38, 57, 68-70, 81, 95-96
New Model Blackhawk, 73-74

Ruger Revolvers (cont.)
New Model Super Blackhawk, 73
Police Service-Six, 38, 68
Redhawk, 70-72, 80
Security-Six, 37-38, 68, 70
Single Action Army, 50
Single-action revolvers, 33, 50, 72-74
Single-Six, 72-74
SP101, 68, 70
Speed Six, 38, 68
Super Blackhawk, 72
Super Redhawk, 70
Vaquero, 33, 34, 74
Russian M1985 Nagant, 138, 148-149
Russian Tokarev pistol. *See* Tokarev pistols
Russian Weapons Factory, 35-36

Saive, Dieudonne Joseph, 120
Sauer, J.P. and Sohn, 58-59, 252
Model 38H pistol, 58, 253
Savage, 110
SIG (Schweizerische Industrie Gesellschaft) pistols,
108, 170, 173, 179-180, 213, 230, 249, 265,
276, 284
Model 49 (SP 47/8), 140
P210, 117, 123-124, 140, 198, 253, 271
P220 (Series), 58, 140, 163-165, 247, 250, 252-
254, 269
P225 (P6), 252-254
P226, 158, 172, 191, 253-254, 274
P228, 254
P229, 160, 254
SIGARMS, 253-254
SIG-Sauer, 252
Sighting devices, general, 291
Signal Co., 111
Simpson & Company, 132-133
Singer Sewing Machine Co., 25-26, 111
Skrzypinski, Jan, 138
Smith & Wesson, 15-18, 24, 28, 60, 63, 65, 65,
67, 68, 88, 89, 95-96, 108, 117, 118, 119, 151,
152, 168, 171, 181, 188, 197, 269, 273
Pistols
Model 39, 42, 112, 141-142, 144, 151, 152, 205-
207, 260, 261
Model 40 single action, 141
Model 59 (Mark 22 "Hush Puppy"), 117, 121,
142-144, 256, 261
Model 410, 255-256
Model 411, 160, 255-256, 257
Model 439, 142
Model 459, 144, 158, 246
Model 469, 142, 217, 255
Model 559, 144
Model 639, 141-142, 144
Model 645, 259
Model 659, 144
Model 915, 255-258
Model 1000 Series, 258-259
Model 1006, 159
Model 1066, 159, 258-259
Model 1076, 159
Model 3900 series, 142
Model 3914, 178
Model 3953, 172
Model 4006, 160
Model 4013/4014, 160
Model 4026, 160
Model 4053, 160
Model 4506, 258, 259-262
Model 4516, 78, 80, 259, 262
Model 4536, 259, 262
Models 4546/4566/4576, 260
Model 4586, 260, 261
Model 5904, 143-144, 256-257, 292
Model 6906, 260
Sigma Series, 262-263, 291
Third Generation series, 143-144, 292

Smith & Wesson (cont.)
Revolvers
Chief's Special, 155, 294
Hand Ejector, 17
J-frame series, 40, 155
K-frame, 41, 42-44, 75, 81, 91
L-frame, 81-83, 91
Military/Police Model 10, 17, 18, 39-42, 43, 44,
45, 75, 81, 87
Military/Police models, 26, 29
Model 13, 43
Model 15 "Combat Masterpiece", 64, 75-76, 87
Model 19 Combat Magnum, 38, 41, 42-44, 81-
83, 85-86, 91-92, 96
Model 25, 78
Model 27, 42, 44-47, 81-82
Model 29, 48, 80-81, 84
Model 38 Bodyguard, 61
Model 57/58, 77-78
Model 64, 41
Model 65, 41, 43-44
Model 66, 41, 42-44, 81, 85-86
Model 625, 77, 78-80
Model 629/629 Classic, 48, 80-81
Model 657, 77-78
Model 686, 57, 81-83, 91-92
Model 686 Powerport, 82
Model 686 Plus Distinguished Combat
Magnum, 82-83
Model 1917, 28, 78
Mountain Revolver, 81
N-frame, 45-47, 78-82
Russian Model of 1871, 18
Safety Hammerless, 16
Société Alsacienne de Construction Mécanique
(SACM), 123-126
Soviet pistols. *See* Makarov and Tokarev pistols
Sphinx Model AT-2000, 160
Spreewerke, 150
Springfield Armory pistols, 110
Model P9, 208, 267-268
M1911-A1 Series, 159, 264, 266
Omega series, 159, 265-266
Springfield, Inc., 264, 267
Stahl, Peters (PSW GmbH), 265-266
Stallard Arms Model JS-40 pistols, 231
Star Bonifacio Echeverria SA pistols, 128, 158
Firestar, 118, 147, 160, 269, 294
Megastar, 269-271
Model A/Super A, 145-146, 147
Model B, 147
Model B Super, 99, 147
Model BKM, 147
Model 28, 271
Model 30, 269, 272
Model 31(M), 31P/31PK, 118, 271-273
Modelo Militar, 147
Ultra Star, 291
Steyr pistols, 117, 138
GB (GB-80), 144, 158, 170, 173, 224, 274-276
-Hahn Model 1912, 189, 276
MAB PA-15, 189
SPP, 189, 238, 276
Stoeger Industries (A.F. Stoeger), 129, 131, 132,
333
Stoner, Eugene, 188
Sturm, Ruger & Company. *See* Ruger
Swiss pistols
W+F 43 Browning, 140
W+F 47 Gasolbensreaktion, 140

Tanfoglio SpA, 196-200, 208-209, 234, 268
Tariq (Iraqi Model 951), 105
Taurus, Forjas, 67, 171, 270
Pistols
PT-92 Series, 91, 107, 170, 173, 175, 189, 277-
280

Taurus (cont.)
Pistols (cont.)
PT-99, 91, 189, 277-280
PT-100/101, 160, 173, 175, 278
Revolvers
Model 44, 84-85
Model 65, 85-86
Model 66, 85-86, 91
Model 80, 86, 87-88
Model 82 and 83, 87-88
Model 431, 64, 88-89
Model 607, 90
Model 669, 86, 91-92
Taurus International, 85, 86, 88, 89, 90, 92
Taylor, Chuck, 179
Technologies, emerging, and future trends, 291-
294
Texas Longhorn Arms Grover's Improved No.5,
93-94
Tokagypt pistol. *See* Hungarian Tokagypt
Tokarev, Feodor, 148
Tokarev pistols, 35, 128, 140, 271
TT-30, 137, 148-149
TT-33, 115, 137, 148-149, 241-243
Turkish flintlock pistol, 12

Uberti, Aldo, 54
Union Switch, 111
U.S. XM9 pistol trials, 108, 158, 167, 223,
226, 246, 247, 254, 274-275, 287
U.S. M11 pistol trials, 254
UZI pistol. *See* Israel Military Industries

"Velo Dog" revolver, 18
Voight, Richard, 176
Voyevodin, P.V., 149

Waffenfabrik Bern, 133
Walther Waffenfabrik (Carl Walther Waffen-
fabrik) pistols, 108, 117, 118, 148, 167,
170, 196, 230, 273
Model 4, 152, 252, 281-285
Model 5, 152, 252
Model HP (Heeres Pistole), 140, 150-151
Model KPK, 155
Model 9, 156
P.38 (P1), 19-20, 26, 39, 104-106, 111, 112,
132, 133, 140, 141, 142, 150-153, 156, 172,
241, 281, 283, 284, 285, 286, 287, 288
P.38K, 283-284
P4, 281-285, 288
P5, 285-286, 288
P5C (Compact), 286, 288
P88, 158, 172, 230, 287-289
P88 Compact, 289
PP (Polizei Pistole), 19-20, 58, 124, 140, 153,
154-156, 281, 284, 291, 295-297
PP Super, 282
PPK, 58, 153, 154-156, 227, 291
Webley & Scott revolvers, 17
Mark IV, 24-26
Mark VI, 24-26
Weihrauch Waffenfabrik, 60-62
Wesson, Dan, Model 14-2/714-2, 95-96
L'il Dan, 95
Wesson, Daniel Baird, 95
White, Rollin, 16,17
Wilniewczyc, Piotr, 138
Wondernine. *See* 9mm-caliber pistols listed
under Calibers